Handbook of Steel Drainage & Highway Construction Products

Prepared under direction of the

HIGHWAY TASK FORCE for

Committee of Galvanized Sheet Producers

Committee of Hot Rolled and Cold Rolled Sheet

and Strip Producers

Published by

AMERICAN IRON AND STEEL INSTITUTE

150 East 42nd Street, New York, N.Y. 10017

Preface

THIS ENGINEERING VOLUME, entitled *Handbook of Steel Drainage and Highway Construction Products*, is intended to serve a long established need. Its major usefulness lies in highway, railway, municipal, agricultural, industrial and other fields where drainage and construction problems must be overcome. While the handbook is new in scope, in text, and in illustrative material, its principal merit can be found in the degree to which consensus has been attained among the numerous reputable contributing authorities on the engineering of drainage structures and related steel products. The text aims to present the best engineering methods and practices compatible with existing technology. Behind these methods are more than 60 years' practical experience by engineers, by public officials, by manufacturers and by contractors for metal drainage structures. Nevertheless, there is still room for individual opinion in these areas.

Design data and designer aids are cited extensively from published literature and supplemented with numerous references to supporting research. We have relied upon the accuracy of the material cited and have not made an independent verification of this data. Theory is kept at a minimum.

Precursors to this text are the *Handbook of Culvert and Drainage Practice* , 1930, and the *Handbook of Drainage and Construction Products* , 1955 (with many editions and printings). These texts were pioneered and published by a major steel producer and participant on various committees of American Iron and Steel Institute which has long been known for its sound work in the engineering of drainage products. Unique in their time and still in widespread use, these earlier handbooks served well to define and to explain the value of corrugated steel pipe and other steel products in highway service. So it is considered appropriate to make this new edition the voice of the steel industry, through American Iron and Steel Institute.

Acknowledgement is due the steel producers cooperating with American Iron and Steel Institute's *Committee of Galvanized Sheet Producers* and *Committee of Hot Rolled and Cold Rolled Sheet and Strip Producers*. Representatives from various steel companies, participating as an AISI Highway Task Force, gave generously of their engineering talent, time, and technical data and illustrations. Special appreciation is acknowledged to the National Corrugated Steel Pipe Association whose Publications Committee has reviewed and approved the text of this handbook.

Thanks are offered also to various practicing engineers, research organizations and government sources, most of whom are listed in the bibliography. A special note of grateful commendation is due Consultant W. H. Spindler, P.E., without whose training and long experience this handbook would not be possible.

Height-of-Cover Tables illustrating how culvert diameter and wall thickness (gage) for several corrugation profiles and conditions of backfill, influence height-of-cover limits, using the design procedures of Chapter 2, are inserted within a pocket affixed to the inside back cover. Fundamental studies, currently underway by American Iron and Steel Institute, within the steel industry, at universities, and by AASHO, BPR, state highway departments and other governmental agencies, may alter presently accepted practices in strength design procedure for flexible steel conduits. This engineering renaissance may result in increased height-of-cover values, such that tables currently in use can and should be updated. At such time, the AISI Committee of Hot Rolled and Cold Rolled Sheet and Strip Producers and the Committee of Galvanized Sheet Producers will print and distribute updated tables, along with changes as may be required in Chapter 2 *Strength Design*.

Suggestions for changes and improvements for future editions will be appreciated.

AMERICAN IRON AND STEEL INSTITUTE

April, 1967

4

Contents

Fig. 0-1. Typical corrugated steel culvert under moderately high fill.

Introduction

THE DESIGN and application of flexible steel underground conduits, along with good installation practices, are described in the first two parts of this book. The third part deals with other steel products for related construction.

APPLICATION OF UNDERGROUND CONDUITS

Uses of underground conduits include:
1. Culverts, small bridges, stream enclosures and sewers, pipe spillways to prevent erosion, and outlets for ponds and dams.
2. Subdrains for drying up and stabilizing subgrades, pavements, runways, tracks, cut slopes, embankments, foundations and retaining walls.
3. Underpasses or tunnels for all kinds of traffic.
4. Special applications, including underground or aerial conduits for equipment and materials, pipelines and sewers.

Engineers, consultants, contractors and public officials are among those having an interest in the proper design and construction of such conduits.

CONSTRUCTION PROJECTS

Projects that require underground conduits include *highways* of the highest type as well as minor roads; *railways* whose concern is revenue-paying traffic moving over main line tracks and in freight yards; *airports* with vast flat areas, and runways with ground water problems.

Also, *municipalities and industries*, with densely populated metropolitan

Fig. 0-2. Maintenance-free twin structural plate pipe-arch culverts serve to replace a small bridge. They are "first cousins" to the shop fabricated culvert pipe sections on the truck-trailer.

7

Fig. 0-3. Battery of 84-in. diameter corrugated steel culvert pipe under 25 ft of cover on a mainline railroad. This shows confidence of the engineers in this type of structure.

areas, industrial parks and some rural conditions; *flood and conservation projects; military and space projects.*

PROGRESS THROUGH RESEARCH

With the purpose of the conduit determined, the engineer next considers which of the various materials will best serve his design needs.

Engineers and contractors are an imaginative lot in seeking improved ways of designing and building their projects. Steel manufacturers and fabricators have cooperated, by aid of their research and manufacturing staffs, to provide engineers and contractors with better materials, products and installation methods.

Manufacturers' sales staffs and associations are made up largely of experienced professional engineers, knowledgeable of the construction industry's problems, who constitute a prime information source on applications, specifications and installation of their products.

ACCEPTANCE OF STEEL

Steel is universally preferred, specified and used as a construction material for corrugated conduits and other products. For many years, steel products have been included in the standard specifications of the American Association of State Highway Officials, the U. S. Bureau of Public Roads, the American Railway Engineering Association, the Corps of Engineers, the Federal Aviation Agency, the American Society for Testing and Materials, and other professional groups. Design engineers in all construction markets include these steel construction products on their plans and in their project specifications.

DURABILITY AND SERVICE LIFE

In determining whether a construction product of a given material will satisfactorily serve the intended purpose, one important question is: "Will it be long-lasting or durable?" Because of changing conditions and possible obsolescence of present highway systems, most engineers consider that a life of 50 or 60 years for a culvert is entirely adequate.

Chapter 3 describes how corrugated steel pipe with its inherent toughness and available economical coatings and linings will give the desired service life—most often at less cost than other products.

The mechanical properties of steel which determine its structural strength are controlled in the producing mill and the finished product is fabricated to exacting specifications. With a properly designed backfill, the engineer can design a corrugated steel conduit of dependable strength and trouble-free serviceability.

CAPACITY

Corrugated steel conduits are made in standard diameters from 6 in. through 24 ft—in round, vertically elongated (elliptical), pipe-arch, horseshoe, arch and other shapes.

Size determination is not an exact science. Factors such as *drift debris*, *sedimentation* and variable *stream conditions* at inlet and outlet require engineering judgment. Under most conditions, a corrugated *culvert* interior is not a hydraulic factor. For *sewers* designed to flow full, a smooth lining can be provided to give maximum capacity.

INSTALLATION FACTORS

The contractor installs culverts ahead of grading operations to eliminate site delays. Strategically located steel pipe fabricating plants and storage yards make for prompt deliveries. Because shop prefabricated steel conduits are not affected by job site temperature extremes or precipitation, these products can be installed with minimum delay.

ECONOMY

The lowest installed cost which is desirable should be considered along with other factors, including strength, material durability, no reduction in capacity during service life, prompt delivery, freedom from excessive maintenance, ease of renewal, and general satisfaction.

———

The first several chapters deal with the product details and structural principles as applied to fabricated corrugated steel conduits. They are based on more than 60 years of experience and are known to be economical, effective and practical. The engineer is free to evaluate these discussions and use his own judgment as to what best fits his immediate problems.

Fig. 1-0. Modern installation procedures are the means of assuring the design engineer of first-class results.

PART I

General Design Considerations

CHAPTER 1 Product Details

DESIGN FACTORS

Which design factor should come first—size, shape, durability, strength, installation methods, economy or others? The engineer is free to choose the sequence and the order of importance to fit his particular problem. Fig. 1-1.

This handbook chooses to begin with an analysis of required strength of the wall of a conduit. This subject continues to challenge the engineer. Its solution offers rewards in personal satisfactions, in technical accomplishments and in ever greater economy.

Fig. 1-1. Problems that confront the design engineer.

BACKGROUND OF CORRUGATED STEEL CONDUITS

Corrugating a flat sheet has long been known to increase its stiffness and strength. Fig. 1-2. Corrugated steel sheets have been produced almost since the first rolling mill was built in England in 1784. But it was not until after 1890, when mass-produced steel sheets became abundant, that their use grew rapidly.[1]

Corrugated metal pipe was first developed and used for culverts in 1896. As experience was gained in the use of this thin-wall, lightweight, *shop-fabricated* pipe, the diameters gradually increased to 96 in. and larger. Fill heights became greater, even exceeding 100 ft. A further development, in 1931, was

Fig. 1-2. Demonstration of how corrugations increase the beam strength of a material.

structural plate pipe with larger corrugations, for *field assembly*. Diameters and arch spans beyond 25 ft. have been successfully installed.

SPECIFICATIONS IN COMMON USE

Specifications for corrugated steel conduits have been prepared by various national engineering authorities in collaboration with steel producers and pipe manufacturers. These are periodically reviewed and brought up to date in the light of research and new product developments. A list of those in common use is found in Table 1-1.

These specifications cover: general description, material, fabrication, testing, and in some cases, design and construction. In part, the *material* specification includes chemical composition of the base metal, and the kind and amount of coatings. The *fabrication* specification includes shape, dimensions and weights, corrugation configurations, seams, end finish and couplings.

Design specifications and tables should include maximum and minimum heights of earth cover from surface to top of structure for the various combinations of diameter or span and gage.

Construction specifications generally include foundation and bedding preparation, how the backfill should be made and other installation information.

Table 1-1 Specifications for Corrugated Steel Drainage Structures

End User	Galvanized	Coated	Structural Plate	Perforated
State and County Highways, Municipal	AASHO M-36	AASHO M-190	AASHO M-167	AASHO M-136
BPR for Federal Highways (including forests, parks, etc.)	(FP-__*)	(FP-__*)	(FP-__*)	(FP-__*)
Fed. Aviation Agency	FAA Standards	FAA Standards		FAA Standards
Railways	AREA 1-4-6	AREA 1-4-13	AREA 1-4-25	AREA 1-4-11
Federal–GSA	WW-P-00405 COM-PR (interim)	WW-P-00405 COM-PR (interim)	WW-P-00405 COM-PR (interim)	WW-P-00405 COM-PR (interim)

*Suffix is last two digits denoting year the manual was published.

Types of Corrugations

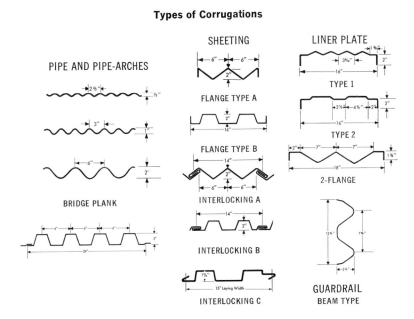

Fig. 1-3. Corrugation types commonly used for galvanized sheet steel conduits and other construction products.

DESCRIPTION OF CORRUGATIONS

There are many kinds of corrugations, some of which are shown in Fig. 1-3. Corrugations commonly used for pipes or conduits are termed "circular arcs connected by tangents," and are described by pitch, depth and inside forming radius. Pitch is measured at right angles to the corrugations from crest to crest.

For *riveted or resistance spot-welded* pipe with circumferential (annular) seams, the corrugations have predominantly been of $2\frac{2}{3}$ in. pitch by $\frac{1}{2}$ in. depth. Recently, 3-in. by 1-in. size has been introduced.

For *lock seam* pipe, the seams and corrugations run helically (or spirally) around the pipe. For small diameters of subdrainage pipe (6, 8, 10 in., etc.) the pitch vs. depth dimension is $1\frac{1}{2} \times \frac{1}{4}$ in. Larger sizes, with helical pipe diameters to 96 in., use $2 \times \frac{1}{2}$ in., $2\frac{2}{3} \times \frac{1}{2}$ in. and 3×1 in. corrugations.

Structural plate pipe was introduced in 1931 with a corrugation of $6 \times 1\frac{1}{2}$ in. Based on the Michigan tests of 1950,[2] the 6×2 in. corrugation was adopted as standard by the American Association of State Highway Officials.

SECTIONAL PROPERTIES

Sectional properties of the arc-and-tangent type of corrugation are derived mathematically.[3] These include area, A, moment of inertia, I, section modulus, S, and radius of gyration, r. Research by American Iron and Steel Institute[1] has shown that failure loads in bending and deflection within the elastic range can be closely predicted by using computed sectional properties of the corrugated sheet. See Tables 1-2 through 1-8.[4,5,6] (*Text continued, page 20*)

Table 1-2 Sectional Properties of Corrugated Steel Sheets and Plates for Drainage Products

Part A. MOMENT OF INERTIA, I, in inches to the fourth power, per Foot of Width

Corrugation Nominal Dimensions	20* Gage	18 Gage	16 Gage	14 Gage	12 Gage	10 Gage	8 Gage	7 Gage	5 Gage	3 Gage	1 Gage
Pitch x Depth											
1½ x ¼ in.	0.00304*	0.00412	0.00527	0.00679	0.01027*	0.01447*	0.01959*				
2 x ½ in.	0.0137*	0.0184	0.0233	0.0295	0.0425*	0.0566*	0.0719*				
2⅔ x ½ in.	0.0135*	0.0180	0.0227	0.0287	0.0411	0.0544	0.0687				
3 x 1 in.	0.0618*	0.0827	0.1039	0.1306	0.1855	0.2421	0.3010				
6 x 2 in.					0.725	0.938	1.154	1.296	1.523	1.754	1.990

*Non-standard. Information only.
Corrugation dimensions are nominal, subject to manufacturing tolerances.

Part B. SECTION MODULUS S, in inches to the third power, per Foot of Width

Corrugation Nominal Dimensions	20* Gage	18 Gage	16 Gage	14 Gage	12 Gage	10 Gage	8 Gage	7 Gage	5 Gage	3 Gage	1 Gage
Pitch x Depth											
1½ x ¼ in.	0.0213*	0.0277	0.0340	0.0419	0.0580*	0.0753*	0.0945				
2 x ½ in.	0.0513*	0.0673	0.0832	0.1025	0.1406*	0.1783*	0.2166*				
2⅔ x ½ in.	0.0503*	0.0659	0.0812	0.0998	0.1360	0.1714	0.2069				
3 x 1 in.	0.1194*	0.1578	0.1961	0.2431	0.3358	0.4269	0.5170				
6 x 2 in.					0.689	0.879	1.066	1.187	1.376	1.562	1.749
Flat Sheet			0.0072	0.0111	0.0219	0.0362	0.0541	0.0643	0.0875	0.1143	0.1447

Bibliography: Sectional Properties of Corrugated Sheets Determined by Formula; D. S. Wolford, *Civil Eng.* Vol. 24, No. 2, Feb. 1954, pp. 103–104.
*Non-standard. Information only. For source of table, see Reference 3 at end of chapter, page 37.

Table 1-3 Sectional Properties of Corrugated Steel Construction Products[5]

Product	Moment of Inertia, in.^{4} per Section; Section Modulus, in.^{3} per Section	14 Gage	12 Gage	11 Gage	10 Gage	8 Gage	7 Gage	5 Gage	3 Gage	1/4 In.	5/16 In.	3/8 In.
LINER PLATE 2-Flange 18 in. wide	Moment, I	0.6202	0.8847		1.1528	1.4306	1.5788	1.8558	2.1470			
	Sect. Modulus, S	0.5809	0.8229		1.0624	1.3064	1.4372	1.6707	1.9166			
Type I. 4-Flange 16 in. wide	Moment, I			0.7431			1.0307		1.8638		2.3845	3.3854
	Sect. Modulus, S			0.3890			0.5516		0.9030		1.1268	1.5462
Type II. 4-Flange 16 in. wide	Moment, I		0.7347		0.9283	1.1156	1.2066	1.3849		1.6196	1.9616	2.2855
	Sect. Modulus, S		0.3716		0.4728	0.5722	0.6210	0.7177		0.8472	1.0412	1.2310
SHEETING Flange Type A 12 in. wide	Moment, I		0.5653		0.7269	0.8885	0.9690	1.1306	1.2922			
	Sect. Modulus, S		0.5180		0.6571	0.7924	0.8585	0.9889	1.1154			
Flange Type B 16 in. wide	Moment, I		1.4937		1.9207		2.5604					
	Sect. Modulus, S		1.185		1.526		2.030					
Interlock-A 14 in. wide overall	Moment, I		0.6788		0.8783	1.0804	1.1820	1.3892				
	Sect. Modulus, S		0.6258		0.8023	0.9776	1.0647	1.2399				
Interlock-B 14 in. wide	Moment, I		1.4582		1.875		2.50					
	Sect. Modulus, S		1.190		1.531		2.040					
GUARDRAIL Beam Type 12¼ in. wide	Moment, I		2.2960		2.9190							
	Sect. Modulus, S		1.3640		1.7322							
BRIDGE PLANK 24⅝ in. wide — 2 x 6 in. Corr.	Moment, I		2.3194		2.9820		3.9758					
	Sect. Modulus, S		2.0609		2.6151		3.4190					
18⅝ in. wide — 3 x 9 in. Corr.	Moment, I						7.81	9.104	10.416			
	Sect. Modulus, S						5.00	5.68	6.40			

Table 1-4 Sectional Properties of Corrugated Steel Sheets[6]
Per Foot of Section Width for Corrugation: **1½x¼ in.** (Helical)
Radius of Curvature: ⁹⁄₃₂ in.

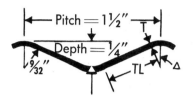

Gage	Uncoated Thickness T In.	Area of Section A Sq. In./Ft	Tangent Length TL In.	Tangent Angle △ Degrees	Moment of Inertia(a) I In.⁴/Ft	Section Modulus(a) S In.³/Ft	Radius of Gyration r In.	Developed Width Factor (b)
20*	0.0359	0.456	0.571	21.44	0.00304	0.0213	0.0816	1.060
18	0.0478	0.608	0.566	21.52	0.00412	0.0277	0.0824	1.060
16	0.0598	0.761	0.560	21.61	0.00527	0.0340	0.0832	1.060
14	0.0747	0.950	0.554	21.71	0.00679	0.0419	0.0846	1.060
12*	0.1046	1.331	0.540	21.94	0.01027	0.0580	0.0879	1.060
10*	0.1345	1.712	0.526	22.17	0.01447	0.0753	0.0919	1.061
8*	0.1644	2.093	0.511	22.42	0.01959	0.0945	0.0967	1.061

Table 1-5 Sectional Properties of Corrugated Steel Sheets[6]
Per Foot of Section Width for Corrugation: **2 x ½ in.** (Helical)
Radius of Curvature: ⅜ in.

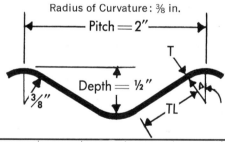

Gage	Uncoated Thickness T In.	Area of Section A Sq. In./Ft	Tangent Length TL In.	Tangent Angle △ Degrees	Moment of Inertia(a) I In.⁴/Ft	Section Modulus(a) S In.³/Ft	Radius of Gyration r In.	Developed Width Factor(b)
20*	0.0359	0.489	0.681	33.12	0.0137	0.0513	0.1676	1.136
18	0.0478	0.652	0.672	33.29	0.0184	0.0673	0.1682	1.136
16	0.0598	0.815	0.663	33.46	0.0233	0.0832	0.1690	1.136
14	0.0747	1.019	0.625	33.68	0.0295	0.1025	0.1700	1.137
12*	0.1046	1.428	0.629	34.13	0.0425	0.1406	0.1725	1.138
10*	0.1345	1.838	0.605	34.62	0.0566	0.1783	0.1754	1.139
8*	0.1644	2.249	0.579	35.13	0.0719	0.2166	0.1788	1.140

*Gages not commonly available. Information only.
(a) Per foot of projection about the neutral axis.
  To obtain *A, I,* or *S* per *inch* of width, divide by 12.
(b) Developed width factor measures the increase in profile length due to corrugating.
  Dimensions are subject to manufacturing tolerances.

Table 1-6 Sectional Properties of Corrugated Steel Sheets[6]

Per Foot of Section Width for Corrugation: **2⅔ x ½ in.** (Annular or Helical)

Radius of Curvature: 1¹¹⁄₁₆ in.

Pitch = 2⅔"

T

Depth = ½"

1¹¹⁄₁₆" 　△ 　TL

Gage	Uncoated Thickness T In.	Area of Section A Sq. In./Ft	Tangent Length TL In.	Tangent Angle △ Degrees	Moment of Inertia(a) I In.⁴/Ft	Section Modulus(a) S In.³/Ft	Radius of Gyration r In.	Developed Width Factor(b)
20*	0.0359	0.465	0.785	26.56	0.0135	0.0503	0.1702	1.080
18	0.0478	0.619	0.778	26.65	0.0180	0.0659	0.1707	1.080
16	0.0598	0.775	0.770	26.74	0.0227	0.0812	0.1712	1.080
14	0.0747	0.968	0.760	26.86	0.0287	0.0998	0.1721	1.080
12	0.1046	1.356	0.740	27.11	0.0411	0.1360	0.1741	1.080
10	0.1345	1.744	0.720	27.37	0.0544	0.1714	0.1766	1.081
8	0.1644	2.133	0.699	27.65	0.0687	0.2069	0.1795	1.081

*Gage not commonly available. Information only.
(a) Per foot of projection about the neutral axis.
　　To obtain A, I, or S per *inch* of width, divide the above values by 12.
(b) Developed width factor measures the increase in profile length due to corrugating.

Dimensions are subject to manufacturing tolerances.

Fig. 1-4. Spot welding is a modern alternative to riveting of corrugated steel pipe.

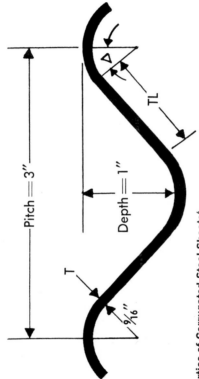

Pitch = 3″

Depth = 1″

9/16″

Table 1-7 Sectional Properties of Corrugated Steel Sheets[6]

Per Foot of Section Width for Corrugation: **3 x 1 in.** (Annular or Helical)

Radius of Curvature: 9/16 in.

Gage	Uncoated Thickness T In.	Area of Section A Sq. In./Ft	Tangent Length TL In.	Tangent Angle Δ Degrees	Moment of Inertia(a) I In.⁴/Ft	Section Modulus(a) S In.³/Ft	Radius of Gyration r In.	De- veloped Width Factor(b)
20*	0.0359	0.534	0.963	44.19	0.0618	0.1194	0.3403	1.239
18	0.0478	0.711	0.951	44.39	0.0827	0.1578	0.3410	1.240
16	0.0598	0.890	0.938	44.60	0.1039	0.1961	0.3417	1.240
14	0.0747	1.113	0.922	44.87	0.1306	0.2431	0.3427	1.241
12	0.1046	1.560	0.889	45.42	0.1855	0.3358	0.3448	1.243
10	0.1345	2.008	0.855	46.02	0.2421	0.4269	0.3472	1.244
8	0.1644	2.458	0.819	46.65	0.3010	0.5170	0.3499	1.246

*Gage not commonly available. Information only.
(a) Per foot of projection about the neutral axis.
To obtain A, I, or S per inch of width, divide by 12.
(b) Developed width factor measures the increase in profile length due to corrugating.
Dimensions are subject to manufacturing tolerances.

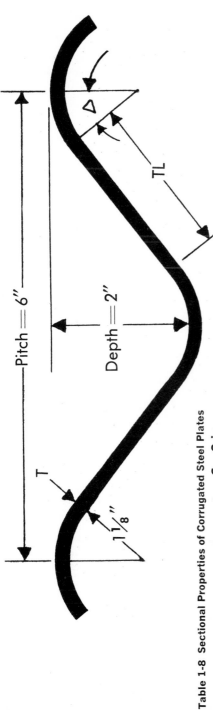

Table 1-8 Sectional Properties of Corrugated Steel Plates

Per Foot of Section Width for Corrugation: **6 x 2 in.**

Radius of Curvature: 1⅛ in.

Gage	Uncoated Thickness T In.	Area of Section A Sq. In./Ft	Tangent Length TL In.	Tangent Angle △ Degrees	Moment of Inertia(a) I In.⁴/Ft	Section Modulus(a) S In.³/Ft	Radius of Gyration r In.	Developed Width Factor(b)
12	0.1046	1.556	1.893	44.47	0.725	0.689	0.682	1.240
10	0.1345	2.003	1.861	44.73	0.938	0.879	0.684	1.241
8	0.1644	2.449	1.828	45.00	1.154	1.066	0.686	1.242
7	0.1838	2.739	1.807	45.18	1.296	1.187	0.688	1.242
5	0.2145	3.199	1.773	45.47	1.523	1.376	0.690	1.243
3	0.2451	3.658	1.738	45.77	1.754	1.562	0.692	1.244
1	0.2758	4.119	1.702	46.09	1.990	1.749	0.695	1.245

(a) Per foot of projection about the neutral axis.
 To obtain A, I, or S per *inch* of width, divide by 12.
(b) Developed width factor measures the increase in profile length due to corrugating.
 Dimensions are subject to manufacturing tolerances.

Table 1-9   Ultimate Longitudinal Seam Strength
of Corrugated Steel Pipe
In Pounds Per Foot of Seam*

Gage of Metal	⁵⁄₁₆″ Rivets		⅜″ Rivets			⁷⁄₁₆″ Rivets
	2⅔″ x ½″		2⅔″ x ½″		3″ x 1″	3″ x 1″
	Single	Double	Single	Double	Double	Double
16	16,750	21,500			28,700	
14	18,200	29,800			35,700	
12			23,400	46,800		53,000
10			24,500	49,000		63,700
8			25,600	51,300		70,700

The above values are based on riveted construction; they also apply to spot welded and helical lock seam fabrication.
*Values in this table are based on tests conducted by Utah State Dept. of Highways, 1964, and by Pittsburgh Testing Laboratories, 1966.[8]

(*Text continued from page 13*)

PIPE SEAMS

Three methods are employed in shop-fabricating the seams of corrugated steel pipe and pipe-arches: riveting, resistance spot-welding and helical lock seam. Recent extensive laboratory tests show that all three methods can develop the full strength of the corrugated walls.

For field-assembled structural plate products, high strength bolts, ¾-in. diameter, provide adequate strength for the plate walls.

Riveted seams. Specifications for 2⅔ x ½ in. corrugation call for the use of ⁵⁄₁₆-in., cold-driven rivets for 16 and 14 gage material and ⅜-in. rivets for 12, 10, and 8 gage. Longitudinal seams are riveted with one rivet in each corrugation, but pipes 42 inches or larger diameter are double-riveted. Circumferential rivets for joining sections are spaced on 6-in. centers. The strength of such seams for steel sheets and rivets is shown in Table 1-9.

For the 3x1 in. corrugation, all longitudinal seams are double riveted with cold-driven rivets as shown in Table 1-9. Rivet diameters are ⅜ in. for 16 and 14 gage sheets, and ⁷⁄₁₆ in. for 12, 10 and 8 gage sheets.

Spot Welded Seams. Resistance spot welding of lapped seams is a relatively new fabricating method resulting in strength equivalent to riveted seams. Elimination of rivet heads allows a smoother pipe interior and better seating of the connecting band on the exterior. Fig. 1-4.

Helical Lock Seams. Helical corrugated steel pipe has been used in diameters 6 to 21 inches since 1935, notably for subdrains but also for culverts and storm sewers. Recently machines have been developed to produce helically corrugated pipe through 96-inch diameter. Fig. 1-5.

Advantages are true roundness, uniform diameter and smoothness. The lock seam product is equivalent in ring compression loading to riveted pipe, as a minimum. There are no longitudinal seams to be specially positioned and the seams are tight.

Fig. 1-5. Beginning with a coil of galvanized steel sheet, this modern equipment rapidly produces continuous lock seam pipe in diameters from 6 to 96 in. Inset view shows the strong, tight lock seam joint that runs helically around the pipe.

Bolted Seams and Joints. High strength bolts have been successfully used for the seams of structural plate pipes, arches and pipe-arches over a period of some 35 years. These bolts are ¾-in. diameter, hot-dip galvanized, meeting ASTM Specification A 325 for high strength carbon steel bolts.

In the Michigan[2] tests, bolted joints were tightened with impact wrenches to a torque of 200 ft-lb, or well within the working limits of the bolt tensile strength. (A torque of 300 ft-lb is recommended as a maximum.) Results of other tests are shown in Table 1-10.

Table 1-10 Ultimate Strength of Bolted Structural Plate Longitudinal Seams[9]

In Pounds Per Foot of Seam

Gage	4 Bolts Per Foot	6 Bolts Per Foot	8 Bolts Per Foot
12	42,000		
10	62,000		
8	81,000		
7	93,000		
5	112,000		
3	132,000		
1	144,000	184,000	220,000

Bolts used in tests were ¾-in. high strength bolts, meeting ASTM A 325.

SHAPES OF CONDUITS

The designer has a wide choice of standard cross-sectional shapes of corrugated steel conduits, as shown in Table 1-11. Size and service use may control the shape selected, with strength and economy as alternate factors. See Tables 1-12 through 1-15 for sizes, weights and other details of corrugated steel pipe and pipe-arch.

Table 1-11 Shapes and Uses of Corrugated Conduits

Shape		Range of Sizes	Common Uses
Round		6 in. to 21 ft	Culverts, subdrains, sewers, service tunnels, etc. All plates same radius. For medium and high fills (or trenches).
Vertically-elongated (ellipse) 5% is common		4 ft to 21 ft nominal; before elongating	Culverts, sewers, service tunnels, recovery tunnels. Plates of varying radii; shop fabrication. For appearance and where backfill compaction is only moderate.
Pipe-arch		span x rise 18 in. x 11 in. to 20 ft 7 in. x 13 ft 2 in.	Where headroom is limited. Has hydraulic advantages. Corner *plate* radius, 18 inches or 31 inches for structural plate.
Underpass*		5 ft 8 in. x 5 ft 9 in. to 20 ft 4 in. x 17 ft 10 in.	For pedestrians, livestock or vehicles (structural plate).
Arch		5 ft to 21 ft	For low clearance large waterway opening, and aesthetics (structural plate).
Specials		Various	For lining old structures or other special purposes. Special fabrication.

*For equal area or clearance, the round shape is generally more economical and simpler to assemble.

Table 1-12 Handling Weight of Corrugated Steel Pipe (2⅔ x ½ in.)

Estimated Average Weights—Not for Specification Use*

Inside Diameter in Inches	Gage No.	Approximate Pounds per Linear Foot**			
		Galvanized	Full-Coated	Full-Coated and Invert Paved	Full-Coated and Full Paved
12	16	10	12	15	
	14	12	14	17	
15	16	12	15	18	
	14	15	18	21	
18	16	15	19	22	
	14	18	22	25	
	12	24	28	31	
21	16	17	21	26	
	14	21	25	30	
	12	29	33	38	
24	16	19	24	30	45
	14	24	29	35	50
	12	·33	38	44	60
30	16	24	30	36	55
	14	30	36	42	60
	12	41	47	53	75
36	16	29	36	44	65
	14	36	43	51	75
	12	49	56	64	90
	10	62	69	77	100
42	16	34	42	51	
	14	42	50	59	85
	12	57	65	74	105
	10	72	80	89	115
48	16	38	48	57	
	14	48	58	67	95
	12	65	75	84	120
	10	82	92	101	130
	8	100	110	119	155
54	14	54	65	76	105
	12	73	84	95	130
	10	92	103	114	155
	8	112	123	134	175
60	14	60	71	85	
	12	81	92	106	140
	10	103	114	128	180
	8	124	135	149	190
66	14	65	77	93	
	12	89	101	117	160
	10	113	125	141	180
	8	137	149	165	210
72	12	98	112	129	170
	10	123	137	154	210
	8	149	163	180	240
78	12	105	121	138	200
	10	133	149	166	230
	8	161	177	194	260
84	10	144	161	179	240
	8	173	190	208	270
90	10	154	172	192	
	8	186	204	224	
96	8	198	217	239	

*Lock seam construction only; weights will vary with other fabrication practices.
**For other coatings or linings the weights may be interpolated.

Table 1-13 Handling Weight of Corrugated Steel Pipe* (3 x 1 in.)

Estimated Average Weights—Not for Specification Use

Inside Diameter, inches	Gage No.	Approximate Pounds per Linear Foot **			
		Galvanized	Full-Coated	Full-Coated and Invert Paved	Full-Coated and Full Paved
36	16	33	44	56	92
	14	41	52	64	100
	12	56	67	79	115
	10	71	82	94	130
	8	87	98	110	146
42	16	39	52	66	107
	14	47	60	74	116
	12	65	78	92	134
	10	83	96	110	152
	8	100	113	127	169
48	16	44	59	75	123
	14	54	69	85	132
	12	74	89	105	152
	10	95	110	126	174
	8	115	130	146	194
54	16	50	66	84	138
	14	61	77	95	149
	12	83	100	118	171
	10	106	123	140	194
	8	129	146	163	217
60	16	55	73	93	153
	14	67	86	105	165
	12	92	110	130	190
	10	118	136	156	216
	8	143	161	181	241
66	16	60	80	102	168
	14	74	94	116	181
	12	101	121	143	208
	10	129	149	171	236
	8	157	177	199	264
72	16	66	88	111	183
	14	81	102	126	197
	12	110	132	156	227
	10	140	162	186	257
	8	171	193	217	288
78	16	71	95	121	198
	14	87	111	137	214
	12	119	143	169	246
	10	152	176	202	279
	8	185	209	235	312
84	16	77	102	130	213
	14	94	119	147	230
	12	128	154	182	264
	10	152	177	206	288
	8	199	224	253	335

(Table continued on following page)

Table 1-13 Handling Weight of Corrugated Steel Pipe* (3 x 1 in.) (Cont.)

Inside Diameter in Inches	Gage No.	Approximate Pounds per Linear Foot**			
		Galvanized	Full-Coated	Full-Coated and Invert Paved	Full-Coated and Full Paved
90	16	82	109	140	228
	14	100	127	158	246
	12	137	164	195	283
	10	175	202	233	321
	8	213	240	271	359
96	16	87	116	149	242
	14	107	136	169	262
	12	147	176	209	302
	10	188	217	250	343
	8	228	257	290	383
102	16	93	124	158	258
	14	114	145	179	279
	12	155	186	220	320
	10	198	229	263	363
	8	241	272	306	406
108	14	120	153	188	295
	12	165	198	233	340
	10	211	244	279	386
	8	256	289	324	431
114	14	127	162	199	312
	12	174	209	246	359
	10	222	257	294	407
	8	271	306	343	456
120	12	183	220	259	378
	10	234	271	310	429
	8	284	321	360	479

*Weights vary slightly with method of fabrication; above table is based on lock seam fabrication.
**For other coatings or linings the weights may be interpolated.

Fig. 1-6. Complicated fittings can be made from corrugated steel pipe.

Table 1-14 Design Details of Corrugated Steel Pipe-Arches* ($2\frac{2}{3}$ x $\frac{1}{2}$ in.)

Diam of Pipe of Equal Periphery, Inches	Span, Inches	Rise, Inches	Waterway Area, Sq Ft	Layout Dimensions			
				B, Inches	R_c, Inches	R_t, Inches	R_b, Inches
15	18	11	1.1	$4\frac{1}{2}$	$3\frac{1}{2}$	$10\frac{1}{16}$	$19\frac{1}{8}$
18	22	13	1.6	$4\frac{3}{4}$	4	$11\frac{7}{8}$	$37\frac{1}{16}$
21	25	16	2.2	$5\frac{1}{4}$	4	$12\frac{3}{4}$	$33\frac{1}{2}$
24	29	18	2.8	$5\frac{1}{2}$	$4\frac{1}{2}$	$14\frac{3}{4}$	55
30	36	22	4.4	$6\frac{1}{4}$	5	$18\frac{1}{4}$	$73\frac{1}{4}$
36	43	27	6.4	7	$5\frac{1}{2}$	$21\frac{9}{16}$	$91\frac{9}{16}$
42	50	31	8.7	8	6	$25\frac{1}{8}$	$97\frac{1}{4}$
48	58	36	11.4	$9\frac{1}{4}$	7	$29\frac{1}{8}$	$115\frac{11}{16}$
54	65	40	14.3	$10\frac{1}{2}$	8	$32\frac{3}{4}$	$129\frac{5}{16}$
60	72	44	17.6	$11\frac{3}{4}$	9	$36\frac{5}{16}$	$142\frac{15}{16}$
66	79	49	21.3	$13\frac{1}{4}$	10	$39\frac{3}{4}$	$145\frac{1}{2}$
72	85	54	25.3	$14\frac{1}{2}$	11	$42\frac{5}{8}$	$154\frac{1}{2}$

*Data in this table is subject to manufacturing tolerances.

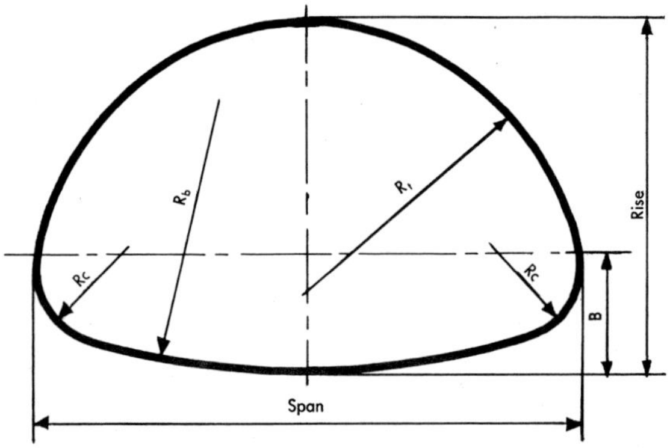

Table 1-15 Design Details of Corrugated Steel Pipe-Arches* (3 x 1 in.)

Diameter of Pipe of Equal Periphery, Inches	Span, Inches	Rise, Inches	Waterway Area, Sq Ft	Layout Dimensions			
				B, Inches	R_c, Inches	R_t, Inches	R_b, Inches
36	43	27	6.4	$9\frac{3}{4}$	$7\frac{3}{4}$	$22\frac{1}{2}$	$54\frac{3}{4}$
42	50	31	8.7	$11\frac{1}{4}$	9	$26\frac{1}{4}$	67
48	58	36	11.4	13	$10\frac{1}{2}$	$30\frac{1}{2}$	82
54	65	40	14.3	$14\frac{3}{4}$	12	$34\frac{1}{2}$	$91\frac{1}{4}$
60	72	44	17.6	$16\frac{1}{4}$	$13\frac{1}{4}$	$38\frac{1}{2}$	$98\frac{1}{2}$
66	73	55	22	21	18	$36\frac{3}{4}$	$76\frac{1}{4}$
72	81	59	26	$21\frac{1}{2}$	18	$40\frac{3}{4}$	$92\frac{3}{4}$
78	87	63	31	22	18	$43\frac{1}{2}$	$100\frac{1}{2}$
84	95	67	35	$22\frac{1}{2}$	18	$47\frac{3}{4}$	116
90	103	71	40	23	18	$51\frac{3}{4}$	$132\frac{1}{2}$

*Data in this table is subject to manufacturing tolerances.

Table 1-16 Details of Uncurved Structural Plate Steel Sections

Net Width in Inches				Over-all Width, Inches	Spaces (N) at 9.6 Inches	Number of Circumference Bolt Holes
Nominal		Detail				
3 N	9 Pi	28.8	28¹³⁄₁₆	33⁹⁄₁₆	3	4
5 N	15 Pi	48.0	48	52¾	5	6
6 N	18 Pi	57.6	57⅝	62⅜	6	7
7 N	21 Pi	67.2	67³⁄₁₆	71¹⁵⁄₁₆	7	8
8 N	24 Pi	76.8	76¹³⁄₁₆	81	8	9

N = 3 Pi = 9.6 inches.   6″ x 2″ Corrugations.

DATA ON STRUCTURAL PLATE—FIELD ASSEMBLED

Description of Plates. Structural plates are field assembled into pipes, arches, pipe-arches, "underpasses" and other shapes. Corrugations of 6-in. pitch and 2-in. depth are at right angles to the length of each plate.

Gage. Thickness or gage of the plates varies from No. 12 to No. 1 (approximately 0.1046 in. to 0.2758 in. for uncoated plates). See table of sectional properties, Table 1-8.

Widths. Standard plates are fabricated in five net covering widths, 28.8 in., 48.0 in., 57.6 in., 67.2 in. and 76.8 in. Table 1-16. Fig. 1-8. These covering widths are listed by the manufacturers either in terms of *pi* or *N* (*N* = 3 *pi*).

The *pi* nomenclature translates circumference directly into nominal diameter, in inches. For example, four 15 *pi* plates gives a diameter of 60 in.; four 21 *pi* plates = 84 in., etc. Various widths may be used to obtain any standard diameters.

To obtain the number *N* in a pipe ring, the nominal diameter is divided by 3. With the number *N* determined, any combination of the four plate widths available in any gage can be used to form the specified pipe section. For example, a 60-in. diameter structural plate pipe contains 20 *N*.

This section is best provided through use of four *5N* plates, or a total of *20N*. Other combinations could be used for *20N*.

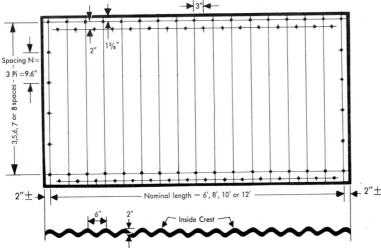

Fig. 1-8. Details of uncurved structural plate.

Table 1-17 Weight of Structural Plate Sections

Net Width		Net Length in Feet	Approximate Weight of Individual Plates Galvanized—in Pounds—without Bolts*							Short Bolts per plate**
No. of N	Inches		12 Gage	10 Gage	8 Gage	7 Gage	5 Gage	3 Gage	1 Gage	
3 N	9 Pi	6	97	124	151	164	191	218	245	22
3 N	9 Pi	8	128	164	199	217	252	288	323	30
3 N	9 Pi	10	161	205	250	272	316	361	405	38
3 N	9 Pi	12	193	246	299	325	379	432	485	46
5 N	15 Pi	6	153	196	238	259	302	344	386	24
5 N	15 Pi	8	203	258	314	342	398	454	510	32
5 N	15 Pi	10	253	323	393	428	498	568	638	40
5 N	15 Pi	12	303	386	470	511	595	678	762	48
6 N	18 Pi	6	182	232	282	307	357	407	457	25
6 N	18 Pi	8	240	306	372	405	471	537	603	33
6 N	18 Pi	10	299	382	465	506	589	671	754	41
6 N	18 Pi	12	357	456	555	604	703	801	900	49
7 N	21 Pi	6	210	267	325	354	412	470	528	26
7 N	21 Pi	8	278	353	429	467	544	620	696	34
7 N	21 Pi	10	345	441	536	583	679	774	869	42
7 N	21 Pi	12	412	526	640	697	810	924	1038	50
8 N	24 Pi	10	396	504	613	667	775	878	986	43
8 N	24 Pi	12	473	603	732	797	927	1050	1176	51
Bolt lengths, in.			1¼ and 1½				1½ and 1¾		1½ and 2	Each plate also has 4 long bolts

*Weights are approximate; based on standard 4-hole punching in longitudinal seams. Plates are galvanized, 2 oz per sq ft of double-exposed surface, AASHO Spec.   6″ x 2″ Corrugations.

**Weight of bolts only   1¼″ = 36 lb   2″ = 46 lb
   in lb per hundred: 1½″ = 40.   3″ = 58.
                   1¾″ = 42.   Nuts = 20.

To compute approximate weight of structures per foot of length: (1) multiply by "no. of plates in periphery" (Tables 1–18 thru 1–20 and 1–22); (2) add weight of bolts and divide by plate length.
N = 3 pi = 9.6 inches

Lengths. Structural plates are furnished either in 6 and 8-ft nominal lengths, *or* 10 and 12-ft nominal lengths. They are punched with ⅞-in. holes on 3-in. centers to provide the standard 4 bolts per ft of longitudinal seam, in two staggered rows on 2-in. centers. They may also be punched to provide either 6 or 8 bolts per ft of longitudinal seam on No. 1 gage material, if required.

The inside crests of the end corrugations are punched for circumferential seams on centers of 9.6 in. or 9¹⁹⁄₃₂ in. (= 3 *pi* or *N*).

Actual length of the square-end structure is about 4 in. longer than its nominal length because a 2-in. lip protrudes beyond each end of every plate for lapping purposes.

Curvature. Plates are furnished curved to various radii as indicated in tables 1-18 through 1-22.

Weights of individual plate sections are shown in Table 1-17. Approximate weights of structural plate structures are readily computed.

Plate sections are clearly marked and delivered to the job site ready for field assembly into full-round pipe, elliptical pipe, arch, pipe-arch or any special shape. Detailed instructions for assembly accompany each structure.

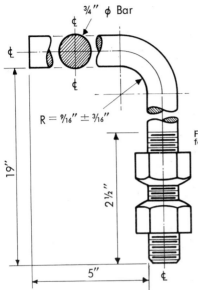

¾" φ Bar

R = 9/16" ± 3/16"

19"

2½"

5"

Fig. 1-9. Hook bolts and nuts
for imbedment in headwalls.

Table 1-18 Sizes of Structural Plate Steel Pipe[13]

Pipe Diameter in Feet	End Area in Sq Ft	Periphery No. of Plates	N	Total Pi	Pipe Diameter in Feet	End Area in Sq Ft	Periphery No. of Plates	N	Total Pi
5	19.6	4	20	60	14.5	165.1	10	58	174
5.5	23.8	4	22	66	15	176.7	10	60	180
6	28.3	4	24	72	15.5	188.7	10	62	186
6.5	33.2	4	26	78	16	201.1	10	64	192
7	38.5	4	28	84	16.5	213.8	10	66	198
					17	227.0	10	68	204
7.5	44.2	6	30	90	17.5	240.5	10	70	210
8	50.3	6	32	96					
8.5	56.7	6	34	102	18	254.5	12	72	216
9	63.6	6	36	108	18.5	268.8	12	74	222
9.5	70.9	6	38	114	19	283.5	12	76	228
10	78.5	6	40	120	19.5	298.6	12	78	234
10.5	86.6	6	42	126	20	314.2	12	80	240
					20.5	330.1	12	82	246
11	95.0	8	44	132	21	346.4	12	84	252
11.5	103.9	8	46	138					
12	113.1	8	48	144					
12.5	122.7	8	50	150					
13	132.7	8	52	156					
13.5	143.1	8	54	162					
14	153.9	8	56	168					

N = 3 Pi = 9.6 in.   6" x 2" Corrugations—Bolted Seams

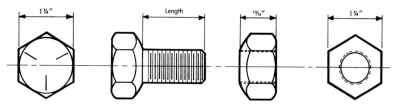

Fig. 1-10. Dimensions of bolts and nuts for structural plate. Lengths include: 1¼ in., 1½ in., 1¾ in., 2 in. and 3 in. The containers and bolt heads may come in individual color markings for ease in identification.

BOLTS AND NUTS

Galvanized ¾-in. diameter bolts and nuts, of special heat-treated steel meeting ASTM Specification A325, are used to assemble structural plate sections. The bolts and nuts must meet ASTM Specification A153 on galvanizing. See Fig. 1-10 for dimensions of bolts and nuts. These are designed for fitting either the crest or valley of the corrugations, and to give maximum bearing area and tight seams without the use of washers.

Power wrenches are generally used, but simple hand wrenches are satisfactory for small structures. The approximate weights of bolts of various lengths and nuts per hundred are: 1¼ in., 36 lb; 1½ in., 40 lb; 1¾ in., 42 lb; 2 in., 46 lb; 3 in., 58 lb; Nuts, 20 lb. Bolt heads are color coded for the different lengths.

Hook Bolts are available for anchoring the ends of structural plate conduits into concrete headwalls or other end treatment (when required). These special galvanized ¾-in. hook bolts must meet ASTM Specification A307 and A325 for the nuts; both bolts and nuts must meet ASTM A153 on galvanizing. Fig. 1-9.

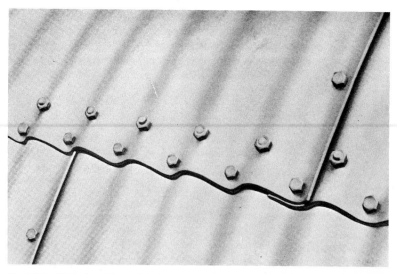

Fig. 1-11. High-strength steel bolts are used for the circumferential and longitudinal seams of structural plate pipe. Four, six or eight bolts per foot of longitudinal seam provide the strength required for the loading conditions.

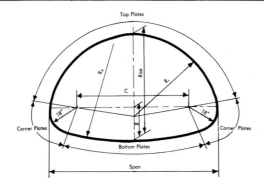

Table 1-19 Sizes and Layout Details—Structural Plate Steel Pipe-Arches
6 in. x 2 in. Corrugations—Bolted Seams
18-inch Corner Radius R_c

Dimensions			Layout Dimensions			Periphery		
Span Ft-In.	Rise Ft-In.	Waterway Area in Sq Ft	B in In.	R_t in Ft	R_b in Ft	No. of Plates	Total N	Pi
6-1	4-7	22	21.0	3.07	6.36	5	22	66
6-4	4-9	24	20.5	3.18	8.22	5	23	69
6-9	4-11	26	22.0	3.42	6.96	5	24	72
7-0	5-1	28	21.4	3.53	8.68	5	25	75
7-3	5-3	31	20.8	3.63	11.35	6	26	78
7-8	5-5	33	22.4	3.88	9.15	6	27	81
7-11	5-7	35	21.7	3.98	11.49	6	28	84
8-2	5-9	38	20.9	4.08	15.24	6	29	87
8-7	5-11	40	22.7	4.33	11.75	7	30	90
8-10	6-1	43	21.9	4.42	14.89	7	31	93
9-4	6-3	46	23.8	4.68	12.05	7	32	96
9-6	6-5	49	22.9	4.78	14.79	7	33	99
9-9	6-7	52	21.9	4.86	18.98	7	34	102
10-3	6-9	55	24.0	5.13	14.86	7	35	105
10-8	6-11	58	26.1	5.41	12.77	7	36	108
10-11	7-1	61	25.1	5.49	15.03	7	37	111
11-5	7-3	64	27.4	5.78	13.16	7	38	114
11-7	7-5	67	26.3	5.85	15.27	8	39	117
11-10	7-7	71	25.2	5.93	18.03	8	40	120
12-4	7-9	74	27.5	6.23	15.54	8	41	123
12-6	7-11	78	26.4	6.29	18.07	8	42	126
12-8	8-1	81	25.2	6.37	21.45	8	43	129
12-10	8-4	85	24.0	6.44	26.23	8	44	132
13-5	8-5	89	26.4	6.73	21.23	9	45	135
13-11	8-7	93	28.9	7.03	18.39	9	46	138
14-1	8-9	97	27.6	7.09	21.18	9	47	141
14-3	8-11	101	26.3	7.16	24.80	9	48	144
14-10	9-1	105	28.9	7.47	21.19	9	49	147
15-4	9-3	109	31.6	7.78	18.90	9	50	150
15-6	9-5	113	30.2	7.83	21.31	10	51	153
15-8	9-7	118	28.8	7.89	24.29	10	52	156
15-10	9-10	122	27.5	7.96	28.18	10	53	159
16-5	9-11	126	30.1	8.27	24.24	10	54	162
16-7	10-1	131	28.7	8.33	27.73	10	55	165

Dimensions are to inside crests and are subject to manufacturing tolerances.
$N = 3$ Pi $= 9.6$ in.

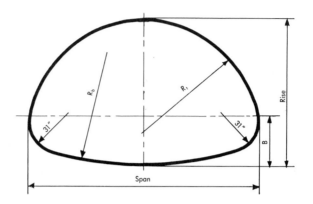

Table 1-20 Sizes and Layout Details—Structural Plate Steel Pipe-Arches[13]
6 in. x 2 in. Corrugations—Bolted Seams
31-inch Corner Radius, R_c

Dimensions			Layout Dimensions				Periphery	
Span Ft-In.	Rise Ft-In.	Waterway Area, in Sq Ft	B in In.	R_t in Ft	R_b in Ft	No. of Plates	Total N	Pi
13-3	9-4	98	38.6	6.68	16.05	8	46	138
13-6	9-6	102	37.8	6.78	18.33	8	47	141
14-0	9-8	106	39.6	7.03	16.49	8	48	144
14-2	9-10	110	38.9	7.13	18.55	8	49	147
14-5	10-0	115	38.0	7.22	21.38	8	50	150
14-11	10-2	119	39.9	7.48	18.98	9	51	153
15-4	10-4	124	41.9	7.76	17.38	9	52	156
15-7	10-6	129	41.0	7.84	19.34	10	53	159
15-10	10-8	133	40.1	7.93	21.72	10	54	162
16-3	10-10	138	42.2	8.21	19.67	10	55	165
16-6	11-0	143	41.2	8.29	21.93	10	56	168
17-0	11-2	148	43.4	8.58	20.08	10	57	171
17-2	11-4	153	42.4	8.65	22.23	10	58	174
17-5	11-6	158	41.4	8.73	24.83	10	59	177
17-11	11-8	163	43.6	9.02	22.55	10	60	180
18-1	11-10	168	42.5	9.09	24.98	10	61	183
18-7	12-0	174	44.8	9.38	22.88	10	62	186
18-9	12-2	179	43.7	9.46	25.19	10	63	189
19-3	12-4	185	46.0	9.75	23.22	10	64	192
19-6	12-6	190	44.9	9.83	25.43	11	65	195
19-8	12-8	196	43.8	9.90	28.04	11	66	198
19-11	12-10	202	42.6	9.98	31.19	11	67	201
20-5	13-0	208	45.0	10.27	28.18	11	68	204
20-7	13-2	214	43.8	10.33	31.13	12	69	207

Dimensions are to inside crests and are subject to manufacturing tolerances.
$N = 3$ Pi $= 9.6$ in.

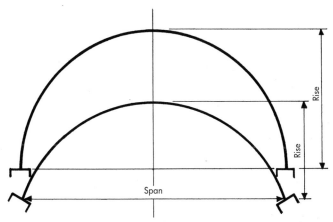

Table 1-21 Representative Sizes of Structural Plate Steel Arches

Dimensions(¹)		Waterway Area, in Sq Ft	Rise over Span(²)	Radius, in In.	Nominal Arc Length	
Span, in Feet	Rise, Ft-In.				N(³)	Pi, In.
6.0	1-9½	7½	0.30	41	9	27
	2-3½	10	.38	37½	10	30
	3-2	15	.53	36	12	36
7.0	2-4	12	.34	45	11	33
	2-10	15	.40	43	12	36
	3-8	20	.52	42	14	42
8.0	2-11	17	.37	51	13	39
	3-4	20	.42	48½	14	42
	4-2	26	.52	48	16	48
9.0	2-11	18½	.32	59	14	42
	3-10½	26½	.43	55	16	48
	4-8½	33	.52	54	18	54
10.0	3-5½	25	.35	64	16	48
	4-5	34	.44	60½	18	54
	5-3	41	.52	60	20	60
11.0	3-6	27½	.32	73	17	51
	4-5½	37	.41	67½	19	57
	5-9	50	.52	66	22	66
12.0	4-0½	35	.34	77½	19	57
	5-0	45	.42	73	21	63
	6-3	59	.52	72	24	72
13.0	4-1	38	.32	86½	20	60
	5-1	49	.39	80½	22	66
	6-9	70	.52	78	26	78
14.0	4-7½	47	.33	91	22	66
	5-7	58	.40	86	24	72
	7-3	80	.52	84	28	84

(*Table continued on following page*)

(¹)Dimensions are to inside crests and are subject to manufacturing tolerances.
(²)R/S ratio varies from 0.30 to 0.52. Intermediate spans and rises are available.
(³)N = 3 Pi = 9.6 in. 6″ x 2″ Corrugations—Bolted Seams.

Table 1-21 Representative Sizes of Structural Plate Steel Arches (Cont'd.)

Span, in Ft	Rise, Ft-In.	Waterway Area, in Sq Ft	Rise over Span[2]	Radius, in In.	N[3]	Pi, In.
15.0	4-7½	50	0.31	101	23	69
	5-8	62	.38	93	25	75
	6-7	75	.44	91	27	81
	7-9	92	.52	90	30	90
16.0	5-2	60	.32	105	25	75
	7-1	86	.45	97	29	87
	8-3	105	.52	96	32	96
17.0	5-2½	63	.31	115	26	78
	7-2	92	.42	103	30	90
	8-10	119	.52	102	34	102
18.0	5-9	75	.32	119	28	84
	7-8	104	.43	109	32	96
	8-11	126	.50	108	35	105
19.0	6-4	87	.33	123	30	90
	8-2	118	.43	115	34	102
	9-5½	140	.50	114	37	111
20.0	6-4	91	.32	133	31	93
	8-3½	124	.42	122	35	105
	10-0	157	.50	120	39	117
21.0	6-11	104	.33	137	33	99
	8-10	140	.42	128	37	111
	10-6	172	.50	126	41	123
22.0	6-11	109	.31	146	34	102
	8-11	146	.40	135	38	114
	11-0	190	.50	132	43	129
23.0	8-0	134	.35	147	37	111
	9-10	171	.43	140	41	123
	11-6	208	.50	138	45	135
24.0	8-6	150	.35	152	39	117
	10-4	188	.43	146	43	129
	12-0	226	.50	144	47	141
25.0	8-6½	155	.34	160	40	120
	10-10½	207	.43	152	45	135
	12-6	247	.50	150	49	147

The table heading above the Span/Rise columns reads "Dimensions[1]".

[1]Dimensions are to inside crests and are subject to manufacturing tolerances.
[2]R/S ratio varies from 0.30 to 0.52. Intermediate spans and rises are available.
[3]N = 3 Pi = 9.6 in.   6″ x 2″ corrugations—Bolted Seams

ARCH CHANNELS

For arch seats, galvanized unbalanced channels with anchor lugs are available. Fig. 1-12.

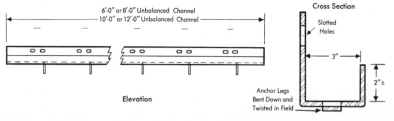

Fig. 1-12. General dimensions of unbalanced channels for structural plate arches.

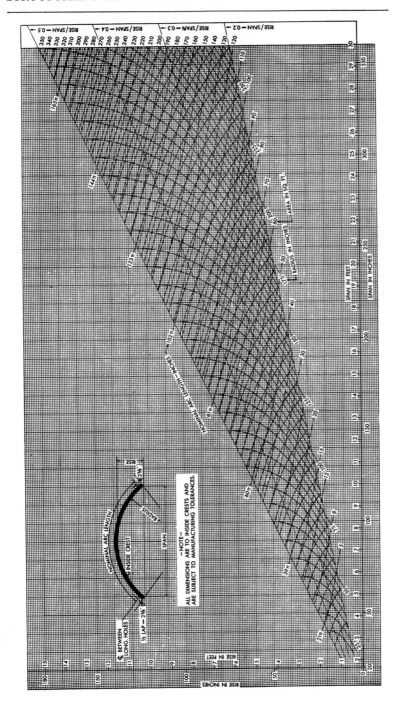

Fig. 1-13. Rise, span radius and area of structural plate arches. (Reference No. 11)

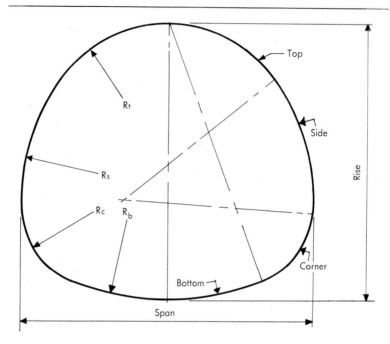

Table 1-22 Structural Plate Steel Underpasses[12]

Sizes and Layout Details

Span x Rise in Ft and In.		Periphery			Layout Dimensions in Inches			
		N	Pi	No. of Plates per Ring	R_t	R_s	R_c	R_b
5-8	5-9	24	72	6	27	53	18	Flat
5-8	6-6	26	78	6	29	75	18	Flat
5-9	7-4	28	84	6	28	95	18	Flat
5-10	7-8	29	87	7	30	112	18	Flat
5-10	8-2	30	90	6	28	116	18	Flat
12-2	11-0	47	141	8	68	93	38	136
12-11	11-2	49	147	9	74	92	38	148
13-2	11-10	51	153	11	73	102	38	161
13-10	12-2	53	159	11	77	106	38	168
14-1	12-10	55	165	11	77	115	38	183
14-6	13-5	57	171	11	78	131	38	174
14-10	14-0	59	177	11	79	136	38	193
15-6	14-4	61	183	12	83	139	38	201
15-8	15-0	63	189	12	82	151	38	212
16-4	15-5	65	195	12	86	156	38	217
16-5	16-0	67	201	12	88	159	38	271
16-9	16-3	68	204	12	89	168	38	246
17-3	17-0	70	210	12	90	174	47	214
18-4	16-11	72	216	12	99	157	47	248
19-1	17-2	74	222	13	105	156	47	262
19-6	17-7	76	228	13	107	158	47	295
20-4	17-9	78	234	13	114	155	47	316

All dimensions, to nearest whole number, are measured from inside crests.
Tolerances should be allowed for specification purposes.   6" x 2" Corrugations.

Fig. 1-14. Bolts may be tightened from the side most convenient or accessible.

REFERENCES AND BIBLIOGRAPHY

1. American Iron and Steel Institute, *Sectional Properties of Corrugated Steel Sheets*, New York, N. Y., 1960, 17 pp.
2. Huber, M. J. and Childs, L. D., *Load Deflection Tests on Corrugated Metal Sections*, Michigan State University, Engineering Experiment Station, E. Lansing, Mich., Bulletin 109, 1951, 62 pp.
3. Wolford, D. S., *Sectional Properties of Corrugated Sheets Determined by Formula*, Civil Engineering, Vol. 24, No. 2, Feb. 1954, pp. 103–104.
4. Unpublished Investigation, *Computer-Calculated Sectional Properties of Arc and Tangent Corrugations as Applied to HEL-COR Pipe*, Macadam, J. N., Sept. 1964. Research and Technology, Armco Steel Corporation, Middletown, Ohio.
5. Unpublished Investigation, *Sectional Properties of Liner Plate, Sheeting, Guard Rail and Bridge Plank*, Jan. 1965. Mullikin, J. D., Armco Steel Corp., Research and Technology, Middletown, Ohio.
6. Unpublished Investigation, *Sectional Properties of Corrugations for Steel Culverts*, Feb. 1965, Macadam, J. N., 12 pp. Armco Steel Corp., Research and Technology, Middletown, Ohio.
7. Kay, B. J., *Culvert Design Based on Structural Strength*, Utah Dept. of Highways. Panel discussion at Annual Meeting of AASHO, Region IV, Phoenix, Ariz., Sept. 15, 1964.
8. Pittsburgh Testing Laboratories Report PG 12590, May 16, 1966.
9. Unpublished Investigation, *Testing of Multi-Plate Seam Strength*, Nov. 1951. Armco Steel Corporation, Research and Technology, Middletown, Ohio.
10. *Hel-Cor Pipe for Culverts and Storm Sewers*, Armco Metal Products Div., Middletown, Ohio. Catalog HC-4563, 1964, 12 pp.
11. *Handbook of Drainage and Construction Products*, Armco Drainage & Metal Products, Inc. Middletown, Ohio, 1955, 529 pp.
12. *Armco Multi-Plate Manual*, Armco Metal Products Div., Middletown, Ohio, 1966, 60 pp.
13. *Armco Multi-Plate Pipe*, Armco Metal Products Div., Middletown, Ohio, Catalog MP-1664, 1964, 16 pp.
14. Lane, W. W., *Comparative Studies on Corrugated Metal Culvert Pipes*, Ohio Dept. of Highways and U.S. BPR, Report No. EES-236, Ohio State Univ. Eng. Experiment Sta., Columbus, Ohio, 1965, 120 pp.

Fig. 2-1. Mainline railroad crosses over twin 20-ft No. 5 gage structural plate highway underpasses.

CHAPTER 2 Strength Design

INTRODUCTION

Half a century of research on the magnitude and distribution of soil pressures on underground conduits has unearthed a vast store of helpful knowledge. One promising field for continued research is that which regards soil as a construction material, combining soil with steel as a composite structure.

Design methods set forth here stem from more than 60 years' satisfactory field experience with buried flexible structures. From such experience has come a newly coordinated design approach that encourages simultaneous consideration of all major variables known to influence performance of the buried structure.

To the extent that it considers the over-all needs of the drainage structure—environment, service demands, strength requirements under dead and live loads—this design procedure represents a significant advance over earlier methods still practiced widely. Continuous computer analysis is practical and is an anticipated future development when sufficient research more completely evaluates the influence of different soils and compactions on the structure.

Major topics in this chapter are treated in the same sequence in which decisions are made in the design of buried structures. These are:

    I *Computation of Loads*
   II *Culvert Structural Design*
  III *Earth Backfill Design*
  IV *Foundation Preparation*
   V *Minimum Cover*
  VI *End Treatment*
 VII *Maintenance*

FUNCTION OF STRUCTURE

Three principal types of underground conduits were introduced briefly in Chapter 1. These types include conduits for:

- Surface drainage, such as culverts, storm sewers and stream enclosures. See Chapter 8 *Culverts*, Chapter 9 *Sewers*, Chapter 12 *Erosion Prevention*, Chapter 13 *Dam and Levee Drainage*.
- Subdrainage for controlling underground water. See Chapter 10 *Subdrainage* and Chapter 11 *Airport Drainage*.
- Traffic underpasses, service passageways, conduits. See Chapter 15 *Underpasses and Service Tunnels*.

SIZE AND SHAPE

The function served by the structure will determine its size and shape. Individual conduit openings can range from 6-in. diameter to 21-ft diameter, or about 350 sq ft. The cross sectional area is determined by procedures outlined in Chapter 4 *Hydraulics* and in related chapters. Several fundamental shapes are available: round, elliptical, pipe-arch and arch.

STRUCTURAL TYPES PRODUCED

An underground conduit may be specified by method of manufacture and assembly, by size and shape of the structure, by dimensions of corrugations, and by gages.

Shop-assembled structures are fabricated in several ways, such as by riveting, by resistance spot welding and by helical lock seam. Field-assembled products are made as individual corrugated and curved plates that are bolted together at the job site. The choice between shop and field assembly must consider handling and shipping limitations as well as manufacturing practices.

Existing manufacturing methods and conduit strength requirements have led to the use of five corrugation profiles (See Table 2-1).

Table 2-1   Steel Conduit Types Generally Available

Size Diam. or Span	Shape	Assembly and Manufacturing Method	Corrugation Type and Size	Gages
6, 8, 10 in.	Round	Shop Assembled Lock Seam	Helical 1½ x ¼ in.	18, 16, 14
12 thru 48 in.	Round, Elliptical, and Pipe-Arch	Shop Assembled Lock Seam	2 x ½ in.	18, 16, 14 12
12 thru 96 in.	Round, Elliptical, and Pipe-Arch	Shop Assembled Lock Seam	2⅔ x ½ in.	18, 16, 14, 12, 10, 8
36 thru 120 in.	Round, Elliptical, and Pipe-Arch	Shop Assembled Lock Seam	3x 1 in.	18, 16, 14, 12, 10, 8
8 thru 96 in.	Round, Elliptical, and Pipe-Arch	Shop Assembled Riveted or Spot Welded Seam	Annular 2⅔ x ½ in.	18, 16, 14, 12, 10, 8
36 thru 120 in.	Round, Elliptical, and Pipe-Arch	Shop Assembled Riveted or Spot Welded Seam	3 x 1 in.	18, 16, 14, 12, 10, 8
5 thru 21 ft	Round, Elliptical, Pipe-Arch, Arch, and Underpass	Field Assembled Bolted	6 x 2 in.	12, 10, 8, 7, 5, 3, 1

Section I—COMPUTATION OF LOADS

First consideration in design is the evaluation of the loads on the conduit. Underground conduits are subject to two principal kinds of loads:

(1) dead loads developed by the embankment or trench backfill, plus stationary superimposed surface loads, uniform or concentrated; and

(2) live loads—moving loads, including impact.*

HISTORY OF LOAD DETERMINATION

Earliest "strength tests" on corrugated steel pipe were quite crude. The tests included circus elephants balanced on unburied pipe and threshing rigs placed over shallow buried pipe.

Laboratory "sand box" and hydraulic tests followed later, by Talbot,

---

*For loads on structures above ground, see Chapter 21 *Aerial Conduits.*

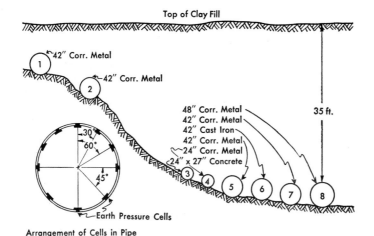

Fig. 2-2. American Railway Engineering Association tests on culvert pipe were run at Farina, Ill. Readings were taken on earth pressure cells.

Fowler and others. Fill loads were measured on buried pipe and on their foundations at Iowa State College (Marston, Spangler and others, 1913)[1] and at the University of North Carolina (Braune, Cain, Janda)[2] in cooperation with the U S Bureau of Public Roads.

Early efforts to rationalize the load-carrying performance of flexible conduits led to the concept of *passive side pressures* and the *Iowa Formula* for predicting deflection[3, 4]. Other formulas, mostly empirical, were devised. All of these have proved valuable in extending the use of flexible structures in larger sizes and under higher fills.

FARINA TEST

Large-scale field tests measuring dead loads were run in 1923 on the Illinois Central Railroad at Farina, Ill.[5] by American Railway Engineering Association (AREA). Measurements with earth pressure cells showed that flexible corrugated pipes carried only 60 per cent of the 35-ft column or prism of fill above it while adjacent soil carried the remaining 40 per cent of the load. These tests demonstrated for the first time that flexible conduit and compacted earth embankment can combine to act as a composite structure. See Figs. 2-2, 2-3.

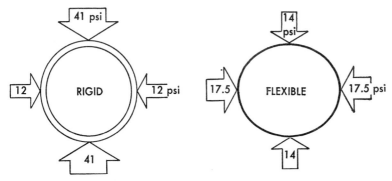

Fig. 2-3. Comparative vertical and horizontal pressures on rigid and flexible pipes of equal diameter in AREA tests at Farina, Ill.

Fig. 2-4. Load test of steel ingots on 20-ft span pipe-arch for a railroad. Special backfill procedures enabled this structure to carry 1000 tons over the center portion without failure.

DEAD LOADS

Dead loads on a buried conduit may be greater or less than the actual weight of the column of fill material above the conduit. The dead load varies with: (1) firmness of the foundation beneath the conduit, (2) firmness of the fill above and beside the conduit, (2a) settlement or consolidation of the fill in a trench, and (3) stiffness of the conduit wall.

If the top of the conduit deflects more than the soil at that elevation, the load will be *reduced* by arching action of the soil when the covering is of sufficient height. Conversely, if the conduit yields less than the soil on both sides at the top of the conduit, the load will be *increased* by development of an inverted earth arch. See Fig. 2-5.

With normal foundation preparation and backfill consolidation, observations to date indicate that corrugated steel conduits can be expected to yield more than the adjacent compacted soil. A value of *80 percent* of the calculated weight of the column above the structure can be reasonably and conservatively assumed. Thus, with normal fill material, about 100 lb per cu ft may be assumed as the earth load on the conduit.

LIVE LOADS

Live loads on an embankment (or trench fill) cause a loading on the conduit that decreases in magnitude as the height of cover above the conduit increases. Several accepted methods exist for determining distribution of live loads; however, no significant difference will be found in the designed structure when any of the accepted methods are used.

Highway. For designing highway culverts and bridges, American Association of State Highway Officials has adopted "standard vehicles" that produce

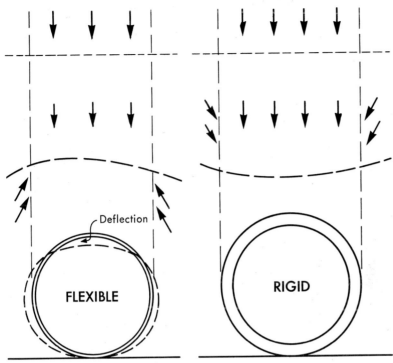

Fig. 2-5. Sketches showing how relative settlement of foundation and backfill and rigidity of conduit influence the load reaching the conduit. For flexible culverts, a value of 80 percent of prism of earth over the structure is considered reasonable.

Fig. 2-6. Twin 15-foot diameter structural plate pipes under an Interstate highway.

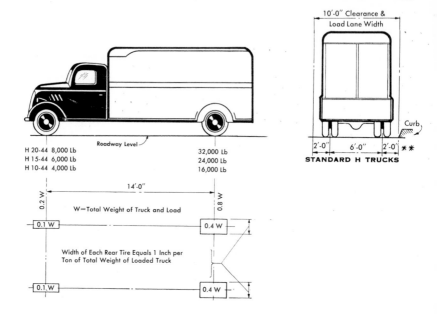

*In the design of floors (concrete slabs, steel grid floors, and timber floors) for H 20 or H 20—S 16 loading, one axle load of 24,000 pounds or two axle loads of 16,000 pounds each, spaced 4 feet apart, may be used, whichever produces the greater stress, instead of 32,000 pound axle shown.

**For slab design the center line of wheel shall be assumed to be 1 foot from face of curb.

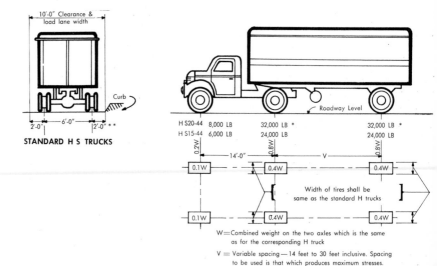

Fig. 2-7. Standard highway loadings, H and HS, for bridge floors (and culverts). After Standard Specifications for Highway Bridges, AASHO.

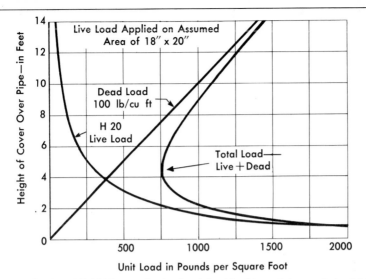

Fig. 2-8. Combined H 20 highway live load and dead load is a minimum at about 4 ft of cover, applied through a pavement 1 ft thick.

representative live loadings on the surface. These loadings, designated H 20, H 15, H 10, HS 20 and HS 15 represent gross load in tons.[6] See Fig. 2–7. AASHO maximum tandem axle loading is 32,000 lbs.

Railway. Similarly, American Railway Engineering Association (AREA) has adopted standard "Cooper Loadings" for live loads on bridges. For Cooper E 72, maximum loading is 72,000 lbs per axle.[7] See Figs. 2-9 and 2-10.

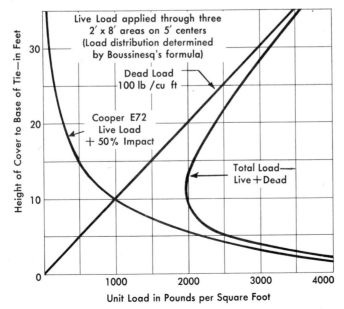

Fig. 2-9. Railroad live load, Cooper E 72, combined with dead load, is a minimum at about 11 ft. Load is applied through three 2 ft by 8 ft areas on 5-ft centers.

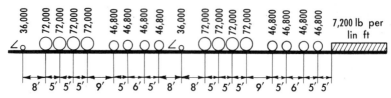

Fig. 2-10. Spacing of wheel loads per axle for a standard Cooper E 72 locomotive loading. Loads are at rail level.—After AREA manual.

In practice, live loads on the conduit due to highway and railway traffic are related to the design of underground conduits through charts prepared by the corrugated steel pipe industry. (Figs. 2-8 and 2-9.) These charts modify the theoretical distribution of live loads to values compatible with observed performance of structures under relatively light covers. Minimum cover recommendations are given in this chapter under Section V *Minimum Cover*.

Table 2-2   Highway and Railway Live Loads

Highway H 20 Loading*   Railway E 72 Loading*

Height of Cover (Ft)	Load, psf	Height of Cover (Ft)	Load, psf
1	1800	2	3400
2	800	5	2200
3	600	8	1400
4	400	10	1000
5	250	12	700
6	200	15	500
7	175	20	300
8	100	30	100

*Neglect live load when less than 100 psf; use dead load only.

Airport. Research is under way in design of minimum cover for airfield conduits, notably by the Corps of Engineers. Tentative recommendations are available from the Federal Aviation Agency.

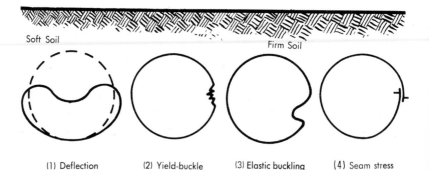

Soft Soil   Firm Soil

(1) Deflection   (2) Yield-buckle   (3) Elastic buckling   (4) Seam stress
   (Flattening)   (Crushing)   (Oil-Can Snap)   (Failure)

Fig. 2-11. Factors to design for in flexible conduits.

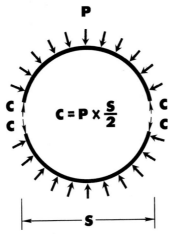

Fig. 2-12. Formula for ring compression design.

Section II—CULVERT STRUCTURAL DESIGN

The structural design of a conduit includes an investigation of seam strength, buckling strength, installation rigidity, and deflection under load. Fig. 2-11. An explanation of these factors and appropriate design equations are given below. A calculation of ring compression must precede the determination of seam strength and buckling strength. Fig. 2-12.

CONDUIT WALL COMPRESSION

As the active dead and live load over a flexible conduit increases, the top of the conduit deflects vertically downward while the sides deflect laterally outward and mobilize passive earth pressures. The combined effects of the active and passive pressures create a relatively uniform circumferential compressive thrust in the conduit wall, while the vertical and lateral movements cause bending stresses. The bending stresses are generally not critical because any resultant yielding is arrested by the support from the surrounding soil mass and do not tend to cause failure of the steel conduit. However, the compressive thrust is important since it can cause either a seam failure or a buckling failure.

It has been shown that the ring compression in a conduit[8] can be obtained from the equation:

$$C = \frac{PS}{2} = (DL + LL)\frac{\text{Span}}{2} \qquad (1)$$

where C = conduit wall compression thrust, lb/ft

$\quad\ \ P$ = dead load + live load, psf

$\quad DL$ = dead load pressure at top of conduit, psf*

$\qquad$ = 100 × height of cover, feet

$\quad LL$ = live load pressure at top of conduit, psf*

Span = maximum horizontal conduit dimension, feet

*See Fig. 2-8 for highways and Fig. 2-9 for railways. Table 2-2 gives values of LL for both highways and railways.

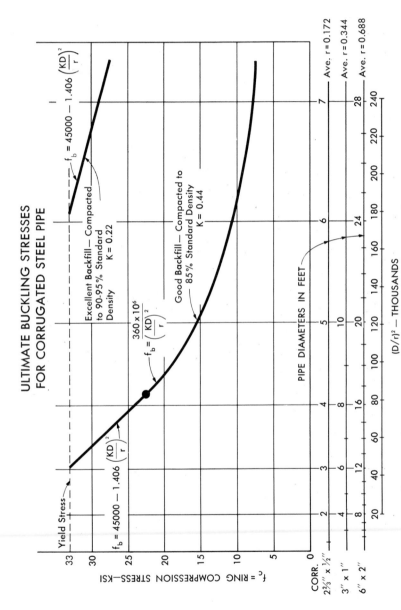

Fig. 2-13. Ultimate buckling stresses for two types of backfill ("good" and "excellent").

SEAM STRENGTH

Design for seam strength is accomplished by limiting the conduit wall compression to the ultimate strength of the seam divided by a factor of safety, *FS*. Values of seam strength obtained from tests are given in Tables 2–4, 2–5, page 52.

BUCKLING STRENGTH

Ultimate buckling stresses for corrugated steel pipe are shown in Fig. 2-13. The curves are based on tests of models placed in compacted soil and tested to failure.[20] As indicated by the two curves, buckling occurs at a higher stress with excellent backfill, compacted to 95 percent AASHO density, than with good backfill, 85 percent AASHO density. The buckling stress may be expressed by the following equations, the first of which represents elastic buckling while the second represents an interaction of buckling and yielding:

$$f_b = \frac{12\,E}{\left(\dfrac{KD}{r}\right)^2} \text{ when } D > 126\frac{r}{K} \tag{2}$$

$$f_b = 45{,}000 - 1.40\left(\frac{KD}{r}\right)^2 \text{ when } 92.4\frac{r}{K} < D < 126\frac{r}{K} \tag{2A}$$

where f_b = ultimate buckling stress, psi

    K = soil stiffness factor (see Fig. 2-13)

    D = conduit diameter, in.

    r = radius of gyration (see Fig. 2-13)

    E = modulus of elasticity, psi

For diameters less than $92.4\ r/K$, wall crushing occurs and f_b may be taken as the yield point, 33,000 psi.

Design for buckling is accomplished by limiting the ring compression to the stress (psi) at buckling, multiplied by the conduit wall area (in.^{2}/ft) and divided by the Safety Factor[9] (*FS*).

HANDLING AND INSTALLATION

Flexible conduits must have adequate rigidity to maintain their shape for handling, shipping, and installation. Under any arbitrary loading, such as those encountered during installation or handling, the relative elastic deflection of a conduit is proportional to the ratio D^2/EI, the flexibility factor, FF. Expressed as a formula:

$$FF = D^2/EI \tag{3}$$

where D = pipe diameter or maximum span, in.

    E = modulus of elasticity of the pipe material, psi

    I = moment of inertia per unit length of cross section of the pipe wall, in., to the 4th power per in. See Table 2-3, p. 50.

Since it would be impractical to determine a theoretical value for this ratio, empirical maximum values have been established based on experience.

MAXIMUM FLEXIBILITY FACTORS

For steel conduits, FF should generally not exceed the following values:

For $2\frac{2}{3}'' \times \frac{1}{2}''$ corrugation   FF = 0.0433
  $3'' \times 1''$ corrugation   FF = 0.0433
  $6'' \times 2''$ corrugation   FF = 0.0200

Table 2-3   Moment of Inertia and Cross Sectional Wall Area of Corrugated Steel Sheets and Plates for Drainage Conduits

Corrugation Dimensions	Moment of Inertia, I in Inches⁴ per Inch of Width								
Pitch x Depth	16 Ga	14 Ga	12 Ga	10 Ga	8 Ga	7 Ga	5 Ga	3 Ga	1 Ga
1½ x ¼ in.	.00044	.00057	.00086	.00121	.00163				
2 x ½ in.	.00194	.00246	.00354	.00472	.00599				
2⅔ x ½ in.	.00189	.00239	.00343	.00453	.00572				
3 x 1 in.	.00866	.01088	.01546	.02018	.0251				
6 x 2 in.			.0604	.0782	.0961	.1080	.1269	.1462	.1659

Cross Sectional Wall Area, in Inches² per Inch of Width

	16 Ga	14 Ga	12 Ga	10 Ga	8 Ga	7 Ga	5 Ga	3 Ga	1 Ga
1½ x ¼ in.	.0634	.0792	.1109	.1427	.1744				
2 x ½ in.	.0679	.0849	.1190	.1532	.1874				
2⅔ x ½ in.	.0646	.0807	.1130	.1453	.1777				
3 x 1 in.	.0742	.0927	.1300	.1673	.2048				
6 x 2 in.			.130	.167	.204	.228	.267	.305	.343

Corrugation dimensions are nominal; subject to manufacturing tolerances.

Fig. 2-14. A comparatively shallow fill will cover this 18-ft diameter steel culvert under a mainline railroad. Backfill was well compacted.

DEFLECTION

Ring deflection of a conduit, defined as change in diameter due to flattening under load, can lead to collapse if shortening of the vertical diameter exceeds 20 percent. Flattening of a conduit indicates inadequate compaction of the backfill, and deflections greater than 10 percent call for periodic inspection to determine when deflection ceases to increase and the soil-structure system has stabilized.

Ring deflection can be limited most effectively by using granular backfill compacted to 90 to 95 percent density. See Fig. 2-13 and Section III *Design of Backfill*, which follows.

The Iowa Deflection Formula provides a rational approach to determination of conduit deflection. It relates pipe deflection to the passive side pressure resisting horizontal movement of the pipe wall and to the inherent strength of the pipe. Unfortunately, soil modulus E' has not been correlated with backfill type and compaction. The formula is thus useful primarily for analysis of installed structures that are under observation and study, but can be used for estimating deflections prior to installation.

The *Iowa Deflection Formula* is

$$\triangle_x = D_1 \frac{KW_c R^3}{EI + 0.061 E'R^3} \tag{4}$$

where $\triangle_x$ = horizontal deflection of the pipe, in.
$\quad D_1$ = deflection lag factor
$\quad K$ = a bedding constant (depends on bedding angle)
$\quad W_c$ = vertical load per unit length of pipe, lb/lin in.
$\quad R$ = mean radius of pipe, in.
$\quad E$ = modulus of elasticity of pipe, psi
$\quad I$ = moment of inertia per unit length of cross section of pipe wall, in.^{4} per in.
$\quad E'$ = horizontal soil modulus, psi

For the purpose of estimating the deflection of a structure prior to installation, and in the absence of a rigorously established correlation between soil modulus E' and degree of soil compaction, the Bureau of Public Roads has used values of $D_1 = 1.5$, $K = 0.100$, and $E' = 700$ psi for good backfill at 85% density, or $D_1 = 1.25$, and $E' = 1400$ psi for excellent backfill at 95% density. Further research will be necessary to define this last relationship more closely. In installed structures, measured values of E' have been found to range from 4000 to 8000 psi.

EXAMPLES

The following limited number of representative examples are included to illustrate the application of design procedures developed in the pages preceding. Other examples involving variations in corrugations, types of seams, factors of safety, etc., may be developed to fit individual engineering needs.

Table 2-4 Ultimate Longitudinal Seam Strength
of Corrugated Steel Pipe
In Pounds Per Foot of Seam

Gage of Metal	⁵⁄₁₆″ Rivets		³⁄₈″ Rivets			⁷⁄₁₆″ Rivets
	2⅔″ x ½″		2⅔″ x ½″		3″ x 1″	3″ x 1″
	Single	Double	Single	Double	Double	Double
16	16,750	21,500			28,700	
14	18,200	29,800			35,700	
12			23,400	46,800		53,000
10			24,500	49,000		63,700
8			25,600	51,300		70,700

The above values are based on riveted construction; they also apply to spotwelded and helical lock seam fabrication.
Values in this table are based on tests conducted by Utah State Dept. of Highways, 1964, and by Pittsburgh Laboratories, 1966.

Table 2-5 Ultimate Strength of Bolted Structural Plate Longitudinal Seams
In Pounds Per Foot of Seam

Gage	4 Bolts Per Foot	6 Bolts Per Foot	8 Bolts Per Foot
12	42,000		
10	62,000		
8	81,000		
7	93,000		
5	112,000		
3	132,000		
1	144,000	184,000	220,000

Bolts used in tests were ¾-in. high strength bolts, meeting ASTM A 325.

Example 1

Given: 36-in. diameter pipe; 2⅔″ × ½″ corr., riveted
       Height of cover, H = 3 ft
       Live load = H20
Find: Gage required

SOLUTION

Ring Compression

$$C = (DL + LL) \times \frac{\text{Span}}{2}$$

where: C = Ring Compression, lb/ft
         DL = Dead Load, psf
         LL = Live Load, psf

$DL = 100 \times H = 300$ psf

$LL = 600$ psf (*from Fig. 2-8, page 45*)

$C = (300 + 600) \times \dfrac{3}{2} = 1350 \ lb/ft$

Seam Strength Required $= 1350 \times FS = 5400$ lb/ft

$$FS = \text{Factor of Safety} = 4$$

16 Ga. steel with $\frac{5}{16}$ in. single riveting, Table 2-4, gives a seam strength of 16,750 lb/ft; which is ample.

Buckling of Wall

From curve "Good Backfill", Figure 2-13
Ultimate buckling stress, $f_b = 33,000$ psi

f_b allowable $= \dfrac{f_b}{2} = 16,500$ psi   where: $FS =$ Factor of Safety $= 2$

$C = 1350$ lb/ft.

$f_c = \dfrac{C}{12 \times A}$

$f_c = \dfrac{1350}{12 \times 0.0646} = 1741$ psi $< 16,500$ psi, and safe against buckling.

$f_c =$ Compressive Stress, psi
$f_b =$ Buckling Stress, psi
$A =$ area of pipe wall, in.^{2}/in.
    (for 16 ga. $= 0.0646$)

Handling and Installation

$$FF = \frac{D^2}{E \times I} = \frac{36^2}{30 \times 10^6 \times 0.00189} = 0.0216$$

where: $FF =$ Flexibility Factor, page 50
$D =$ Diameter, inches
$E =$ Modulus of Elasticity, psi
$I =$ Moment of Inertia in.^{4}/in.
    (for 16 ga. $= 0.00189$)

which is less than $FF = 0.0433$ and is, therefore, satisfactory.

Deflection

$$\triangle_x = \frac{D_1 \times K \times W_c \times R^3}{E \times I + 0.061 \times E' \times R^3}$$

$$W_c = \frac{(DL + LL) \times \text{Span}}{12}$$

$$W_c = \frac{900 \times 3}{12} = 225 \text{ lb/in.}$$

where:
$\triangle_x =$ Deflection, inches
$D_1 = 1.5$, Deflection Lag Factor
$K = 0.1$, Bedding Factor
$W_c =$ Load on Pipe, lb/in.
$R = 18$ in., Radius
$E = 30 \times 10^6$ psi, Modulus of Elasticity of Pipe
$I = 0.00189$ in.^{4}/in., Moment of Inertia of pipe wall
$E' = 700$ psi, Horizontal Soil Modulus

$$\triangle_x = \frac{1.5 \times 0.1 \times 225 \times 18^3}{(30 \times 10^6 \times 0.00189) + (0.061 \times 700 \times 18^3)}$$

$$= \frac{196,830}{56,700 + 249,026}$$

$\triangle_x = 0.644$ in.

Allowable $\triangle_x = 36 \times 0.05 = 1.80$ in. > 0.644 in., therefore satisfactory.

"Good backfill", $E' = 700$ psi, is satisfactory for deflection requirement.

Answer:

No. 16 gage meets all the requirements.

Example 2

Given: 66-in. diameter pipe; $3'' \times 1''$ corr., riveted
      Height of cover, $H = 30$ ft
      Live Load = H 20
Find: Gage required

SOLUTION

Ring Compression
$$C = (DL + LL) \times \frac{Span}{2}$$
where: C = Ring Compression, lb/ft
         DL = Dead Load, psf
         LL = Live Load, psf

$DL = 100 \times H = 3000 \; psf$
$LL = 0 \; (from \; Fig. \; 2\text{-}8, \; page \; 45)$
$C = 3000 \times \dfrac{5.5}{2} = 8{,}250 \; lb/ft$

Seam Strength Required $= 8250 \times FS = 33{,}000$ lb/ft
                                FS = Factor of Safety = 4
From Table 2-4, 14 Ga. steel with $\frac{3}{8}$ in. rivets gives a seam strength of 35,700 lb/ft, which is sufficient.

Buckling of Wall

          where:

From curve "Good Backfill", Figure 2-13 FS = Factor of Safety = 2
Ultimate buckling stress, $f_b = 33{,}000$ psi f_c = Compressive Stress, psi

$$f_b \; allowable = \frac{f_b}{FS} = \frac{f_b}{2} = 16{,}500 \; psi$$

          f_b = Buckling Stress, psi
          A = area of pipe wall =

$C = 8250 \; lb/ft$
$$f_c = \frac{C}{12 \times A} = \frac{8250}{12 \times 0.0927} = 7416 \; psi$$

          0.0927 in.²/in.
          for 14 ga., Table 2-3, p. 50

$f_c = 7416 < f_b$ allowable, and safe against buckling.

Handling and Installation

          where:
$$FF = \frac{D^2}{E \times I} = \frac{66^2}{30 \times 10^6 \times .01088} = 0.0133$$

          FF = Flexibility Factor
          D = Diameter, inches
          E = Modulus of Elasticity, psi
          I = Moment of Inertia, .01088

which is less than FF = 0.0433 and is, in.⁴/in.
therefore, satisfactory.   Table 2-3, p. 50

Deflection

          where:
$$\triangle_x = \frac{D_1 \times K \times W_c \times R^3}{E \times I + 0.061 \; E' \; R^3}$$

          $\triangle_x$ = Deflection, inches
          D_1 = 1.5, Deflection Lag Factor
          K = 0.1, Bedding Factor

$$W_c = w \times H \times S/12$$

          W_c = Load on Pipe, lb/in.
          R = 33 in., Radius

$$= \frac{100 \times 30 \times 5.5}{12}$$

          E = 30 × 10⁶ psi, Modulus of
          Elasticity of Pipe
          I = .01088 in.⁴/in., Moment of

$$= 1375 \; lb/in.$$

          Inertia of pipe wall
          E' = 700 psi, Horizontal Soil
          Modulus
          w = Weight of Earth, lb/ft³

$$\triangle_x = \frac{1.5 \times 0.1 \times 1375 \times 33^3}{(30 \times 10^6 \times .01088) + (0.061 \times 700 \times 33^3)} = \frac{7,400,000}{1,857,000}$$

$\triangle_x = 3.98$ *in.*

Allowable $\triangle_x = 66 \times 0.05 = 3.3$ *in.* < 3.98 *in.*

Therefore, if "good backfill" is used, the 14 ga pipe must be vertically elongated 5 percent.

Check "excellent backfill" with $E' = 1400$ psi

$$\triangle_x = \frac{1.5 \times 0.1 \times 1375 \times 33^3}{(30 \times 10^6 \times .01088) + (0.061 \times 1400 \times 33^3)} = 2.18 \ in.$$

Allowable $\triangle_x = 3.3$ *in.* > 2.18 *in.;* therefore is satisfactory.

Answer: Gage required is 14. Use round pipe in "excellent backfill" or elongated pipe in "good backfill".

Example 3

Given: 18-ft diameter pipe; $6'' \times 2''$ corrugation, bolted
      Height of cover, H = 38 ft
      Live Load (railroad) E 72
Find: Gage required

SOLUTION

Ring Compression

$$C = (DL + LL) \times \frac{Span}{2}$$

where: C = Ring Compression, lb/ft
          DL = Dead Load, psf
          LL = Live Load, psf

$DL = 100 \times H = 100 \times 38 = 3800$ psf

$LL = less \ than \ 100$ psf, *from*
    Fig. 2-9; therefore, neglect

$$C = 3800 \times \frac{18}{2} = 34,200 \ lb/ft$$

Seam Strength Required $= 34,200 \times FS = 136,800$ lb/ft
                              FS = Factor of Safety = 4
Bolt Joint Values; see Table 2-5. Seam strength = 144,000 lb/ft
Plate Gage Required = No. 1.

Buckling of Wall

From curve "Good Backfill", Figure 2-13
Ultimate buckling stress, $f_b = 18,900$ psi

f_b allowable $= \dfrac{f_b}{2} = 9450$ psi

$C = 34,200$ lb/ft

$$f_c = \frac{C}{12 \times A} = \frac{34,200}{12 \times .343}$$

$f_c = 8,309$ psi $< 9,450$ psi; safe against buckling.

where: FS = Factor of Safety = 2
        f_c = Compressive Stress, psi
        f_b = Buckling Stress, psi
        A = Area of pipe wall = 0.343
           in.^{2}/in. for No. 1 ga.
           Table 2-3, p. 50

Handling and Installation

$$FF = \frac{D^2}{E \times I} = \frac{216^2}{30 \times 10^6 \times .1659}$$

$$= 0.0094, < 0.02 \text{ and is,}$$
therefore, satisfactory.

Deflection

$$\triangle_x = \frac{D_1 \times K \times W_c \times R^3}{EI + 0.061 \, E' \, R^3}$$

$$W_c = \frac{w \times H \times \text{Span}}{12}$$

$$W_c = \frac{100 \times 38 \times 18}{12} = 5,700 \, lb/in.$$

where: FF = Flexibility factor = 0.02, p. 50
D = Diameter, inches
E = Modulus of Elasticity, psi
I = Moment of Inertia = 0.1659 in.^{4}/in. for No. 1 gage, p. 50

where:
$\triangle_x$ = Deflection, inches
D_1 = 1.25, Deflection Lag Factor
K = 0.1, Bedding Factor
W_c = Load on Pipe, lb/in.
R = 108 in., Radius
E = 30 × 10⁶ psi, Modulus of Elasticity of pipe
I = 0.1659 in.^{4}/in., Moment of Inertia of pipe wall
E' = 1400 psi, Horizontal Soil Modulus
w = Weight of Earth, lb/ft³

$$\triangle_x = \frac{1.25 \times 0.1 \times 5700 \times 108^3}{(30 \times 10^6 \times .1659) + (0.061 \times 1400 \times 108^3)}$$

$\triangle_x = 8.3 \, in.$

Allowable $\triangle_x = 216 \times 0.05 = 10.8 \, in. > 8.3 \, in.;$ therefore is satisfactory.

"Excellent Backfill", E' = 1400 psi, is required to control deflection.

Answer:
    Gage required is No. 1.

Example 4

Given: Pipe-arch 18 ft - 1 in. × 11 ft - 10 in.; 6″ × 2″ corrugation, bolted
    Height of cover, H = 10 ft
    Live Load = E 72
    Corner plate radius, R_c = 31 in.
Find: Gage required

SOLUTION

Ring Compression

$$C = (DL + LL) \times \frac{\text{Span}}{2}$$

$DL = 100 \times H = 100 \times 10 = 1000 \, \text{psf}$

$LL = 1000$ psf (*from Fig. 2-9*)

$$C = (1000 + 1000) \times \frac{18.08}{2} = 18,080 \, lb/ft$$

where: C = Ring Compression, lb/ft
DL = Dead Load, psf
LL = Live Load, psf

Seam Strength Required = 18,080 × FS = 72,320 lb/ft

FS = Factor of Safety = 4

Bolt Joint Values: Table 2–5 shows seam strength 81,000 lb/ft for No. 8 ga., 4 bolts per ft, which is greater than 72,320 lb/ft, and therefore is adequate.

Buckling of Wall

From curve "Excellent Backfill", Figure 2-13
(Using span for diameter.)
Ultimate compressive ring stress, $f_b = 33,000$ psi

f_b allowable $= \dfrac{f_b}{2} = 16,500$ psi

$C = 18,080$ lb/ft

$f_c = \dfrac{C}{12 \times A}$

$f_c = \dfrac{18,080}{12 \times .204} = 7386$ psi $< 16,500$ psi and safe against buckling.

where:
$FS =$ Factor of Safety $= 2$
$f_c =$ Compressive Stress, psi
$f_b =$ Buckling Stress, psi
$A =$ Area of pipe wall $= 0.204$
in.^{2}/in. for No. 8 ga.
(Table 2-3)

Handling and Installation

$FF = \dfrac{D^2}{E \times I} = \dfrac{217^2}{30 \times 10^6 \times .0961} = .0163$

which is less than $FF = .02$ and is
therefore, satisfactory.

where:
$FF =$ Flexibility Factor
$D =$ Span of Pipe - Arch, in.
$E =$ Modulus of Elasticity, psi
$I =$ Moment of Inertia $= 0.0961$ in.^{4}/in. for No. 8 ga. (Table 2-3)

Deflection

Pipe-arches are normally furnished under fill heights that do not require investigation of deflection.

Pressure at Corner Plates

$P_c = C \times \dfrac{12}{R_c} = 18,080 \times \dfrac{12}{31} = 7000$ psf

where:
$P_c =$ Soil Pressure at Corner Plates, psf
$R_c =$ Radius of Corner Plates, inches

Therefore, an "excellent" grade of backfill compacted to a minimum Proctor density of 95 percent must be placed against the corner plates. Since the corner pressure exceeds 3000 psf, consult a soils engineer for further requirements on design of the backfill. For the remainder of backfill and embankment, use a good backfill material.

HEIGHT-OF-COVER TABLES

Height-of-cover tables illustrating how culvert diameter and wall thickness (gage), for several corrugation profiles and conditions of backfill, influence height-of-cover limits, using the design procedures of Chapter 2, are inserted within a pocket affixed to the inside back cover. Fundamental studies, currently underway by American Iron and Steel Institute, within the steel industry, at universities, and by AASHO, BPR, state highway departments and other governmental agencies, may alter presently accepted practices in strength design procedure for flexible steel conduits. This engineering renaissance may result in increased height-of-cover values, such that tables currently in use can and should be updated. At such time, the AISI Committee of Hot and Cold Rolled Sheet and Strip Producers and the Committee of Galvanized Sheet Producers will print and distribute updated tables, along with changes as may be required in Chapter 2 *Strength Design*.

Fig. 2-15. A granular material makes the best backfill. However, cohesive materials can be used if the moisture is controlled.

Section III—EARTH BACKFILL DESIGN

For the roadway conduit to support the pavement or track above it adequately and uniformly, a stable composite structure is vital. Stability in a soil-structure interaction system requires not only adequate design of the structure barrel, it also presumes a well engineered backfill. Performance of the flexible conduit in retaining its shape and structural integrity depends greatly on selection, placement and compaction of the envelope of earth surrounding the structure and distributing its pressures to the abutting soil masses.

Requirements for selecting and placing backfill material around or near the conduit are similar to those for a roadway embankment. The main difference in requirements is due to the fact that *the conduit generates more lateral pressure than would the earth within the embankment if no structure existed.*

CHOICE OF MATERIAL

All highway and railroad engineering departments have adequately detailed specifications for selecting and placing material in *embankments*. These specifications provide for wide variations in terrain and for available local materials, and so can generally apply to backfill material *around conduits* for normal installations. If abnormal conditions exist at a specific site or if unusual performance is expected of a conduit and embankment, a competent soils engineer should be consulted for designing the backfill.

Backfill material should preferably be granular to provide good shear strength. Cohesive type material can also be used if careful attention is given to compaction at optimum moisture content. Very fine granular material may infiltrate into the structure and should be avoided when high ground water table is anticipated. Bank run gravel or similar material compacted to 90 to 95 percent standard density has produced completely satisfactory installations.

What constitutes good backfill performance is being clarified through laboratory research. Model structures tested in granular environment at different compactions have led to laboratory observations of a "critical density range." Within this range, those tested below 85 percent show large deflections while those tested at 90 percent or greater density show very small deflections.

FILL TECHNIQUE

Backfill should cover the conduit at least one foot* and extend along both sides at least one diameter away from the conduit surface at midheight where (1) for construction reasons, backfill is placed before building the embankment, or (2) backfill around the conduit differs from that used in the rest of the embankment. This material should be placed and compacted in simultaneous layers on each side of the conduit.

Conduits of pipe-arch or underpass shape exert greater pressures against the soil at the corner plates than elsewhere around the conduit. Excessive pressures at the corners will require material of better bearing capacity which should extend far enough to transfer distributed pressures to the abutting embankment at acceptably low intensities. See *Example 4, page 56.*

*For completed height of minimum cover, see Section V *Minimum Cover.*

Section IV—FOUNDATION PREPARATION

Purpose. A good foundation for an underground conduit will maintain the elevation and grade of the invert to a planned position (1) with the conduit in the desired cross-sectional shape, (2) without concentration of foundation pressures that tend to produce excessive stresses in the conduit.

FOUNDATION SOILS

Evaluation of the conduit site may require subsurface exploration to detect undesirable foundation material, such as muck or rock ledges. Either of these gives uneven support, and in muck the conduit can shift after the embankment is constructed. Any large structure, and any size structure under high fill, is especially sensitive to inferior foundation material. Materials of poor or non-uniform bearing capacity should be removed and replaced with suitable fill to provide uniform continuous support. Large rocks or ledge rock should be replaced with suitable material, such as sand.

WIDTH OF FOUNDATION

Where foundation soils must be replaced, excavation should extend along the entire length of the conduit to a width at least one diameter on both sides of the conduit's greatest width. Soft materials must be removed and replaced across the entire foundation width, but ledge rock or rocks beyond the bedding may be left. Foundation preparation in a trench bottom, while based on these principles, should be confined to practical widths.

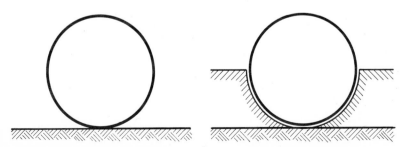

Fig. 2-16. Two extremes of bedding for a conduit—neither of which is desirable.

BEDDING

Bedding is that portion of the foundation which is shaped to contact the bottom of the conduit. This contact area can vary from practically a straight line to a half cylinder—the first foundation being a flat transverse surface and the second being shaped to the entire bottom of the structure. See Fig. 2-16. Both extremes are undesirable. The flat surface makes compaction difficult at the very bottom of large structures. Foundation shaping to fit the entire bottom interferes with assembly of field-bolted structures and is costly. Bedding or shaping should therefore be wide enough to permit efficiently compacting the remainder of the backfill under the haunches of the structure, but not so wide as to interfere with bolting procedures.

A uniform blanket of loose material should cover the shaped bedding to a depth sufficient to allow the corrugations to become filled with the material.

CAMBER

An embankment exerts more load on the foundation at the center of the embankment than at the toe of slope, so more settlement will occur in the center area. A corresponding settlement of the conduit will occur. Hence, the bedding profile should be cambered longitudinally. The upstream half of the pipe may be laid on almost a flat grade and the downstream half on a steeper grade. Fig. 2-17. The mid-ordinate of the curve should be determined by the soils engineer. For further details on foundation preparation see Chapter 7 *Installation.*

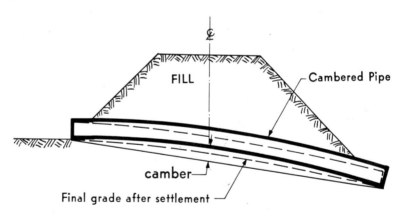

Fig. 2-17. Camber allows for settlement of a culvert under a high fill. Most of the fall is in the outlet half. Diameters 10 ft and smaller are easier to camber, as are the lighter gages.

Section V—MINIMUM COVER

Section II of this chapter, *Culvert Structural Design,* implies sizeable fills and dead loads. However, with decreasing fill height, live loads assume increasing importance. Strength design that involves the minimum cover possible with a specific conduit and known live load requires further research to define completely.

Nonetheless, satisfactory minimum cover requirements have been formulated. These are based on long-time observations by the corrugated steel pipe industry of structure performance under live loads. See Figs. 2-8 and 2-9. From these field observations, a minimum cover requirement has been tentatively established of one eighth of the barrel diameter (or span) for highway conduits and one quarter of the diameter for railway conduits, with a minimum of 1 ft.

Note that this minimum cover requirement is not always adequate during construction. When construction equipment—frequently heavier than traffic loads for which the conduit has been designed—is to be driven over or close to the buried structure, it is the responsibility of the contractor to provide the additional cover required to avoid damage to the conduit.

Section VI—END TREATMENT

Designing the ends of a flexible culvert differs in analysis from designing the barrel of that structure.

SKEWS AND BEVELS

Cutting the ends of a corrugated drainage structure to a skew or bevel, to conform with the embankment slopes, destroys the ability of the end portion of the structure to resist ring compression. Headwalls, riprap slopes or slope pavements may in some cases be required to serve as flanges on the ends of the

Fig. 2-18. This 66-in. culvert under 64 ft of rock and earth is 340 ft long. Properly installed, it should give many decades of excellent service.

structure to stiffen them against asymmetric loading from the embankment and the dynamic forces of the water. Such "flanges," when needed, can vary from half-headwalls with cutoff walls (on the inlet end particularly), to elaborate headwalls which not only stiffen the structure end against damage from water energy, but also improve the hydraulic efficiency of the inlet.

Structures designed to flow under pressure head are more vulnerable to end problems than those designed to flow less than full. Also, large diameter structures, and those structures where there is a combination of skew and bevel offer problems of end distortion. In general, a skew of 20 degrees with a 2:1 bevel should not be exceeded.

Cut ends should be anchor-bolted to headwalls or slope pavements at approximately 18-in. intervals. Uncut, square-end structures may be anchored to a headwall with bolts in alternate standard circumferential holes.

TEMPORARY BRACING

During backfill and the construction of headwalls, the ends of structures may require temporary bracing, generally horizontal, to prevent unsightly distortion. The overhang of a conduit cut on an extreme skew and bevel may require support by shoring until the slope pavement is completed.

STANDARD DESIGNS

Most highway and railway design offices have adequate design standards suitable to their terrain. Reference to these is valuable for design of headwalls, riprap protection and slope pavements.

Section VII—MAINTENANCE

Preventive maintenance of drainage structures can often stop minor structural damage from becoming a major repair or replacement project—especially for large structures. A partial list of spots to watch, with suggestions for remedying, includes:

- *Distortion in structure walls*, if caused by voids in the backfill, can be arrested by pressure grouting before the distortion becomes critical. Structural repairs can also be accomplished in limited areas by welding, blind fasteners, or strengthening with ring beams.

- *Damaged pipe ends*, headwalls or slope pavements should be repaired before high water conditions cause washout of the embankment or collapse of the structure.

- *Invert erosion* can be repaired by field paving with reinforced concrete.

- *Structural or material deterioration* may be repaired by relining with threaded-in pipe or tunnel liner plates, with the annular space grouted.

Periodic inspection will detect accumulated debris and allow removal before high water conditions cause trouble.

SUMMARY

Chapter 2 *Strength Design* aims to crystallize a broad pattern of contemporary engineering thought regarding the most efficient and economical approach to the design of buried structures. It draws extensively on newly correlated research, as tempered by 60 years' experience with service performance of underground conduits, and so extends the capabilities and uses of these structures in larger sizes and under higher fills.

One of the more fruitful areas of structural research has been that of composite structures of steel and earth. As research continues to evaluate dead loads more precisely, and heavier live loads on structures under minimum cover, more sophisticated design criteria will result.

REFERENCES AND BIBLIOGRAPHY

1. Marston, Anson, *The Theory of External Loads on Closed Conduits*, Bulletin No. 96, Iowa Eng. Experiment Sta., Ames, Iowa, 1930, pp. 5–8.
2. Braune, G. M., Cain, William and Janda, H. F., *Earth Pressure Experiments on Culvert Pipe*, Public Roads, Nov. 1929, p. 157.
3. Spangler, M. G., *Underground Conduits—An Appraisal of Modern Research*, ASCE Transactions, (Discussion), Vol. 113, p. 346, 1948.
4. Spangler, M. G., *Field Measurement of the Settlement Ratios of Various Highway Culverts*, Iowa Eng. Experiment Sta., Bull. No. 170, 1950.
5. American Railway Engineering Association, *Culvert Load Determination*, Bulletin 284, Vol. 27, Chicago, Ill., 1926.
6. American Association of State Highway Officials, *Standard Specifications for Highway Bridges*, Washington, D. C., 1961, 286 pp.
7. American Railway Engineering Assn., *Manual of Recommended Practice*, Chicago.
8. White, H. L. and Layer, J. P., *The Corrugated Metal Conduit as a Compression Ring*, Highway Research Board Proceedings, Vol. 39, 1960, pp. 389–397.
9. Brockenbrough, R. L., *Influence of Wall Stiffness on Corrugated Metal Culvert Design*, Highway Research Record #56, Highway Research Board, Pages 71–82, 1964.
10. *Armco Multi-Plate Pipe*, Armco Metal Products Div., Middletown, Ohio, Catalog MP-1664, 1964, 16 pp.
11. Brockenbrough, R. L., *Structural Design of Pipe-Arch Culvert with 1- by 3-inch Corrugation*, United States Steel, Applied Research Laboratory, Monroeville, Pa. Tech. Report No. 57.019-400(5), 1965.
12. Barnard, R. E., *Design and Deflection Control of Buried Steel Pipe Supporting Earth Loads and Live Loads*. Proceedings of American Society for Testing and Materials, Philadelphia, Pa. Vol. 57, 1957.
13. Spangler, M. G., *The Structural Design of Flexible Pipe Culverts*, Bulletin 153, Iowa Engineering Experiment Station, Ames, Iowa, 1941.
14. Meyerhof, G. G., and Fisher, C. L. *Composite Design of Underground Steel Structures*. Engineering Journal of the Engineering Institute of Canada, Montreal, Que., Sept. 1963.
15. Spangler, M. G., Discussion by Walter Lum of *Stresses in Pressure Pipe Lines and Protective Casing Pipes*, ASCE, Journal of the Structural Division, Vol. 83 No. ST1, Proc. Paper 1156, Jan. '57.
16. Watkins, R. K. and Smith, A. B. *Ring Deflection of Buried Pipes*, Utah State University, Engineering Experiment Station, Logan, Utah, May 1966.
17. *Multi-Plate Compression Measurements at Cullman, Alabama, Installation*, 1951, Timmers, J. H., Research & Technology, Armco Steel Corporation, Middletown, Ohio.
18. *Flexible Culverts Under High Fills*, Highway Research Board, Bulletin 125. Committee report, 34th Annual Meeting, Washington, D. C., 1955.
19. *Handbook of Drainage and Construction Products*, Armco Drainage & Metal Products, Inc. Middletown, Ohio, 1955.
20. Meyerhof, G. G. and Baikie, L. D. *Strength of Steel Culvert Sheets Bearing Against Compacted Sand Backfills*, with Discussion by R. K. Watkins, Highway Research Record #3, Highway Research Board, Pages 1–19, 1963.

Fig. 3-1. Confidence in the durability of steel culverts and sewers comes from inspecting many individual installations that have served many decades. This veteran culvert was installed over 50 years ago.

CHAPTER 3 Service Life

INTRODUCTION

In designing his drainage structures, the engineer is confronted with the problem of choosing the materials best suited for meeting a wide variety of service conditions. He requires an amply long service life but at an economical cost. Fig. 3-1.

Steel drainage structures are available in a wider range and combination of physical and chemical properties, gages, protective coatings and other durability factors than any other culvert material. The engineer has a greater choice.

This chapter on service life confirms that corrugated steel drainage structures can be economically designed not only for normal conditions but also for highly corrosive industrial and sanitary sewers and for mining, salt water and other tough service conditions. The chapter deals with:

Section I—Inspection Methods and Results
Section II—Soil and Water Conditions
Section III—Designing for Service Life

Section I—INSPECTION METHODS AND RESULTS

DESTRUCTIVE FORCES

Any satisfactory engineering structure regardless of type or material must possess sufficient but not wasteful durability. This durability implies resistance both to structural forces and material deterioration, including:

1. Excessive dead or live loads, impact, soil movements, undermining.
2. Longitudinal stresses tending to pull the structure apart.
3. Corrosion, rotting, disintegration and other forms of chemical or electrolytic deterioration (underground and underwater rather than atmospheric).
4. Erosion or abrasive action by hydraulic traffic through the structure.

The first two items pertain to structural forces and have been discussed in preceding chapters. The third and fourth are covered here.

METHODS OF DETERMINING DURABILITY

Extensive tests on material durability of all types of drainage structures and other buried materials have been made by the American Society for Testing and Materials, the U.S. Bureau of Standards, state highway departments, and by other engineering associations, industries and materials producers. These investigations cover not only the basic materials but also protective coatings, linings and other factors.

Research on service life has been of three principal kinds—laboratory tests, special field test installations, and inspection-evaluation of actual structures in service.

LABORATORY TESTS

Laboratory tests on material durability are useful in that they enable the factors to be controlled and varied. Also they permit accelerating the aging conditions. Researchers, however, are wary of making any predictions about the comparative or absolute service life expectancy of any material as the result of these accelerated tests, which at best can serve only as a rough guide.

Special Test Installations. Research projects are constantly underway to de-

Figs. 3-2, 3-3. Installed during the horse and wagon days of the early 1900's, this same corrugated galvanized steel culvert still looks young when photographed after more than 50 years of service.

termine the comparative durability of various materials and products. These are not necessarily accelerated or full-scale tests of actual structures. Rather they may involve exposure of many samples of materials to atmospheric, water immersion or underground and effluent conditions in various typical geographic areas. Included in this category are some test installations of stainless steel culverts under conditions particularly corrosive to the steels ordinarily used in culverts and sewers. These tests span long periods of time. Data obtained from them are distinctly more reliable than those from accelerated laboratory tests, but are not necessarily convertible to all service conditions.

Field Service Investigations. The most reliable way to estimate the life expectancy of a conduit or other engineering structure is to examine the records of a *large number* of these structures that have served their *full useful life*, as contrasted to design life. Since the use for the structure is often ended prior to its full life span, complete records of structures under various service conditions are not generally available.

However, many structures of various ages have been re-examined periodically. By applying a widely accepted method of predicting life expectancy, it is possible to reach acceptable conclusions. Figs. 3-2 and 3-3.

Uniform methods have been set up for inspecting, re-examining and rating a culvert according to its structural and its material condition and age and then predicting the number of years of service remaining.

These rating methods originated some forty years ago and have been used extensively by various state highway departments, the Bureau of Public

Roads and numerous railroads. Several general conclusions drawn from culvert investigations are:

1. No one type of culvert investigated is ideal for all conditions.
2. Weaknesses of existing culvert types and methods for improving them are revealed.
3. Sufficient facts on durability are available to make economic selection of culverts possible.

HIGHWAY CULVERT INSPECTIONS

The earliest organized culvert inspections, around 1920, were made on galvanized corrugated steel and iron culverts, cast iron, vitrified clay, concrete pipe and boxes. These revealed the comparative structural strength and durability of corrugated steel culverts. They also led to development of bituminous pavements and coatings for more severe conditions.

The California Division of Highways was a pioneer (1926) in culvert inspections and reinspections on a large scale to determine probable durability under various service conditions. Over the past 40 years it has evaluated more than 12,000 corrugated metal culverts.

More recently, California engineers have emphasized the importance of over-all culvert design including: (1) size and shape to fit the hydraulics of a given site, (2) rational determination of structural strength, and (3) a logical method of estimating service life.

Pennsylvania Turnpike. One of the notable uses of bituminous paved invert steel culverts was under the Pennsylvania Turnpike in 1938–1939. Diameter of the 47 pipe structures inspected ranged up to 72 in. with fill heights to 80 ft. These were inspected in 1949 and again in 1959 with highly satisfactory results reported as to material and structural service life prospects.[1] Fig. 3-4.

Comprehensive inspections of structural plate pipe and arches began in 1943–1944 and have been repeated at ten year intervals since. These have led to positive durability information and to improvements in design.

Fig. 3-4. Under the famous Pennsylvania Turnpike, an inspector finds this 66-in. bituminous coated and paved culvert in very good structural and material condition after a quarter century of service.

Fig. 3-5, 3-6. Reinspection of 60-in. galvanized steel culvert under 77 ft. of cover shows that care in installation 38 years ago assures top structural durability.

RAILWAY CULVERT INSPECTIONS.

Railroads in the United States and Canada annually examine all culverts under their lines—a commendable practice. This has led to confidence in and greater use of corrugated steel culverts in a wide range of sizes, under normal and severe service conditions.

The American Railway Engineering Association Committee 15, Iron and Steel Structures, issued in 1953 a progress report on the inspection of some 300 corrugated metal pipes 60 in. and larger.[2] These pipes were of riveted and bolted construction, installed with and without vertical diameter elongation, and in different degrees of compacted embankments. The results were reassuring. Figs. 3-5 and 3-6.

Another inspection on a mid-western railroad in 1952 included 125 structures in four states under a wide variety of service conditions. Here are a few typical conclusions from the report:

1. Plain galvanized pipe 20 to 25 years old can be expected to give 15 to 25 years more of service. (Total: 35 to 50 years)
2. Most affected by corrosion is the bottom 25 per cent of the structure.
3. Chief installation faults were: grade lines too low, resulting in silting; inclusion of cinders in backfill material; and installing multiple pipes too close together.

In general, inspections such as these are helpful in revealing the results of improper manufacture and installation practices and in avoiding them on subsequent installations.

SEWER INSPECTIONS

Photographic surveys of sewers can now be made with closed circuit television cameras for instant or later viewing. These take on-the-spot movies of the condition of sewers of almost any size from the smallest to the largest.

Pipe manufacturers have made comprehensive field studies of corrugated steel sanitary and combined sewers as well as storm sewers. Inspections first made in 1940 were repeated in 1950 and 1960 to learn if the rates of deterioration originally estimated were realistic and substantially correct. Fig. 3-7.

The value of coatings, pavements and other protective means was found to be substantial and economical. They resisted sewer gases and their condensates, as well as active industrial wastes. The report concludes, "Only slight changes have taken place in the past 10 years in most (of the 199) installations."

Special investigations of corrugated steel sewers were also made in coastal areas where soils include a high percentage of decaying vegetable matter and are subject to tidal salt water inundation twice daily. These conditions were successfully resisted by economical coatings and linings.[3]

AIR FORCE BASE DRAINAGE INSPECTION

In extension of storm drainage lines at Sheppard Air Force Base, Wichita Falls, Tex., suitability of plain galvanized steel pipe was questioned. As a result, field inspections of a representative group of 26-year old culverts in the area were conducted. Involved in the investigation were a metallurgical consultant, a testing laboratory, a local professional engineer, city, county and state highway engineers, and operators of underground pipe line systems in the Wichita Falls area.

Even though the soil in the area is considered corrosive, the investigation concluded that a service life up to 50 years could be expected, versus a design service life of 25 years. The Corps of Engineers' Office and the consulting engineer subsequently approved the use of galvanized steel for the installations. These included a triple line of 144-in. diameter, 10 gage structural plate pipe with 8 gage invert plates.[4]

AIRPORT DRAINAGE

Beginning in 1927, several large installations of perforated corrugated steel pipe drainage were made on the municipal airports at Buffalo and Rochester,

Fig. 3-7. Inspection of a 36-in. 30-yr. old galvanized steel storm sewer to determine what the life expectancy might be. Such inspections can be reassuring.

Figs. 3-8, 3-9. Installed about the time Lindbergh made his solo flight across the Atlantic, this half-coated and paved 30-in. perforated subdrain pipe on the Buffalo, N.Y., airport looks in good condition (photo at left) when inspected almost 40 years later.

N.Y. Figs 3-8 and 3-9. During the same period, numerous pipe-arches and a structural plate storm sewer were installed at Mitchell Field, Milwaukee County Airport, Wisc. At Charleston, South Carolina, 1928, 1930, 1936, several miles of perforated steel pipe were installed. Reinspections at several of these and other locations during the past few years indicate that perforated corrugated steel pipe properly installed will serve almost indefinitely.

LEVEE CULVERTS AND SEWERS

Long life, tightness and safety are required for culverts and sewers through major river levees. In 1962 the St. Louis District, Corps of Engineers, re-inspected corrugated steel drainage structures through levees on the Mississippi River just below St. Louis, Mo., and on several tributaries.[5] Earlier inspections of these structures had been made in 1945, 1949 and 1954. Fig. 3-10. Structural condition of all inspected pipe was excellent or good despite yielding soil foundations. Joints have proved tight against leakage. Asphalt pavements and coatings continue to protect the galvanized coating and base metal after service periods of 20 to 29 years. Most diameters range from 36 to 84 in. As levees have been raised or widened, existing corrugated steel culverts have been extended.

Fig. 3-10. Levee culvert service is punishing. This 60-in. bituminous coated and paved steel culvert was installed under a Mississippi River levee in Illinois in 1933, reinspected in 1940, 1956 and 1962. Condition, structurally and materially, rated as good.

Section II—SOIL AND WATER CONDITIONS

SERVICE CONDITIONS

Major soil and water conditions under which drainage structures may be called on to serve are: mine, acid, alkaline, salt, normal and sewage. The important factors that influence the corrosion rate of metal and reinforced concrete culverts are:[6]

1. The presence of flowing water
2. Average annual rainfall
3. Frequency of wetting
4. Formation of corrosion inhibiting films
5. Soil bacteria growth
6. pH or hydrogen ion concentration
7. Minimum electrical resistivity of soil
8. Sulfate (SO_4) concentration
9. Total alkalinity (expressed as $CaCO_3$)
10. Dissolved solids, and
11. Total calcium (expressed as $CaCO_3$)

MINE WATERS

Coal mines and certain other mining operations produce waters which are corrosive to nearly all materials normally used for drainage structures. This is due to free acid or acid forming elements in the soil and waters.

Every stream in a mining area is not necessarily contaminated with chemical constituents harmful to structures through which they flow. Where analysis shows concentrations of free sulfuric acid or presence of sulfates (SO_4) in the water, additional protection is recommended for corrugated metal (steel and aluminum) and concrete.

ACID WATERS

Beyond mine acids are the aggressive acidic waters, contaminated with organic acids present in marsh and swamp land and other locations where vegetable matter decays in quantity. The generally unstable nature of organic acids makes identification difficult by laboratory analysis. Acidic waters often occur in conjunction with soft and unstable foundations and both tend to increase the difficulties of drainage construction.

Additional protection for all drainage structure materials is recommended used in this type of exposure.

ALKALI SOILS AND WATERS

Alkali regions are generally classified as being white or black; white alkali usually contains sufficient sulfates or carbonates to leave a white deposit upon evaporating. The black alkali—sodium carbonate—does not deposit white "snow" on evaporating.

White alkalis, particularly the sulfates, attack ordinary portland cement concrete quite rapidly. Drainage structures of this material most often fail to provide satisfactory service in this soil type. These same alkalis also attack aluminum pipe, and the zinc coating on steel pipe, more rapidly than does normal soil.

Where soil is known to be highly alkaline, additional protective coating for all drainage structures is recommended.

SALT AND SALT MARSH

In sea water, the chlorides are largely responsible for the corrosion of aluminum and steel, while chlorides, sulfates and certain magnesium salts are considered to cause deterioration of concrete. The chemical deterioration of concrete in sea water is accelerated by the mechanical disintegration resulting from alternate wetting and drying and frost action in cold climates (spalling). All ordinary culvert materials exposed to sea water should carry additional protective coatings.

NORMAL AND ARID CONDITIONS

Galvanized corrugated steel culverts installed in normal, arid and semi-arid regions can be expected to have a great many years of life.

SEWAGE

A *storm sewer* carries storm and surface water and street wash, of which little, if any, will be more corrosive than rural watershed runoff. However, erosion by the hydraulic traffic may be a factor.

A *sanitary sewer* is designed to carry domestic sewage and the discharge from commercial and light industrial plants. The general nature of fresh sanitary sewage is slightly alkaline or neutral and usually well-diluted. In a well designed and normally maintained sanitary sewer system the velocity of flow is sufficient to carry the sewage to its point of disposal before putrefaction begins, so the problem of corrosion is minimal. If flow is sluggish or stagnant and the temperature and oxygen content favorable, bacterial action can take place and sewer gas is released. This condition can be especially corrosive above the flow line in the sewer.

Industrial wastes may be handled in sanitary or combined sewers, or in some cases in sewers built especially to cope with highly corrosive wastes.

Sanitary and industrial sewers generally require protective linings or liner plates. Joint materials, and seam sealants if used, should be acid resistant.[7]

Section III—DESIGNING FOR SERVICE LIFE

HOW MUCH DURABILITY IS NEEDED?

With an eye to economics, the engineer usually does not build drainage structures or conduits to last forever. He considers the following factors: (1) a conservative life expectancy for the project or structure, (2) possible future change causing inadequacy or obsolescence, and (3) cost or inconvenience of replacing or perpetuating a structure.

For some structures, 25 years may be sufficient life expectancy; for others, 50 years. Most highway, railway and sewer engineers will settle for 40 to 60 years.

SERVICE CONDITIONS

Obsolescence is unpredictable but structural and material durability lend themselves to engineering judgment and design.

Material durability of steel drainage structures is affected primarily by elements in the soil or water—acids, alkalis, salts, cinders, sewage—in the presence of moisture and oxygen. Also, gases, electrolysis and bacteria can be harmful. Corrosion is the consequence unless proper steps are taken to counteract these elements.[8]

BASE METALS

Corrugated steel pipe and other fabricated products are manufactured from ferrous metal sheets or plates made either by the basic open-hearth process or by the basic oxygen process. These conform in chemical properties to one of the classes listed in Table 3-1, with copper-bearing steel the most commonly specified and used. Low cost, corrosion-resistant stainless steels have been developed and are being tested for durability under severe soil and effluent conditions. These may obviate the need for additional protective coatings.

Table 3-1   Chemical Composition of Base Metals for Culvert Sheets by Ladle Analysis

Elements (Max. Per Cent Except as noted)	Kind of Base Metal					Tolerance by Check Analysis of Finished Sheets
	Pure Iron	Copper Bearing Pure Iron	Copper Iron	Copper Molybdenum Iron	Copper Steel	
Carbon...................						
Manganese...............						
Phosphorus...............	.015	.015	.015	.015		
Sulphur...................	.040	.040	.040	.040	.050	.010
Silicon...................						
Copper, Min. Per Cent.....		.20	.20	.40	.20	.02
Molybdenum, Min. Per Cent..				.05		
Sum of First 5 Elements.....		.10	.25	.25	.70	.04
Sum of First 6 Elements.....	.10					.04

From AREA and AASHO Specifications.

GALVANIZED COATINGS

The service life of steel structures can be greatly increased by use of a metallic coating. Especially for underground service, zinc is one of the most beneficial and economical coatings. Therefore, practically all drainage conduits and many other structures are galvanized before or during fabrication.

Under normal soil conditions, zinc corrodes much slower than steel. Consequently a zinc coating on steel protects it by shielding it from the corrosive environment. Furthermore, if the zinc coating is locally damaged and exposes the steel, the zinc will sacrifice itself and continue to serve by providing the steel with cathodic protection.

"When different metals are electrically bonded and immersed in an electrolyte—such as water in streams or ditches, as well as wet soils—there is a difference in potential between the metals.[9] This potential difference results in a flow of current through the electrolyte. If the conductivity of the electrolyte is high (sea water) a greater current will flow than if it is low (fresh water). The magnitude of the current flow determines the extent of galvanic protection that results. Fig. 3-11.

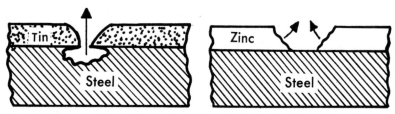

Fig. 3-11. Because of its position on the electro-chemical scale, the steel base is sacrificed to a tin coating, whereas a zinc coating (galvanizing) sacrifices itself to protect the steel against corrosion.

"Many tables arranging metals in order of potential differences have been published. These can be abbreviated to include only metals commonly used in construction or as metallic coatings, as shown in the following table.

ANODIC—CORRODED

Magnesium

Zinc

Iron

Lead

Tin

Copper

CATHODIC—PROTECTED

"A metal near the anodic end of the list will corrode faster when coupled with a metal below it. Extent of corrosion will be determined by the particular combination of metals and by the characteristics of the corroding environment. Magnesium or zinc frequently is used as a sacrificial anode to protect not only steel structures, but also steel-reinforced concrete and cast iron structures. Zinc coatings on steel accomplish the same purpose. However, such protection results only when both metals are immersed in an electrolyte. Thus, in atmospheric applications, the extent of this galvanic protection is limited.

Fig. 3-12. All corrugated steel culverts are given a heavy galvanized coating—ample for normal and mildly severe service conditions.

"Zinc coated sheets do not corrode significantly at cut edges. Also, scratches in the coating do not develop rust of thè base metal. However, the galvanic protection afforded in atmosphere rarely extends laterally beyond $\frac{1}{16}$ of an inch. By contrast, in sea water a small area of zinc will prevent rusting of large areas of bare iron."

PRE-GALVANIZING

Most sheets and plates from 18 gage ($\frac{1}{20}$ in.) through 8 gage ($\frac{1}{6}$ in.) are pre-galvanized by a continuous hot coating process *prior to* corrugating and forming into drainage or other structures. Weight of coating is usually specified as commercial 2 oz of zinc per sq ft of sheet (1 oz on each side).

Structural plates, liner plates and other heavy-gage structures are customarily hot-dip galvanized *after* corrugating and/or forming (from 2 to 3 oz per sq ft total of both sides).

Most steel guardrail and steel retaining walls are galvanized before forming.

SERVICE LIFE OF GALVANIZED COATINGS

Many thousands of galvanized culverts and storm sewers have service records of 35 to 50 years or more, as verified by engineers in field inspections. The value of zinc galvanized coatings as a means of overcoming corrosion is also recognized for structural members for bridges, bridge decking, bridge rail, fencing, lamp standards, signs and many other related construction purposes.

NON-METALLIC COATINGS AND LININGS

Where a metal structure is completely accessible, its life may be prolonged indefinitely by periodic painting or coating.

Bituminous coating affords additional low cost protection when applied over the basic galvanized coating. To be most effective, it must adhere well to the underlying metal and insulate it from the corrosive environment.

Fig. 3-13. Corrugated steel pipe and pipe-arches may be double dipped, full or half coating, over the galvanizing for additional service life.

Non-metallic coatings may be asphalt, tar, rubber or plastic compounds. They are applied either by hot dipping in a tank, or by spraying. Their cost should be in keeping with the purpose and importance of the installation. Figs. 3-13 and 3-14.

For example, under severely corrosive conditions such as highly acid soils, mine drainage, tidal drainage or certain industrial wastes, a special asbestos bonding for the bituminous coating has been found effective and economical

Fig. 3-14. A heavy pavement in the bottom of the pipe or pipe-arch covers the corrugations to a minimum of ⅛ in. Such pavement protects against scour, erosion and impact of sand, gravel and boulders.

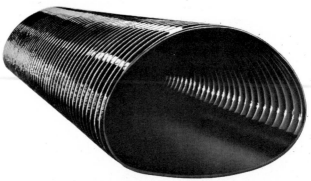

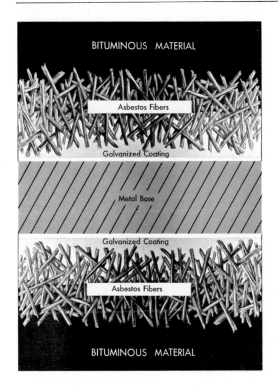

Fig. 3-15. Cross section of asbestos-protected galvanized steel sheet showing how asbestos fibers are imbedded in the galvanized coating. This provides a permanent bond for bituminous coating or pavement. Both sheet sides are thus protected.

over a 30-year period. Asbestos bonding consists of applying inert, rot-proof asbestos fibers to the molten zinc surface during manufacture of the sheet. The fibers become imbedded in the zinc as it solidifies. The sheets are then passed through specially designed equipment that thoroughly saturates the mass of fibers with a bituminous material that is compatible with such nonmetallic coatings as may be added later. Fig. 3-15.

These sheets are then corrugated and formed further into pipe. Subsequent treatment may consist of a seal coat or an asphaltic coating and a paved invert of the same material.

PAVEMENTS IN PIPE

Field inspections show that, where erosion is a factor, structures such as culverts and sewers generally wear faster in the bottom or invert than in the upper three-fourths. In order to protect the bottom against erosion and give it a balanced wear pattern, a heavy bituminous pavement completely filling the corrugations in the invert (25% of periphery) can be placed in the pipe. For diameters up to 96 inches and comparable pipe-arches, such protection ordinarily is factory applied. Fig. 3-16.

Fig. 3-16. Paved pipe gives extra protection in the bottom where the greatest wear takes place. It supplies "balanced wear design."

Galvanized or Asbestos Protected   ┌─ Asphalt Lining
Corrugated Steel Pipe   Smooth Interior Surface

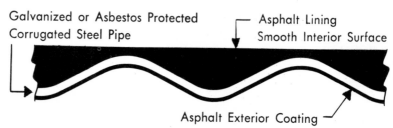

Asphalt Exterior Coating ─┘

Fig. 3-17. Cross section of bituminous spun lining over the complete interior periphery of corrugated steel pipe.

For maximum hydraulic advantage (see Chapter 4) the pavement may cover the complete interior periphery as a smooth, centrifugally applied lining. Figs. 3-17 and 3-18.

Where erosion is a factor in *structural plate* pipe and pipe-arches, which are field assembled, they can be paved after installation. Concrete, plain or reinforced, is used for this purpose, as is asphaltic concrete pavement. Fig. 3-20. For cattle passes, underpasses and other structures, a floor or roadway of earth, asphalt or concrete may be specified.

CALIFORNIA DETERMINATION OF SERVICE LIFE

Based on extensive research, the California Division of Highways recently included in their Planning Manual the following instructions.[10]

(C) Service Life and Special Requirements

The service life of metal culverts shall be determined from the pH (hydrogen ion concentration) and electrical resistivity tests covered in Test Method No. Calif. 643 and the following criteria. To meet the 25 or 50-year criteria for certain installations, both types of metal culverts (steel and aluminum) may require added gage thickness besides additional treatment such as bituminous coating with or without a paved invert as well as other approved coatings.*

. . . The guide values for culverts and coating range may be modified where field observations of existing installations show that other values are more accurate.

The California test method for rationally estimating service life of metal culverts has been thoroughly researched and appears to offer a practical solution under a wide range of geographical and climatic conditions. Test results compare favorably to actual culvert corrosion rates observed in the field.[6]

---

*Aluminum is considered as an alternate only for use under intermediate and low type pavement and for side drains; also for sizes of 48 in. and smaller, under depths of cover of less than 10 ft.

Fig. 3-18. Greatest hydraulic efficiency arises with a complete bituminous lining, centrifugally spun for a durably smooth surface and the lowest Manning's "n" factor. Its primary use is for sewers.

By correlating the *p*H (hydrogen ion concentration) with the electrical resistivity of various kinds of soil, a chart (Fig. 3-19) has been designed to determine the "years required to perforate 16 gage galvanized corrugated steel pipe." Gage factors have been devised as a multiplier for gages other than 16. By means of tables in the Planning Manual, the designer may vary the gage and, where necessary, add coatings, pavements or other protection to provide the service life required.

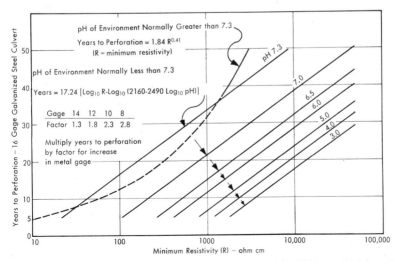

Fig. 3-19. Method of estimating service life as developed by California Division of Highways. This correlates pH with electrical resistivity of soils to determine years to perforate a steel sheet. Local durability records are used for confirmation or control.

Fig. 3-20. Asphaltic or cement concrete pavement in liner plate culvert.

MISCELLANEOUS PRODUCTS AND CONDITIONS

Subdrainage. Plain galvanized steel pipe has been entirely satisfactory on many installations for over thirty years. For areas where corrosive conditions exist, including abundant soil fertilizers, bituminous coating of the subdrain pipe is recommended.

Steel End Sections. Being attached to the ends of culverts, storm drains and spillways, steel end sections or headwalls are readily accessible for maintenance. The galvanized coating assures ample durability under most conditions.

Steel Retaining Walls. Steel retaining walls are supplied with a galvanized finish. Where soil or atmospheric conditions are known to be corrosive, the units comprising the wall may be furnished with bonded asbestos or be suitably field coated.

Liner Plates. For tunnel lining of a temporary nature, bare (black) steel plates are used. For permanent linings or conduits, the plates may be hot-dip galvanized at the factory or be asphalt coated on the job over the galvanized coating.

Sheeting. Steel sheeting or piling used as a temporary structure need not be coated. However, for permanent dams, cutoff walls and the like, the sheeting may be galvanized or bituminous coated, or both.

Guardrail. Most guardrail since 1960 is made from pre-galvanized strip or is hot-dip galvanized after fabrication. If painting becomes desirable for visibility reasons, it can be confined to the surface facing traffic.

Table 3-2 Dates of Introduction of Fabricated Steel Products

Structure	Year	Remarks
Corrugated steel pipe	1895	Patented May 1896
		Some of earliest structures still in service.
Bituminous paved-invert pipe	1926	Developed to resist erosion in bottom—gives a pipe of "balanced design"
Structural plate pipe and arches	1931	Field assembled, bolted construction
Metal retaining walls	1931	Cribbing; replaced by bin-type
Beam-type guardrail	1933	Corrugated plate rail
Asbestos-protected pipe	1934	Developed to give better adhesion of bituminous coating and pavement. Found to give superior resistance to corrosion
Liner plates	1935	For tunneling or relining
Pipe-arches	1937	For limited headroom.
		Found to be more efficient hydraulically
Sheeting, light-weight	1937	Interlocking and flange types
Bridge plank	1946	Replacement of old bridge flooring
Fully paved sewer pipe	1955	Spun-lined; maximum flow

REFERENCES AND BIBLIOGRAPHY

1. Rankin, R. W., *After 20 Years— Pennsylvania Turnpike Culverts Get Inspection OK*, Roads and Streets, Chicago, March 1960.
2. AREA, *Design of Metal Culverts of 60-in. Diam. and Larger*, Progress Report of Committee 15, Bulletin 506, Jan. 1953, pp. 918–929.
3. *1962 Inspection of Armco Sewers in Salt Water Service*, Report of Metal Products Division, Armco Steel Corp., Middletown, Ohio, 1962, 16 pp.
4. *Durability Studies in Wichita County, Texas*, Report of Armco Drainage & Metal Products, Inc., Houston, Texas, 1957, 30 pp.
5. Corps of Engineers, St. Louis District, *1962 Reinspection of Coated & Paved Corr. Steel Pipe in Flood Control Levees*, Report published by Armco Metal Products Division, Middletown, Ohio, 44 pp.
6. Beaton, J. L. and Stratfull, R. F., *Field Test for Estimating Service Life of Corrugated Metal Pipe Culverts*, Calif. Div. of Highways, Highway Research Board, Proc. Vol. 41, 1962, p. 258.
7. American Society of Civil Engineers; Water Pollution Control Federation, New York, N. Y., *Design and Construction of Sanitary and Storm Sewers*, Manuals of Engineering Practice, Nos. 37 and 9, 1960, 283 pp.
8. Stratfull, R. F., *Field Method of Detecting Corrosive Soil Conditions*, Calif. Div. of Highways, Proc. 15th Annual Street & Highway Conf., Jan. 1963.
9. Ellis, O. B., *Economical Corrosion Protection*, Highway Magazine, Middletown, Ohio, 1st Quarter 1963, pp. 8–10.
10. *Planning Manual of Instructions, Part 7-Design, Section 7-800*. Calif. Div. of Highways.

Fig. 4-1a. Vortex at submerged upstream end of culvert.
Fig. 4-1b. Vigorous discharge at outlet end of same culvert. Courtesy: Bureau of Public Roads.

CHAPTER 4 Hydraulics

Section I—INTRODUCTION

The engineering study determining drainage structure size and shape is termed *Hydraulics*, one of the spokes in the "wheel of design factors" (Fig. 1-1). Other factors include strength, durability, installation and economy.

This handbook chapter is directed to various drainage structures, including open channels, culverts, storm drains and sanitary sewers. Subdrains are covered in Chapter 10.

Emphasis here is placed on culverts. Many millions of dollars have been spent and will continue to be spent on small waterway structures vital to the protection of streets, highways and railroads. If inadequate, they can jeopardize the roadway and bring excessive property damage and loss of life. Overdesign means extravagance. Good engineering can find an economic medium.

METHODS OF DESIGN

The aim of hydrologic design is to determine the peak discharge that can be handled safely and economically by a structure. A Bureau of Public Roads official* comments, "while the tools of design have been greatly improved in recent years, they are not perfect by any means."[1] Approximations are still employed.

Various methods of design include: (1) Judgment. (2) Classification and diagnosis. (3) Empirical rules (of thumb). (4) Formulas. (5) Tables and curves. (6) Direct observations. (7) Rational method. (8) Correlating factors. (9) Hydrographic synthesis.[2] Several among these are described here.

Because topography, soil and climate combine in infinite variety, drainage sites should be designed individually from reasonably adequate data for each particular site. In addition, the designer is advised to consult with those of long experience in maintaining culverts in the area. One state highway engineer** comments:

"With the exception of the riding qualities of the traveled way, no other single item requires as much attention on the part of the maintenance man as highway culverts. Many of the problems of culvert maintenance stem from the fact that designers in all too many instances consider that culverts will be required to transport only clear water. This is a condition hardly ever realized in practice, and in many instances storm waters may be carrying as much as 50 per cent detrital material which, due to a rapid change in grade line at the culvert entrance, causes complete blockage of the culvert, with resulting overflow across the highway and in some cases, especially where high fills are involved, the intense static pressure results in loss of the embankment."

---

*Lester A. Herr, Chief, Hydraulics Branch, Bridge Division, U.S. Bureau of Public Roads.

**P. M. Hine, District Maintenance Engineer, Operations, California State Division of Highways.

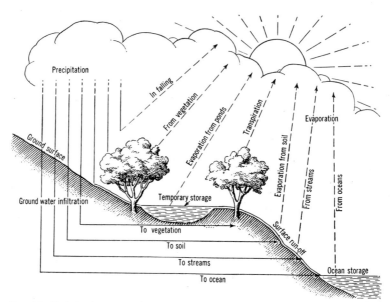

Fig. 4-2. Hydrologic cycle—where water comes from and where it goes.—From M. G. Spangler's "Soil Engineering."

The same source adds: "Many engineers recognize the importance of the various items mentioned; however, due to the increased initial cost of an adequate structure, they are reluctant to provide culverts with all of the foregoing features." These include deflecting debris at inlet; maintaining velocity of approach through the culvert; providing for possible settlement of culvert; protecting against erosion at outlet.

FACTORS IN DRAINAGE DESIGN

The design procedure for the solution of drainage problems consists of:

(1) collecting complete field data by the locating engineer,
(2) compiling facts about the proposed roadway,
(3) determining how much water to expect under flood conditions, and
(4) then determining the kind, proper size, shape, alignment, slope and end treatment of drainage structure to handle water and debris with minimum damage to embankment, structure and property above and below the site.

Item (4) is properly known as "hydraulics."

Section II—ESTIMATING RUNOFF FROM SMALL AREAS

GENERAL

"Many formulas have been developed for estimating the peak storm runoff, but most were developed from data collected from a limited area and can be considered applicable only to that area and under the conditions for which the data were collected."[3]*

Some storm runoff formulas (including Talbot's) give the size of waterway opening directly and these continue to be used because of their simplicity. However, modern practice is to first calculate the anticipated discharge and then design the waterway or channel to accommodate that discharge.[4]

RAINFALL INTENSITY—FREQUENCY ANALYSIS

"The expected frequency of occurrence of the design discharge is of concern ... Overdesign and underdesign both involve excessive costs on a longtime basis," says the Bureau of Public Roads.[3]

Memorandum PPM 20-4 of the Bureau of Public Roads requires that on Interstate System projects, all drainage facilities other than culverts and bridges be designed to keep the traveled way usable during storms at least as great as that for a 10-year frequency, except that a 50-year frequency shall be used for underpasses or other depressed roadways where ponded water can be removed only through the storm drain system.

Rainfall intensity data are taken from the U.S. Weather Bureau Atlas,[5] or from Weather Bureau Technical Paper 25.[6]

Approximate rainfall intensity—duration—frequency data can also be obtained from Fig. 4-3 by the use of coefficients.[3] The 2-year rainfall inten-

---

*The Highway Research Board Surface Drainage Committee in June 1965 initiated a research project entitled "Improved Methods for Estimating Runoff Rates from Small Watersheds." Because of the economic importance of this information, the project is labeled as "urgent."

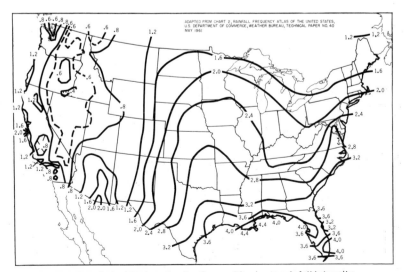

Fig. 4-3. Map of the United States, showing 2-year, 30-minute rainfall intensity.

Table 4-1 Rainfall Intensity Conversion Factors[3]

Duration in Minutes	Factor	Duration in Minutes	Factor
5	2.22	40	0.8
10	1.71	50	0.7
15	1.44	60	0.6
20	1.25	90	0.5
30	1.00	120	0.4

From BPR Circular 4, p. 9
Note: U.S. Weather Bureau says "Rainfall amounts for the 5-, 10-, and 15-minute durations may be obtained by multiplying the 30-minute values by 0.37, 0.57 and 0.72 respectively.[5]

Table 4-2 Recurrence Interval Factors[3]

Recurrence Interval in Years	Factor
2	1.0
5	1.3
10	1.6
25	1.9
50	2.2

sity for other durations is obtained by multiplying the 30-minute intensity for the project location from Fig. 4-3 by the factors listed in Table 4-1.

To convert 2-year recurrence interval rainfall for a given duration to other frequencies (recurrence intervals) multiply by the factors in Table 4-2 to obtain acceptable results.

Another chart, Fig. 4-4, applying only to conditions east of the Rocky Mountains shows the relationship between intensity of storms and their frequency of recurrence.

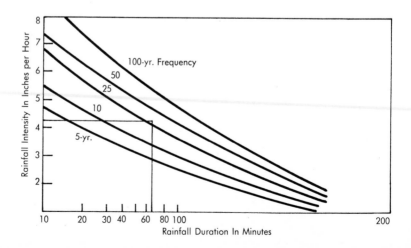

Fig. 4-4. Rainfall intensities for various storm frequencies vs. rainfall duration.

RUNOFF: THE RATIONAL METHOD

Total or peak rainfall can be converted into estimated storm runoff or design discharge by the rational method or formula.

For **storm sewers,** most engineering offices in the United States use the *rational method* of design which has been in use since 1889. This method, recommended by the BPR for roadside channels draining less than about 200 acres, uses the equation:

$$Q = CiA \tag{1}$$

where Q = peak rate of runoff, in cfs

$\quad C$ = weighted runoff coefficient, expressing the ratio of rate of runoff to rate of rainfall (Table 4-4)

$\quad i$ = average intensity of rainfall, in inches per hour (for the selected frequency and for duration equal to the time of concentration)

$\quad A$ = drainage area, in acres, tributary to the point under design

This formula although not dimensionally correct, gives numerically correct results, since 1 cfs runoff equals 1.008 in. per hour per acre.

Table 4-3 World's Greatest Observed Point Rainfalls

Duration	Depth in Inches	Station	Date
1 min	1.23	Unionville, Maryland	July 4, 1956
5 min	2.48	Porto Bello, Panama	Nov. 29, 1911
8 min	4.96	Fussen, Bavaria	May 25, 1920
14 min	3.95	Galveston, Tex.	June 4, 1871
15 min	7.80	Plumb Point, Jamaica	May 12, 1916
20 min	8.10	Curtea-de-Argés, Roumania	July 7, 1889
40 min	9.25	Guinea, Va.	Aug. 24, 1906
42 min	12.00	Holt, Mo.	June 22, 1947
1 hr	10.00	Catskill, N.Y.	July 26, 1819
1 hr, 20 min	11.50	Campo, Calif.	Aug. 21, 1891
2 hr, 10 min	19.00	Rockport, W. Va.	July 18, 1889
2 hr, 45 min	22.00	D'Hanis, Tex. (17 miles NNW)	May 31, 1935
3 hr	16.00	Concord, Pa.	Aug. 5, 1843
4 hr	23.00	Bassetere, St. Kitts, West Indies	Jan. 12, 1880
4 hr, 30 min	30.8†	Smethport, Pa.	July 18, 1942
12 hr	26.58	Baguio, Philippine Islands	July 15, 1911
15 hr	34.50	Smethport, Pa.	July 17–18, 1942
18 hr	36.40	Thrall, Tex.	Sept. 9, 1921

Source: Monthly Weather Review, Jan. 1950, p. 4, U.S. Weather Bureau, Washington, D.C., April 1962.

Note: Maximum recorded U.S. point rainfall for 207 first-order stations in the U.S. for periods of 5 min. to 24 hrs. can be found in Technical Paper No. 2, 1947, U.S. Weather Bureau.

Table 4-4 Values of Relative Imperviousness[3]

Type of Surface	Factor C
For all watertight roof surfaces...............................	.75 to .95
For asphalt runway pavements...............................	.80 to .95
For concrete runway pavements.............................	.70 to .90
For gravel or macadam pavements...........................	.35 to .70
*For impervious soils (heavy)................................	.40 to .65
*For impervious soils, with turf..............................	.30 to .55
*For slightly pervious soils...................................	.15 to .40
*For slightly pervious soils, with turf.........................	.10 to .30
*For moderately pervious soils...............................	.05 to .20
*For moderately pervious soils, with turf.....................	.00 to .10

*For slopes from 1% to 2%

WATERSHED CHARACTERISTICS

Some of the watershed characteristics that influence the amount and rate of runoff are:

1. Area and shape

2. Steepness and length of slopes

3. Kind and extent of vegetation or cultivation

4. Condition of surface—dry, saturated, frozen—pervious or impervious soil

5. Number, arrangement and condition of drainage channels on the watershed

The changes of land use during the lifetime of a drainage structure should be considered in evaluating runoff characteristics. Where the drainage area is composed of several types of ground cover, the runoff should be weighted according to the area of each type of cover present.

TIME OF CONCENTRATION

An important factor is the time required for runoff from the remotest part of a drainage area to reach the point under design. This is known as the time of concentration. It is used in the rational design method but must be clearly understood to avoid misapplication of the method and its proposed refinements.[3]

A minimum time of 5 minutes is recommended by the Bureau of Public Roads. See Fig. 4-5.

DRAINAGE AREA

The drainage area can be measured on a topographic map or determined in the field by estimation, pacing, aerial photos, or a survey comparable in accuracy to a stadia-compass traverse.

Example:[3]

Find the discharge for a 10-year frequency rainfall at the outlet of a grassed roadside channel 400 ft from the crest of a hill with the contributing area 238 ft wide, consisting of 12 ft of concrete pavement, 26 ft of gravel shoul-

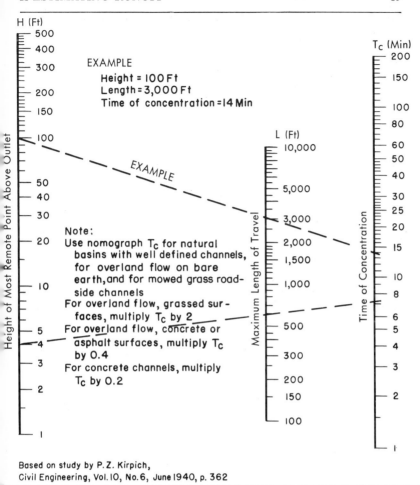

EXAMPLE

Height = 100 Ft
Length = 3,000 Ft
Time of concentration = 14 Min

Note:
Use nomograph T_C for natural
   basins with well defined channels,
   for overland flow on bare
   earth, and for mowed grass roadside channels
For overland flow, grassed surfaces, multiply T_C by 2
For overland flow, concrete or
   asphalt surfaces, multiply T_C
   by 0.4
For concrete channels, multiply
   T_C by 0.2

Based on study by P. Z. Kirpich,
Civil Engineering, Vol. 10, No. 6, June 1940, p. 362

Fig. 4-5. Time of concentration of rainfall on small drainage basins.

der, channel, and 200 ft backslope of grassed pasture—giving a weighted
$C = 0.35$. The channel grade is 0.5 per cent; and the outer edge of the contributing area is 4 ft above the channel. Location is near Washington, D.C.

The distance from the channel to the ridge of the area is 210 ft and that of
the channel is 400 ft making $L = 610$ ft. The height of the most remote
point above the outlet $= 4$ ft $+ (0.005 \times 400) = 6$ ft. From Fig. 4-5, the
time of concentration, $Tc = 7$ min.

The rainfall intensity for a 7 minute duration and 10-year return period is
6.8 in. per hr. (Fig. 4-6).

The drainage area $= 238 \times 400 = 95,200$ sq ft or
$$\frac{95,200}{43,560} = 2.2 \text{ acres}$$

Then $Q = 0.35 \times 6.8 \times 2.2 = 5.2$ cfs.

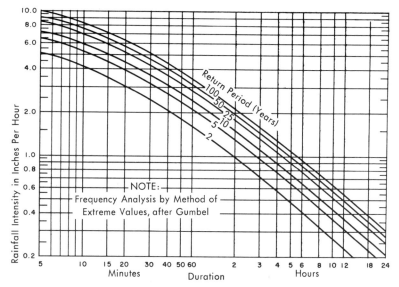

Fig. 4-6. Rainfall intensity for various durations and return periods.

THE TALBOT FORMULA

The Talbot formula continues to find extensive use by engineers in many localities. This can be attributed to its simplicity and the fact that when used by individuals well acquainted with local conditions, results have been satisfactory.

The Talbot formula is empirical, based on observations in the Middle West around the beginning of the 20th Century. It does not take into account the intensity of rainfall, velocity of flow or other factors. This formula gives the area of the culvert opening directly:

$$A = C\sqrt[4]{M^3} \tag{2}$$

where

A = waterway necessary, in sq ft

M = area drained, in acres

C = contour coefficient

The coefficient C depends upon the contour of the land drained, and the following values are recommended for various conditions of topography.

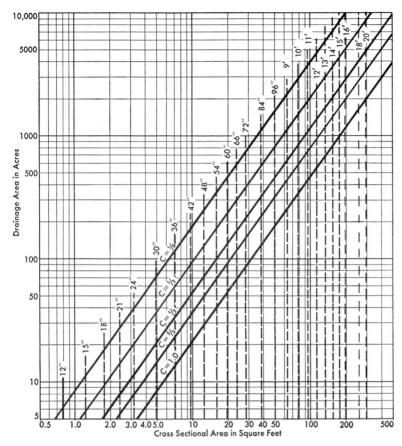

Fig. 4-7. Culvert size determination by diagram for Talbot formula $A = C\sqrt[4]{M^3}$.

$C = 1$, for steep and rocky ground with abrupt slopes

$C = \frac{2}{3}$, for rough hilly country of moderate slopes

$C = \frac{1}{2}$, for uneven valleys, very wide as compared to length

$C = \frac{1}{3}$, for rolling agricultural country where the length of valley is three or four times the width

$C = \frac{1}{5}$, for level district not affected by accumulated snow or severe floods. For still milder conditions or for subdrained lands, decrease C as much as 50 per cent; but increase C for steep side slopes or where the upper part of the valley has a much greater fall than the channel of the culvert.

Example: Required, the cross-sectional area of a culvert suitable for draining 75 acres in level country. Assuming $\frac{1}{5}$ as the value of C, locate the intersection of the 75-acre line with the first curve of Fig. 4-7, then trace directly down to the base line. This point lies almost exactly at 5 sq ft.

From Table 4-5 find the nearest waterway opening corresponding to 5.0, in this case 4.91. A 30-in. culvert is the nearest stock size.

Engineers have in some cases modified the factors in this formula, based on experience with it in their own section of the country.

Table 4-5 Acres Drained by Culverts of Various Diameters[3]
(Talbot Formula)

Diameter of Culvert in Inches	Area of Waterway Opening in Sq Ft	Mountainous Country C = 1	Rolling Country C = ⅓	Level Country C = ⅕
12	.79	¾	3	6
15	1.23	1	6	11
18	1.77	2	9	18
21	2.40	3	14	28
24	3.14	5	20	39
30	4.91	8	36	71
36	7.07	14	59	115
42	9.62	20	89	175
48	12.6	29	125	250
54	16.0	40	175	345
60	19.6	55	230	455
66	23.8	70	295	585
72	28.3	85	375	735
78	33.2	105	460	910
84	38.5	130	560	1110
90	44.2	160	680	1340
96	50.3	190	800	1590
102	56.7	220	940	1860
108	63.6	250	1100	2170
114	70.9	290	1270	2510
120	78.5	340	1450	2870
126	86.6	380	1660	3270
132	95.0	430	1880	3710
138	103.9	490	2110	4180
144	113.1	550	2370	4680
150	122.7	610	2640	5210
156	132.7	680	2930	5780
162	143.1	750	3240	6400
168	153.9	820	3570	7050
174	165.1	910	3920	7740
180	176.7	990	4290	8480

BURKLI-ZIEGLER FORMULA

Dozens of other empirical formulas have been devised to fit peak flows in various parts of the country. These generally give the answer in quantity of flow expected for peak discharge. The second part of the problem then consists of designing the culvert by hydraulic methods, based on $Q = AV$, (see page 95 for nomenclature).

One convenient formula frequently used is the Burkli-Ziegler as follows:

$$Q = MRc\sqrt[4]{\frac{S}{M}} \tag{3}$$

in which:

Q = quantity of water reaching culvert or sewer, cfs

M = drainage area, in acres

R = average rate of rainfall in inches per hour during the

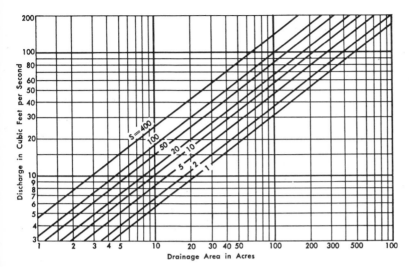

Fig. 4-8. Graphical solution of Burkli-Ziegler formula.

heaviest rainfall (2.75 in. per hr is commonly used in the Middle West)

S = average slope of ground, in feet per 1000 ft

c = a coefficient depending upon the character of the surface drained and determined approximately as shown in Table 4-4 or, more briefly, as follows:

c = .75 for paved streets and built up business blocks

c = .625 for ordinary city streets

c = .30 for village with lawns and macadam streets

c = .25 for farming country

Example: Assume an area of 100 acres in a suburban district with gardens, lawns and paved streets ($c = 0.30$), rainfall 2.4 in. per hour exceeded only once every 10 years, and slope $S = 10$ ft per 1000. From the Burkli-Ziegler diagram, Fig. 4-8, it is found that the quantity of water reaching the culvert is about 56 cu ft per sec. To obtain runoff for $R = 2.4$ and $c = 0.3$ multiply as follows: $56 \times 2.4 \times 0.3 = 40.3$ cu ft per sec. For determining the size of opening required, see later in this chapter.

SUMMARY

Section II dealing with hydrology has been the subject of a great deal of research, but as experienced engineers will agree, scientifically the surface has just been scratched. The subject is still loaded with educated guesses, estimates and economic factors. In many respects it still is an art, rather than a science.

The fact that we are not dealing with "clean" water but also with driftwood, debris and changing runoff characteristics as land is developed, puts a premium on experience and judgment as against pure theory.

So the design of drainage channels and structures as described in following sections continues to be a challenge to engineering skills.

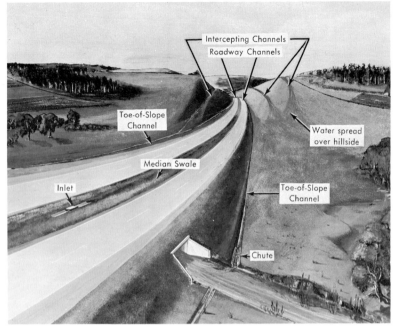

Fig. 4-9. Types of roadside drainage channels.

Section III—HYDRAULICS OF
OPEN DRAINAGE CHANNELS

GENERAL

Before designing culverts, storm sewers and other drainage structures, it is well to consider the design of ditches, gutters, chutes, median swales, and other channels leading to these structures. Fig. 4-9.

The design engineer with needs beyond the scope of this handbook will wish to refer to the publication, *Design of Roadside Drainage Channels*,[3] which includes numerous examples of calculations and a list of 55 authoritative references on all phases of the subject.

Rainfall and runoff, once calculated, are followed by design of suitable channels to handle the peak discharge with minimum erosion, maintenance and hazard to traffic.

The AASHO *Policy on Geometric Design of Rural Highways* recommends:

"Where terrain permits, roadside drainage channels built in earth should have side slopes not steeper than 4:1 (horizontal to vertical), and a rounded bottom at least 4 ft wide. (Minimum depth 1 ft to 3 ft.) . . . Dimensions can be varied by the use of different types of channel surfacing."

Systematic maintenance is recognized as essential to any drainage channel and therefore should be considered in the design of those channels.

CHEZY EQUATION

A basic hydraulic formula developed by Chezy for determining the flow of water particularly in open channels is written as follows:

$$Q = AV \qquad V = c\sqrt{RS} \qquad \text{and} \qquad Q = Ac\sqrt{RS} \tag{4}$$

in which:

Q = discharge, cfs

A = cross-sectional area of flow in sq ft, at right angles to the direction of flow

V = mean velocity of flow, fps

c = a coefficient of roughness whose value depends upon the character of surface over which water is flowing

R = hydraulic radius in ft = $\dfrac{A}{WP}$

WP = wetted perimeter or length, in ft, of wetted contact between a stream of water and its containing channel measured at right angles to the direction of flow

S = slope, or grade in ft per ft

This fundamental formula is the basis of most capacity formulas.

MANNING'S EQUATION

Manning's formula, published in 1890, gives the value of c in the Chezy formula as:

$$c = \frac{1.486}{n} R^{1/6} \tag{5}$$

the complete Manning formula being:

$$V = \frac{1.486}{n} R^{2/3} S^{1/2} \tag{6}$$

and combining with the Chezy Equation:

$$Q = A \frac{1.486}{n} R^{2/3} S^{1/2} \tag{7}$$

in which:

A = cross-sectional area of flow in sq ft

S = slope in ft per ft

R = hydraulic radius in ft

n = coefficient of roughness (see Tables 4-6, 4-7)

In many computations, it is convenient to group the properties peculiar to the cross section in one term called conveyance (K) or:

$$K = \frac{1.486}{n} AR^{2/3} \tag{8}$$

then $$Q = KS^{1/2} \tag{9}$$

Uniform flow of "clean" water in a straight, unobstructed channel would be a simple problem but is rarely attained. Manning's formula gives reliable results if the channel cross section, roughness, and slope are fairly constant over a sufficient distance to establish uniform flow.

Table 4-6 Coefficient of Roughness *n* for Channels

Type of Lining	*n* (Manning)
Ordinary earth, smoothly graded	.02
Sod, depth of flow over 6 in	.04
Sod, depth of flow under 6 in	.06
Type A riprap, rough	.04
Concrete paved gutter	.016

Source: Ohio Hydraulic Treatise, 1947.

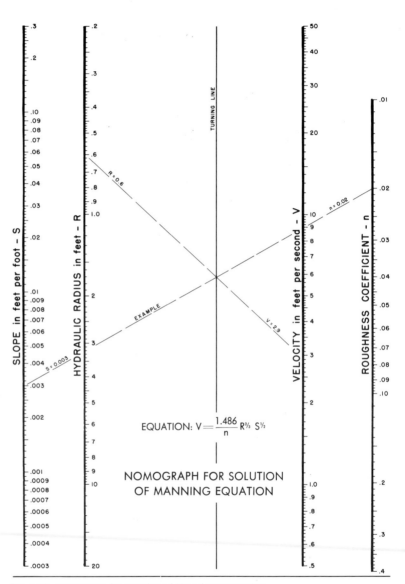

Fig. 4-10. Nomograph for solution of Manning's equation.

Table 4-7 Manning's *n* for Natural Stream Channels
Surface width at flood stage less than 100 ft.

1. Fairly regular section:
   a. Some grass and weeds, little or no brush............................. 0.030—0.035
   b. Dense growth of weeds, depth of flow materially greater than weed height.. 0.035—0.05
   c. Some weeds, light brush on banks.................................... 0.035—0.05
   d. Some weeds, heavy brush on banks................................... 0.05 —0.07
   e. Some weeds, dense willows on banks................................. 0.06 —0.08
   f. For trees within channel, with branches submerged at high stage, increase all
      above values by.. 0.01 —0.02

2. Irregular sections, with pools, slight channel meander; increase values given
   above about... 0.01 —0.02

3. Mountain streams, no vegetation in channel, banks usually steep, trees and
   brush along banks submerged at high stage:
   a. Bottom of gravel, cobbles, and few boulders........................... 0.04 —0.05
   b. Bottom of cobbles, with large boulders............................... 0.05 —0.07

THE USE OF CHARTS AND TABLES

While design charts[7,8,9] for open-channel flow reduce work, "they cannot replace engineering judgment and a knowledge of the hydraulics of open-channel flow . . . and flow through conduits with a free water surface."[3]

These design charts contain the channel properties (area and hydraulic radius) of many channel sections and tables of velocity for various combinations of slope and hydraulic radius. Their use is explained in the following examples.

Example 1

Given: A trapezoidal channel of straight alignment and uniform cross section in earth, bottom width 2 ft, side slopes 1:1, channel slope 0.003, and normal depth 1 ft.

Find: Velocity and discharge.

Solution:

1. In Table 4-6 for an excavated channel in ordinary earth, *n* is 0.02.

2. Cross-sectional area, A, of the channel is 3.0 sq ft and the hydraulic radius is 0.6 ft.

3. Using the nomograph (Fig. 4-10), lay a straightedge between the outer lines at the values of $S = 0.003$ and $n = 0.02$. Mark where the straightedge intersects the turning line.

4. Then place the straightedge so as to line up the point on the turning line and the hydraulic radius of 0.6 ft.

5. Read the velocity 2.9 fps on the velocity line.

6. The discharge, $Q = AV$, is 3.0 sq ft times 2.9 fps or 8.7 cfs.

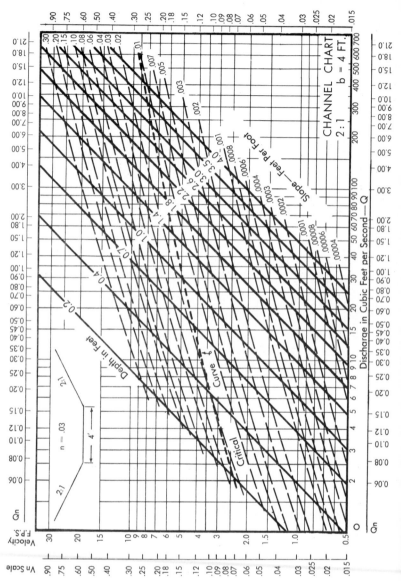

Fig. 4-11. Open-channel chart for bottom width of 4 ft and 2:1 side slopes.

Example 2

Given: A trapezoidal channel with bottom width 4 ft, side slopes 2:1, $n = 0.03$, channel slope 0.005, and discharge 100 cfs.

Find: Depth d and velocity V.

Solution: (by trial and error)

$$A = (4 + 2d)d$$
$$WP = 4 + 2d\sqrt{5} = 4 + 4.47d$$

Try: $d = 2.5$ ft

$A = (4 + 5) \times 2.5 = 22.5$ sq ft

$WP = 4 + (4.47)(2.5) = 15.2$ ft

$R = 1.48$ ft

From the nomograph, $V = 4.6$ fps

$Q = 22.5 (4.6) = 104$ cfs

This figure is slightly higher than the required 100 cfs, but inasmuch as "exact" solution is $d = 2.45$, the greater refinement does not seem justified. See Fig. 4-11. To the value $d = 2.5$ ft some freeboard should be added.

SAFE VELOCITIES

The ideal situation is one where the velocity will cause neither silting nor erosion. In designing a channel, the approximate grade can be determined from a topographic map, from the plan profiles, or from both.

To prevent the depositing of sediment, the *minimum* gradient for earth and grass-lined channels should be about 0.5 per cent and that for smooth paved channels about 0.35 per cent. Furthermore it should be kept constant or increasing, if possible, to avoid deposition.

Safe or permissible velocities for erodible channels are given in Table 4-8.

Table 4-8 Comparison of Limiting Water Velocities and Tractive Force Values for the Design of Stable Channels
Straight channels after aging. Canal depth, 3 ft.

Material	n	For Clear Water		Water Transporting Colloidal Silts	
		Velocity ft/sec	Tractive* Force lb/sq ft	Velocity ft/sec	Trac- tive* Force lb/sq ft
Fine sand colloidal..........................	0.020	1.50	0.027	2.50	0.075
Sandy loam noncolloidal...................	.020	1.75	.037	2.50	0.075
Silt loam noncolloidal......................	.020	2.00	.048	3.00	0.11
Alluvial silts noncolloidal..................	.020	2.00	.048	3.50	0.15
Ordinary firm loam.........................	.020	2.50	.075	3.50	0.15
Volcanic ash................................	.020	2.50	.075	3.50	0.15
Stiff clay very colloidal....................	.025	3.75	.26	5.00	0.46
Alluvial silts colloidal......................	.025	3.75	.26	5.00	0.46
Shales and hardpans.......................	.025	6.00	.67	6.00	0.67
Fine gravel.................................	.020	2.50	.075	5.00	0.32
Graded loam to cobbles when non-colloidal...	.030	3.75	.38	5.00	0.66
Graded silts to cobbles when colloidal........	.030	4.00	.43	5.50	0.80
Coarse gravel noncolloidal.................	.025	4.00	.30	6.00	0.67
Cobbles and shingles......................	.035	5.00	.91	5.50	1.10

*"Tractive force" or shear is the force which the water exerts on the periphery of a channel due to the motion of the water. The tractive values shown were computed from velocities given by S. Fortier and Fred C. Scobey and the values of n shown.

The tractive force values are valid for the given materials regardless of depth. For depths greater than 3 ft, higher velocities can be allowed and still have the same tractive force. From U.S. Bureau of Reclamation, Report No. Hyd-352, 1952, 60 pp.

Table 4-9 Maximum Permissible Velocities in Vegetal-lined Channels

Cover average, uniform stand, well maintained	Slope Range	Permissible Velocity[a]	
	Per cent	Erosion Resistant Soils	Easily Eroded Soils
		f p s	f p s
Bermudagrass	0–5 5–10 over 10	8 7 6	6 5 4
Buffalograss Kentucky bluegrass Smooth brome Blue grama	0–5 5–10 over 10	7 6 5	5 4 3
Grass mixture[b]	0–5 5–10	5 4	4 3
Lespedeza sericea Weeping lovegrass Yellow bluestem Kudzu Alfalfa Crabgrass	0–5	3.5	2.5
Common lespedeza[b] Sudangrass[b]	0–5[c]	3.5	2.5

[a]From "Handbook of Channel Design for Soil and Water Conservation," Soil Conservation Service SCS-TP-61, Revised June 1954
[b]Annuals—used on mild slopes or as temporary protection until permanent covers are established
[c]Use on slopes steeper than 5 per cent is not recommended

CHANNEL PROTECTION

If the mean velocity exceeds that permissible for the particular kind of soil, the channel should be protected from erosion. Grass linings are valuable where grass can be supported. Ditch bottoms may be sodded or seeded with the aid of temporary quick growing grasses, mulches, jute bagging or fiberglass. Grass may also be used in combination with other, more rigid types of linings, the grass being on the upper bank slopes.

Linings may consist of stone—dumped, hand placed or grouted, preferably laid on a filter blanket of gravel or crushed stone.

Asphalt and concrete lined channels are used on many steep erodible channels.

Corrugated steel flumes or chutes (and pipe spillways) are favored especially in wet, unstable or frost heaving soils. See Fig. 4-12. They should be anchored to prevent undue shifting. Most types of fabricated or poured channels should be protected against buoyancy and uplift, especially when empty. Cutoff walls, half diaphragms, or collars are used to prevent undermining.

Ditch checks (slope-control structures) are used in arid and semi-arid areas where grass won't grow. However, where grass will grow, the use of ditch

Fig. 4-12. Riveted corrugated steel flume used as ditch lining to prevent erosion. Precautions should be taken to anchor against uplift and other forces.

checks in roadway or toe-of-slope channels is discouraged because they are a hazard to traffic and an impediment to mowing equipment.

High velocity at channel exits must be considered and some provision made to dissipate the excess energy.

Fig. 4-13. Refined culvert design and field conditions may vary greatly. These four 84-in. culverts clogged with debris can function only partly, with the value of "*n*" being meaningless.

Section IV—HYDRAULICS OF CULVERTS

INTRODUCTION

Designing a culvert has not yet reached the stage where two or more individuals will always arrive at the same answer, or where actual service performance matches the designer's anticipation. The reason is that the engineer's interpretation of field data and hydrology is often influenced by personal judgment, based on his own experience in a given locality. However, field data, hydrology and hydraulic research are hopefully closing the gap to move the art of designing a culvert a little closer to becoming a science.

Up to this point, the design procedure has consisted of (1) collecting field data, (2) compiling facts about the roadway, and (3) making a reasonable estimate of maximum flood flow. The fourth step now is to design an economical culvert to handle the flood flow (including debris) with little or no damage to the highway, street, railway or adjacent property. Fig. 4-13.

Factors to consider include: type of structure; area and shape of waterway opening; approximate length and slope of culvert barrel; and treatment of inlet and outlet ends.

The locator and designer have a choice and an obligation. They must mix laboratory facts and theories with field facts and experience and come up with designs that are reasonably economical, both as to first cost and annual cost. They must protect the roadway against washout, and their organization against lawsuits for damage up or down the waterway.

Meanwhile, the various material interests and pipe manufacturers associations are trying to be helpful and neutral. If culverts are inadequate in size or in other features, the manufacturer stands to suffer along with the engineer. Costs increase much more slowly than capacity does, so the manufacturer prefers to furnish a pipe with a reasonable factor of safety, believing it to be most economical during the service life.

TWO BASIC APPROACHES TO DESIGN

A culvert is in most instances a change in cross-sectional area and shape of the waterway from the stream above and below. Under some conditions the barrel runs full; in other cases it does not. The effects of slope of the barrel, slope of the stream profile, velocity of flow, headwater and tailwater, roughness of interior walls—all follow fairly well known laws of hydraulics.

By *ponding* the water above a culvert and submerging the inlet, the discharge can be increased up to several hundred per cent. However, it also appreciably reduces the peak discharge on flashy streams. A temptation will exist which must be restrained, to use this head or pressure to get greater capacity from a structure, whereas the structure may actually be unable to withstand resultant pressures, that will endanger embankment, culvert and property up and downstream.

The two schools of thought are: (1) design with little or no ponding by using a larger structure that will pass drift and debris with a factor of safety, or (2) design for ponding and spend more money on debris interceptors, special inlets, diaphragms, watertight joints, velocity retarders downstream and add to the maintenance forces. In the first instance, larger pipes alone will often not reduce velocity or avoid leakage.

Fig. 4-14. Large culverts justify careful design with an adequate size factor for the class of roadway, and experience under local conditions.

HIGHWAY ASSOCIATION CRITERIA

The American Association of State Highway Officials' specifications for Highway Bridges for 1961 reads:

> In general, culverts shall be proportioned to carry the maximum flood discharge without head. If the maximum flood discharge occurs only at rare intervals, culverts may be designed to carry it under slight head, provided they are protected against undermining by means of adequate pavement and apron or cutoff walls and that adjacent embankments are protected from erosion by riprap or other suitable means.

Memorandum 20-4 of the Bureau of Public Roads states:

> Design for all culverts and bridges over streams shall be in accord with the Standard Specifications for Highway Bridges of the American Association of State Highway Officials to accommodate floods at least as great as that for a 50-year frequency or the greatest flood of record, whichever is the greater, with runoff based on land development expected in the watershed 20 years hence and with *backwater limited* to an amount which will not result in damage to upstream property or to the highway.

The California Division of Highways recommends as general rules that (a) culverts pass a 10-year flood without static head on crown of culvert at entrance, and that (b) designs be balanced for 100-year floods.[17] (One step in balancing design is for the locator or designer to select a combination of conduit and gradient that will carry the 100-year flood with full section to the outlet, so as to control the velocity of effluent.)

This procedure limits the ponding possible on 100-year flows, since the pipe size required for the 10-year flow without ponding is large enough to carry the 100-year flow with ponding of only about one half a pipe diameter. This can be seen from Table 4-10 where a 100-year storm is only 45 per cent more than a ·10-year storm.

Table 4-10   Storm Rating Based on 50-Year Maximum Rainfall

Storm Rating	One-Hour Maximum Rainfall
1 year	0.428
5 years	0.659
10 years	0.762
25 years	0.898
50 years	1.000
100 years	1.108

The amount of ponding is also modified at the entrance by the effect of storage. It can be shown that a culvert will not flow full (inlet controls), and then only under special conditions, until the headwater depth is 1.5 HW/D. (HW=headwater; D=diameter.) This indicates it might be possible to have a full flow in a 100-year flood. Many textbook examples of culverts show excessive HW/D values, some as high as 6.0. These examples are mathematically correct but are not a practical answer to the problem of culvert design.

The ASCE Task Force on Hydraulics of Culverts, 1961, offers the following recommendations for "Attributes of a Good Highway Culvert":[10]

1. The culvert, appurtenant entrance and outlet structures should properly take care of water, bed-load, and floating debris at all stages of flow.

2. It should cause no unnecessary or excessive property damage.

3. Normally, it should provide for transportation of material without detrimental change in flow pattern above and below the structure.

4. It should be designed so that future channel and highway improvement can be made without too much loss or difficulty.

5. It should be designed to function properly after fill has caused settlement.

6. It should not cause objectionable stagnant pools in which mosquitoes may breed.

7. It should be designed to accommodate increased runoff occasioned by anticipated land development.

8. It should be economical to build, hydraulically adequate to handle design discharge, structurally durable and easy to maintain.

9. It should be designed to avoid excessive ponding at entrance which may cause property damage, accumulation of drift, culvert clogging, saturation of fills, or detrimental upstream deposits of debris.

10. Entrance structures should be designed to screen out material which will not pass through the culvert, reduce entrance losses to a minimum, make use of the velocity of approach insofar as practicable, and by use of transitions and increased slopes, as necessary, facilitate channel flow entering the culvert.

11. The design of culvert and outlet should be effective in re-establishing tolerable non-erosive channel flow within the right-of-way or within a reasonably short distance below the culvert.

12. The outlet should be designed to resist undermining and washout.

13. Culvert dissipaters, if used, should be simple, easy to build, economical and reasonably self-cleaning during periods of easy flow.

DESIGN FOR CULVERT SIZE

A recent hydraulics study by the U.S. Bureau of Reclamation summarizes this subject as follows:[11]

The three most generally used methods of determining culvert size are:
(1) On the basis of old structures in the vicinity.
(2) Using an empirical formula relating drainage area and culvert size, such as Talbot's formula.
(3) Using hydrologic and physiographic data to determine the quantity of water reaching the culvert, then designing the culvert to pass that quantity of water.

"The first two methods are still retained in design handbooks . . . Their popularity is due to the simplicity of the computations required. The third method requires a consideration of hydrologic factors, drainage area, slope and cover of terrain, as well as knowledge of culvert hydraulics. Two expressions which have attempted to relate these variables are the *Burkli-Ziegler Formula* and the *Rational Formula*. Although the third method listed above is the most reasonable approach, exact results are not obtainable because the science of hydrology is still in its infancy. Engineering experience and judgment (are) indispensable when computing the amount of flow a culvert will be required to pass."

The *Talbot, Burkli-Ziegler* and *Rational* formulas are given in this chapter, under Section II Estimating Runoff from Small Areas.

HYDRAULIC CONDITIONS AND DEFINITIONS

Some of the definitions, discussions, examples and other hydraulic design data that follow are reprinted by permission from Hydraulics Engineering Circular No. 5, prepared by Lester A. Herr, Chief, Hydraulics Branch, Bridge Division, U. S. Bureau of Public Roads, in collaboration with Herbert G. Bossy, Highway Research Engineer, Hydraulic Research Division, April 1964, 54 pp.[12]

By the same authors, this circular has been supplemented by *Circular No. 10*, entitled "Capacity Charts for the Hydraulic Design of Highway Culverts," March 1965, 90 pp.[13]

Both circulars give identical answers in certain ranges, but the *nomographs* of HEC No. 5 must be used for the higher headwater depths and in cases of submerged outlets. HEC No. 10 contains a series of *hydraulic capacity charts* which permit direct selection of a culvert size for a particular site without making detailed computations. Included in HEC No. 10 is a brief discussion of other design considerations to emphasize that culvert capacity is only one of many problems confronting the engineer in the design of a culvert.

The various conditions, precautions and limitations of the data and charts are made as clear as possible. They should not be used without full knowledge of their practical limitations. They should be used under the supervision of engineers experienced in design, construction and maintenance.

Conventional Culverts considered here are circular pipes and pipe-arches, with uniform barrel cross-section throughout. The culvert ends may project from the roadway fill or be beveled (mitered) to fit the slope. (See Fig. 4-15) Headwalls, wingwalls, and end sections are considered separately.

Inlet and Outlet Control. There are two major types of culvert flow—with

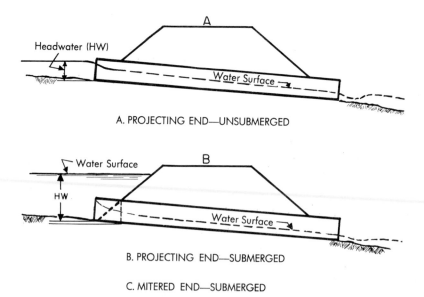

A. PROJECTING END—UNSUBMERGED

B. PROJECTING END—SUBMERGED

C. MITERED END—SUBMERGED

INLET CONTROL

Fig. 4-15. Inlet control is one of the two major types of culvert flow. Condition A with unsubmerged culvert inlet is preferred to the submerged end. Slope, *roughness* and length of culvert barrel are no consideration.

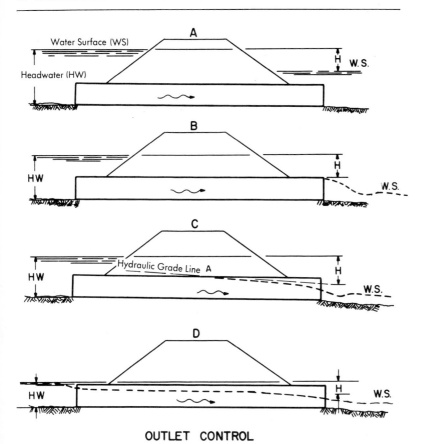

OUTLET CONTROL

Fig. 4-16. Outlet control involves these factors: cross sectional area of barrel; inlet "geometry"; ponding; tailwater; and slope, roughness and length of culvert barrel.

inlet control or outlet control. Under **inlet** control, (1) the cross-sectional area of the barrel, (2) the inlet configuration or "geometry" and (3) the amount of headwater or ponding are of primary importance. (Fig. 4–15) **Outlet** control involves (4) the additional consideration of the tailwater in the outlet channel, and (5) the slope, *roughness* and length of the culvert barrel. (Fig. 4–16)

Hydraulic Slope. The hydraulic slope or hydraulic grade line, sometimes called the pressure line is defined by the elevations to which water would rise in small vertical pipes attached to the culvert wall along its length. (See Fig. 4–17) The energy line and the pressure line are parallel over the length of the barrel except in the vicinity of the inlet where the flow contracts and re-expands. The difference is the velocity head, $\dfrac{V^2}{2g}$.   (10)

Head (H). The head (Fig. 4–17) or energy required to pass a given quantity of water through a culvert flowing in outlet control (with barrel full) is made up of (1) velocity head $H_v = \dfrac{V^2}{2g}$, (2) an entrance loss H_e, and (3) a friction loss H_f. This energy is obtained from ponding at entrance and slope of pipe, and is expressed in equation form:

$$H = H_v + H_e + H_f \qquad (11)$$

Entrance Loss, (H_e) depends upon the geometry of the inlet edge. This loss is expressed as a coefficient k_e multiplied by the barrel velocity head or

$$H_e = k_e \frac{V^2}{2g} \tag{12}$$

Entrance loss coefficients, k_e, for various types of entrances are given in Table 4-11.

Friction Loss, (H_f) is the energy required to overcome the roughness of the culvert barrel and is expressed in the following equation:

$$H_f = \frac{(29 \ n^2 L)}{(R^{1.33})} \frac{V^2}{2g} \tag{13}$$

where: n = Manning's friction factor (See Table 4-12)
L = length of culvert barrel (ft)
V = mean velocity of flow in barrel (ft/sec)
g = acceleration of gravity, 32.2 (ft/sec^2)
R = hydraulic radius, or $\dfrac{A}{WP}$ (ft)

Table 4-11 Entrance Loss Coefficients for Corrugated Metal Pipe or Pipe-Arch[12]

Inlet End of Culvert	Coefficient k_e
Projecting from fill (no headwall)	0.9
Headwall, or headwall and wingwalls square-edge	0.5
Mitered (beveled) to conform to fill slope	0.7
*End-Section conforming to fill slope	0.5
Headwall, rounded edge	0.1

*End Sections available from manufacturers.

Table 4-12 Values of Coefficient of Roughness n for Corrugated Metal (Manning Formula)*

Corrugations (Annular)	2⅔ x ½ in.	3 x 1 in.	Structural Plate 6 x 2 in.
Diam.	1 to 8 ft	3 to 8 ft	5 to 20 ft
Unpaved	.024	.027	.031**
25% Paved	0.021	0.023	0.026
Fully Paved	0.012	0.012	0.012

*BPR Circ. 5, p. 30, April, 1964, except following:
**BPR Circ. 10, Mar. 65, p. 78. Based on 108-in. diam.

Caution: 1. Most published coefficient of roughness values, n, are based on experimental work under controlled laboratory conditions, using clear or clean water; the lines are straight and with perfect joints. Design should take into account the actual construction and service conditions which vary greatly for different drainage materials.
2. Roughness of drainage structure walls is not a controlling factor in a majority of culvert design criteria.

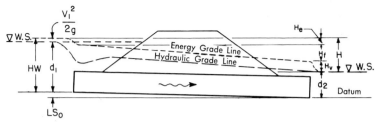

Fig. 4-17. The difference between the energy grade line and the hydraulic grade line is shown here.

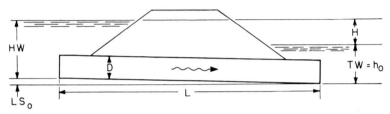

Fig. 4-18. Relationship of headwater to high tailwater and other terms in formula (15).

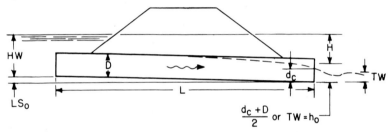

Fig. 4-19. Low tailwater in relation to terms of the flow equation.

Substituting in equation (12) and simplifying (for Bernoulli's Theorem) we get for *full flow:*

$$H = \left(1 + k_e + \frac{29\,\dot{n}^2 L}{R^{1.33}}\right)\frac{V^2}{2g} \tag{14}$$

See Fig. 4-17. Nomographs for solving equation 14 may be found in Reference 13.

Headwater Depth (HW). The headwater depth is the vertical distance from the culvert invert at the entrance (full cross-section) to the energy line of the headwater pool (depth + velocity head). Water surface and energy line at the entrance are assumed to coincide.

where: $HW = H + h_o - LS_o$ (15)
    H = head (ft)
    h_0 = TW (under conditions shown here)
    L = length of culvert (ft)
    S_0 = slope of barrel (ft per ft)

Tailwater Depth, (TW) is the depth from water surface at outlet end to culvert invert. See Figs. 4–18 and 4–19.

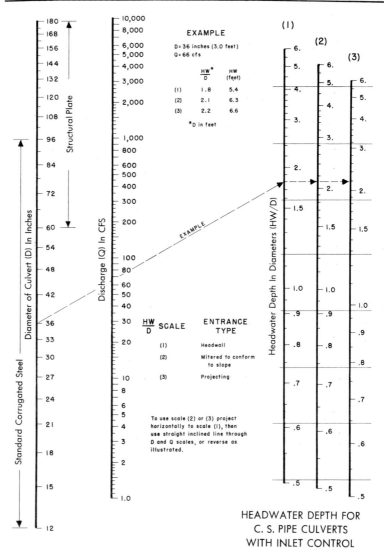

EXAMPLE

D = 36 inches (3.0 feet)
Q = 66 cfs

	$\frac{HW^*}{D}$	HW (feet)
(1)	1.8	5.4
(2)	2.1	6.3
(3)	2.2	6.6

*D in feet

$\frac{HW}{D}$ SCALE	ENTRANCE TYPE
(1)	Headwall
(2)	Mitered to conform to slope
(3)	Projecting

To use scale (2) or (3) project horizontally to scale (1), then use straight inclined line through D and Q scales, or reverse as illustrated.

HEADWATER DEPTH FOR
C. S. PIPE CULVERTS
WITH INLET CONTROL

BUREAU OF PUBLIC ROADS JAN. 1963

Fig. 4-20. Inlet control nomograph for corrugated steel **pipe** culverts. The manufacturers recommend keeping HW/D to a maximum of 1.5 and preferably to no more than 1.0. **Abbreviation CS** in nomograph refers to "corrugated steel" or to corrugated metal pipe, shop fabricated. This is in contrast to structural plate or bolted pipe, as in ig. 4-24.

HYDRAULIC COMPUTATIONS

Referring again to the two major types of culvert flow—with inlet and with outlet control—the question may be asked; which applies in a given case? Generally, inlet control applies in average to steep slope conditions, and outlet control applies on mild slopes.

INLET CONTROL

Figure 4-20 for Corrugated Metal Pipe shows a šample from BPR Circular 5

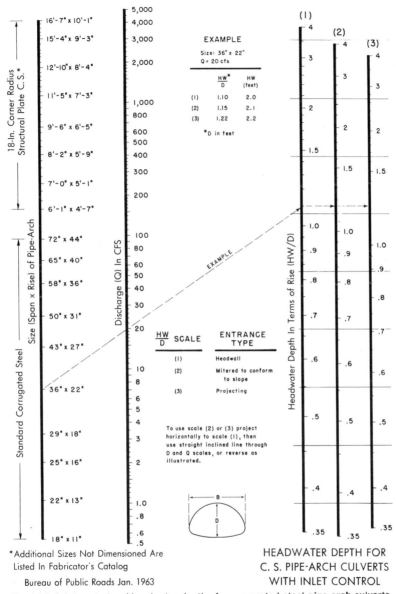

18-In. Corner Radius Structural Plate C.S.*

Size (Span x Rise) of Pipe-Arch

Standard Corrugated Steel

16'-7" x 10'-1"	
15'-4" x 9'-3"	
12'-10"x 8'-4"	
11'-5" x 7'-3"	
9'-6" x 6'-5"	
8'-2" x 5'-9"	
7'-0" x 5'-1"	
6'-1" x 4'-7"	
72" x 44"	
65" x 40"	
58" x 36"	
50" x 31"	
43" x 27"	
36" x 22"	
29" x 18"	
25" x 16"	
22" x 13"	
18" x 11"	

Discharge (Q) In CFS

EXAMPLE

Size: 36" x 22"
Q = 20 cfs

	$\frac{HW^*}{D}$	HW (feet)
(1)	1.10	2.0
(2)	1.15	2.1
(3)	1.22	2.2

*D in feet

EXAMPLE

$\frac{HW}{D}$ SCALE

	ENTRANCE TYPE
(1)	Headwall
(2)	Mitered to conform to slope
(3)	Projecting

To use scale (2) or (3) project horizontally to scale (1), then use straight inclined line through D and Q scales, or reverse as illustrated.

Headwater Depth In Terms of Rise (HW/D)

*Additional Sizes Not Dimensioned Are Listed In Fabricator's Catalog

Bureau of Public Roads Jan. 1963

HEADWATER DEPTH FOR
C. S. PIPE-ARCH CULVERTS
WITH INLET CONTROL

Fig. 4-21. Inlet control and headwater depths for corrugated steel **pipe-arch** culverts. Headwater depth should be kept low because pipe-arches are generally used where headroom is limited.

of an **inlet control** nomograph from which the headwater can be found, given a culvert size and discharge. **It should be noted that slope, length and roughness of the barrel are not shown because they are not used in the determination of headwater when a culvert is flowing with inlet control.** Figure 4-21 is for Corrugated Metal Pipe-Arch culverts (standard corrugated metal and structural plate).

OUTLET CONTROL

See Fig. 4-22 for Standard Corrugated Metal Pipe Culverts *Flowing Full*, and Fig. 4-23 Standard CS Pipe-Arch Culverts *Flowing Full*. See Figs. 4-24 and 4-25 for Structural Plate Pipe and Pipe-Arch Culverts *Flowing Full*.

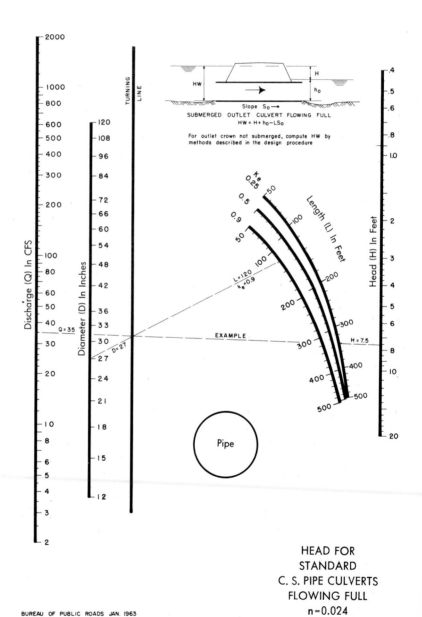

HEAD FOR
STANDARD
C. S. PIPE CULVERTS
FLOWING FULL
n=0.024

BUREAU OF PUBLIC ROADS JAN. 1963

Fig. 4-22. Head for corrugated steel **pipe** culvert with submerged outlet and culvert flowing full. Manufacturers recommend keeping outlet crown not submerged. See note under sketch at top.

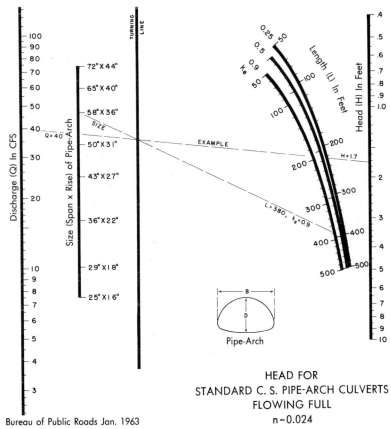

HEAD FOR
STANDARD C. S. PIPE-ARCH CULVERTS
FLOWING FULL
n = 0.024

Bureau of Public Roads Jan. 1963

Fig. 4-23. Head for corrugated steel **pipe-arch** culvert with submerged outlet and flowing full.

See Figs. 4-27 and 4-28 Critical Depths for Standard Pipe-Arch and Structural Plate Pipe-Arch. See Fig. 4-26 Critical Depth for Circular Pipe. (All charts, Figs. 4-15 through 4-29, have been reproduced by courtesy of the Bureau of Public Roads.)

For a culvert flowing full (outlet control), the length, slope and roughness of barrel are used in the computation. In addition to determining head, (H), it is necessary to use the tailwater (h_o) and slope and length of installation to find the headwater. See Equation (15).

Velocity of Culvert Flow, (V) mean or average velocity in the culvert barrel, is expressed as discharge Q, in cfs, divided by the cross-sectional area A, in sq ft, of the barrel.

$$V = \frac{Q}{A} \tag{4}$$

Outlet Velocity for a culvert flowing with inlet control may be approximated by (computing the mean velocity for the culvert cross section) using Manning's equation.

$$V_o = \frac{1.486}{n} R^{2/3} S_o^{1/2} \tag{16}$$

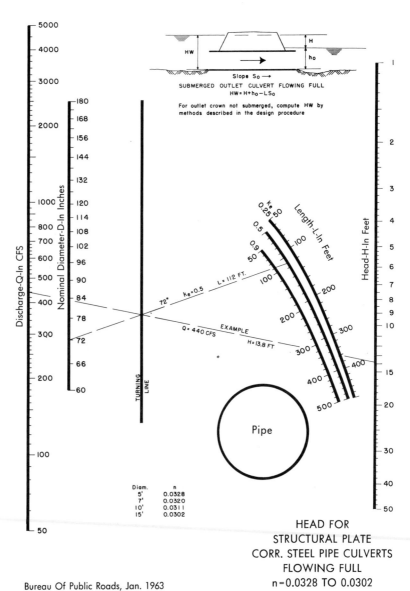

HEAD FOR
STRUCTURAL PLATE
CORR. STEEL PIPE CULVERTS
FLOWING FULL
n=0.0328 TO 0.0302

Bureau Of Public Roads, Jan. 1963

Fig. 4-24. Head for **structural plate pipe** culvert—with submerged outlet and flowing full. See note under sketch at top.

Critical Depth[13] (d_c) is the flow depth in a pipe placed on the critical slope, with flow at critical velocity. (Sub-critical depth—on a mild slope; super-critical depth—on a steep slope.)

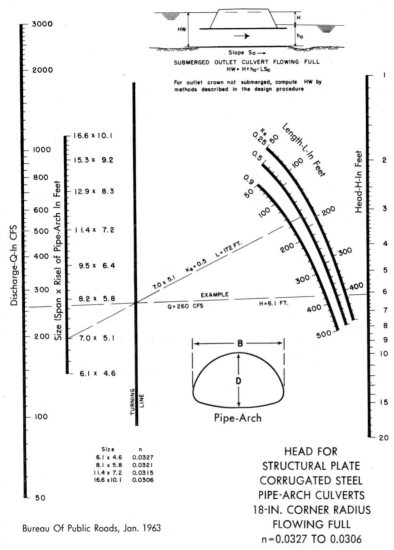

Fig. 4-25. Head for **structural plate pipe-arch** culvert with **18-in.** corner radius. Submerged outlet, flowing full.

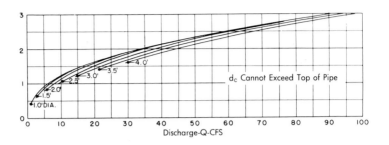

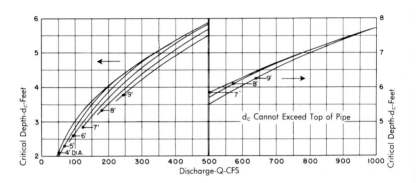

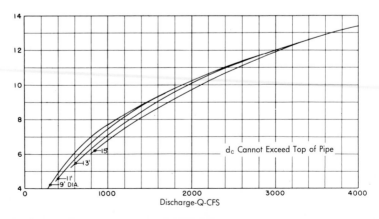

Fig. 4-26. Critical depth curves for circular **pipe**. Same for corrugated steel and other types of pipe.

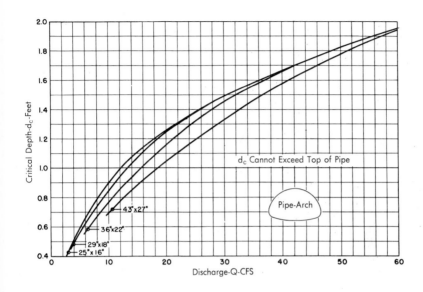

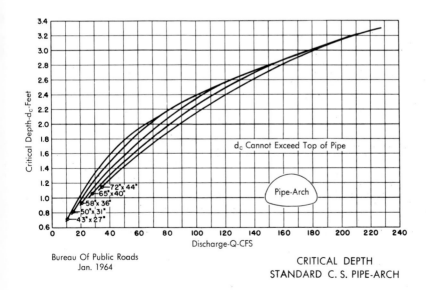

Bureau Of Public Roads
Jan. 1964

CRITICAL DEPTH
STANDARD C. S. PIPE-ARCH

Fig. 4-27. Critical depth curves for standard corrugated steel **pipe-arch.** See d_c in Fig. 4-19.

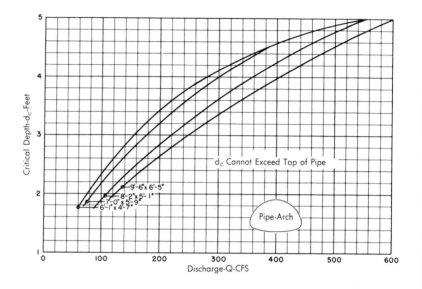

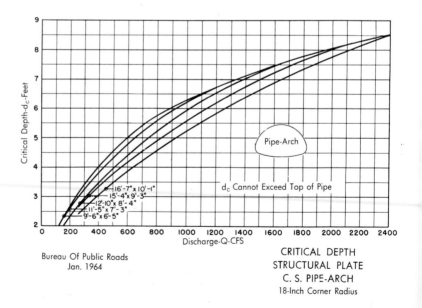

Bureau Of Public Roads
Jan. 1964

CRITICAL DEPTH
STRUCTURAL PLATE
C. S. PIPE-ARCH
18-Inch Corner Radius

Fig. 4-28. Critical depth curves for **structural plate pipe-arch** with **18-in.** corner radius.

HYDROLOGIC AND CHANNEL INFORMATION

$Q_1 =$ __180 cfs__ $= Q_{25}$ $TW_1 =$ __3.5__

$Q_2 =$ __225 cfs__ $= Q_{50}$ $TW_2 =$ __4.0__

(Q_1 = DESIGN DISCHARGE, SAY Q_{25})
(Q_2 = CHECK DISCHARGE, SAY Q_{50} OR Q_{100})

SKETCH

STATION: __6+21__

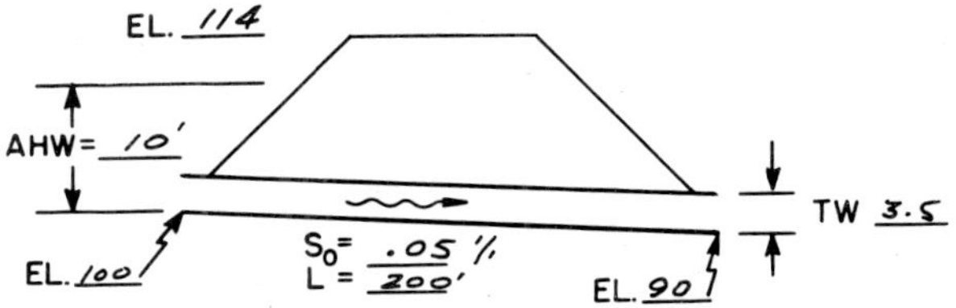

EL. __114__

AHW = 10'

TW __3.5__

EL. __100'__ $S_0 =$ __.05__ % $L =$ __200'__   EL. __90'__

MEAN STREAM VELOCITY = __10'/sec__

MAX. STREAM VELOCITY = __18'/sec__

HEADWATER COMPUTATION

CULVERT DESCRIPTION (ENTRANCE TYPE)	Q	SIZE	INLET CONT.		OUTLET CONTROL								CONTROLLING HW	OUTLET VELOCITY	COST	COMMENTS
			$\frac{HW}{D}$	HW	K_e	H	d_c	$\frac{d_c+D}{2}$	TW	h_o	LS_0	$HW=H+h_o-LS_0$	HW	VELOCITY		
CIRCULAR CMP PROJ. ENT.	180		Assume 1.5	7.5	D=60"	Try smaller size PHW=10'							=10'			
"	180	54"	2.2	9.9	.9	9.7	3.9	4.2	3.5	4.2	10.0	3.9	9.9	16.5		
"	225	54"	3.15	14.2	.9	15.3	4.2	4.4	4.0	4.4	10.0	9.7	14.2	17.0		HW high for Q_{50} - try 60"
"	180	60"	1.51	7.55	.9	5.9	3.9	4.4	3.5	4.4	10.0	0.3	7.55	16.7		
"	225	60"	2.1	10.5	.9	9.3	4.2	4.6	4.0	4.6	10.0	3.9	10.5	17.5		

Fig. 4-29. Typical culvert computation form with illustrative problem for a given set of conditions.

PROCEDURE FOR DETERMINING CULVERT SIZE[15]

Step 1: List the design data
    2: Estimate a first trial size
    3: Find headwater depth, first assuming inlet control; then assuming outlet control; compare the headwaters and choose the higher.
    4: Select culvert size which keeps headwater depth below allowable limit.
    5: Compute outlet velocity to determine need for channel protection.

The BPR has a suggested tabulation form (Fig. 4-29) and given detailed instructions for use of inlet-control nomographs (Figs. 4-20 and 4-21) and outlet-control nomographs (Figs. 4-22 to 4-25). Table 4-12 lists Manning's values of n for corrugated metal. Coefficient k_e. (Table 4-11) is applied to velocity head $\dfrac{V^2}{2g}$ for determination of head loss at entrance to a structure, such as a culvert or conduit, operating full or partly full.

OTHER HYDRAULIC EFFECTS

Hydraulic capacity of a culvert is affected by factors other than size of opening. In order of consideration here, these include:
1. Flow conditions through culvert
2. Shape of culvert
3. Single vs. multiple opening

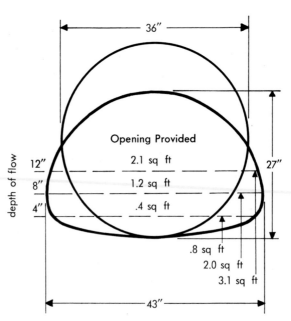

Fig. 4-30. Comparison of waterway cross-sectional areas at equal depths of flow in steel pipe and pipe-arch. The pipe-arch handles a larger volume of water at the lower levels of flow.

4. Slope of culvert
5. Length of culvert
6. Roughness of culvert interior
7. Approach channel
8. Type of culvert inlet
9. Type of culvert outlet
10. Ponding at entrance
11. Height of tailwater

1. Flow Conditions Through Culvert

For culverts on a steep slope, the discharge is controlled at the inlet, depending on headwater depth[12]; on mild slopes, outlet control usually exists.

For full flow with a free outlet, data are sparse, but investigators have found the hydraulic grade line to be below the crown of the pipe.

2. Shape of Culvert

The shape of a corrugated metal culvert—circular pipe, vertically elongated pipe, pipe-arch or arch—is generally chosen for reasons of headroom and/or strength rather than for hydraulic reasons. However, as the accompanying chart shows, a pipe-arch carries roughly 50 per cent more water at depths up to half full. See Fig. 4-30. This is advantageous in keeping the headwaters at a lower level of flow. Need for further research is indicated.

3. Single vs. Multiple Opening

A single culvert opening is, in general, the most satisfactory because of its greater ability to handle floating debris and driftwood. However, in many cases the greater portion of the waterway should be kept low to get the water through quickly without ponding or flooding of the land upstream. In such cases, the solution may consist of using either an arch or pipe-arch, or using a battery of two or more openings, or both. See Fig. 4-31.

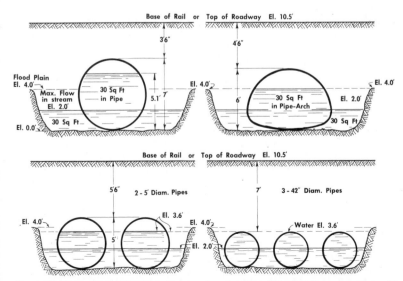

Fig. 4-31. Diagrams showing four choices of a culvert opening. For the assumed conditions, a single large pipe will cause the water to back up and flood the adjacent land. A twin or triple opening, while less efficient hydraulically, offers the best solution.—from *Railway Track & Structures.*

4. Slope of Culvert

Culvert location and length are described and pictured in detail under the subject of Culvert Applications, Chapter 8.

For hydraulic and other reasons, a culvert may be installed on the same general grade as the approach and exit channels of the stream or waterway. However, on steeply sloping areas or hillsides, the culvert may be put on the critical slope or a flatter grade to reduce outlet velocities or for other reasons of discharge control.

The use of drop inlets, pipe spillways, paved aprons and cantilevered ends are means of controlling the slope and consequently the outlet velocity.

For culverts flowing with **inlet control,** increasing the barrel slope reduces the headwater depth slightly. The slope is classified as steep, critical or mild; the flow is uniform on these slopes when the water surface is parallel to the culvert bottom.

For culverts flowing with **outlet control,** the slope of the hydraulic grade line is more important than the slope of the culvert barrel. When the culvert is not flowing full, the slope of the culvert barrel can affect the hydraulic grade line.

5. Length of Culvert

The length of the culvert is influenced not only by the slope and direction of the barrel, but also by the width of roadway, fill height and steepness of fill slopes.

From a hydraulics standpoint, the length of the culvert barrel is a factor only on culvert flow with **outlet control.** It then becomes a factor in the formula for determining the loss of head.

For full flow in culverts on mild slopes, the discharge in long culverts is less than in short culverts. However on steep slopes, if the inlet permits full flow, the discharge in long culverts is **greater** than in short culverts, due to siphoning action.

Culverts are of relatively short length, so that the loss-of-head factor is not significant even where the culvert flows with outlet control. Culverts of long length, 400 ft or more, are generally located in very hilly country where fills are high where inlet control governs, with tailwater being generally of little consequence.

6. Roughness of Culvert Interior

Laboratory research on models and prototype sizes has in recent years helped to clarify the values of roughness coefficients n as used in Manning's formula and others. Fig. 4-32. These apply to various pipe and pipe-arch sizes and for various materials and shapes. However they are limited to "clean water" conditions and should be applied with judgment and experience.

A general design assumption has been that the roughness coefficient remains constant for pipes flowing either full or partly full. However, some investigators have found that the roughness coefficient increases slightly for pipes flowing full. It has also been determined that as the diameter increases, there is a slight reduction in the coefficient.

Values of the coefficient of roughness n for Manning's formula for long pipes and canals are given in Table 4-12 (modified by recent findings).[14] These are for ideal conditions and can be modified on the basis of local experience.

A large share of culvert installations fall under the classification of flow with

Fig. 4-32. Test section of structural plate steel pipe, in Laboratory of the Corps of Engineers' Waterway Experiment Station at Vicksburg, Mississippi.

inlet control.* Also, designers are aware that on the flatter grade lines, the factor of debris, sediment, boulders and irregular joints can neutralize or offset the hydraulic advantages gained by clear water experiments in laboratory and field research. Therefore, many engineers design their culverts on the basis of equal cross-sectional areas regardless of kind of materials.

7. Approach Channel

When a culvert is placed either in a natural channel or in a new channel, the alignment should be as direct as possible or follow moderate curvature. Where erosion or eddying of approach channel banks is anticipated, proper revetment, linings or deflectors should be designed to keep the flow as constant as possible.

Where upstream land use is likely to produce driftwood or debris, proper deflectors, screens, racks or risers should pass or divert such materials so they cannot clog the culvert entrance, or so they can be removed by the maintenance crew before the next storm. Drift can create buoyancy that can have a destructive effect, even if not submerged.

If headwater is permitted to pond and submerge the crown of the culvert, more extensive measures must be taken to protect the embankment and channel slopes against erosion and the culvert inlet against possible uplift forces.

A circular[16] prepared by the Bureau of Public Roads, and based largely on

---

*Roughness of culvert interior is not a factor. See page 111.

California Culvert Practice[17] describes the purposes of debris control structures and illustrates many different types of such structures.

Pictured here is one type of corrugated metal pipe risers and debris cages used by the California Division of Highways. Fig. 4-33.

8. Type of Culvert Inlet

The head required for a culvert has several components: (1) velocity head, (2) entrance loss and (3) friction loss. Streamlining the entrance by rounding or expanding can measurably improve the flow into the culvert and thereby decrease the backwater above the culvert. Inlet improvement is most beneficial for culverts operating under inlet control.

Corrugated steel culverts are ordinarily supplied with "square-cut" ends, but may also be supplied with mitered ends. The end either (1) projects beyond the fill, (2) is flush with a headwall, or (3) is supplemented with a manufactured steel end section. Structural plate pipe and pipe-arches may be supplied with the ends beveled (mitered) or skewed to coincide with the fill slope. These various forms of entrance treatments may be supplemented by means of revetment or slope paving. The purpose is generally for improving the appearance, with hydraulic benefits or cost saving being secondary.

Particularly for large structures, the Bureau of Public Roads advocates that provision be made to resist possible structural failure by hydrostatic uplift forces. This trouble can occur where rapid and unprecedented runoff, plus clogging with debris, causes ponding and possible overtopping of the embankment. Inlet protection is suggested in the form of headwalls, collars, slope paving and other means.

8a. Research on Inlets

The Bureau of Public Roads has tested beveled or rounded inlet edges.[18]

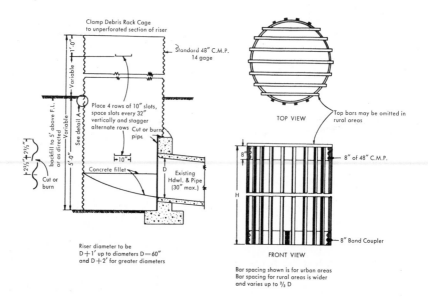

Fig. 4-33. Typical pipe riser with debris rack cage as applied to existing culverts by California Division of Highways.

Fig. 4-34. Tapered inlet on standard corrugated steel pipe culvert under an Interstate highway.

Considerable increases in discharge are indicated under some conditions.

The next step is to determine the cost of manufacturing such collars and inlets to determine whether they can be justified as compared to increasing the size of the culvert barrel cross section. They have been used in the Northwest for about 10 years. (For further discussion of hydraulic factors see Chapter 8, Section II Culvert Location and Length. Also Section III End Finish.)

9. Type of Culvert Outlet

The principal hydraulic problem at the outlet end of a culvert is to avoid blockage by sedimentation, or damage by undermining of culvert and embankment, or erosion of the downstream channel. High velocities are damaging and should be considered in culvert design.

Greater roughness of the culvert interior is an advantage in reducing outlet velocities, particularly when the pipe is flowing with inlet control, where roughness is not a factor in capacity.

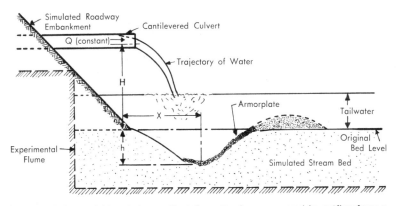

Fig. 4-35. Some variables that can affect the rate of scour caused by outflow from a cantilevered steel culvert into a rectangular channel with rigid sides and an alluvial bed. Armor-plated stilling basin effectively dissipated the energy.

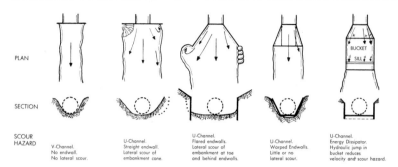

Fig. 4-36. Influence of transition shape on hazard of lateral scour at outlet of culvert—based on California practice.

Energy dissipators have been designed and used in some instances, especially in irrigation channels. They add to the cost of the culvert. The BPR suggests computing outlet velocities and comparing with alternate culvert designs, existing culverts in the area, or the natural stream velocities to determine need for channel protection.

Tests have been conducted with impact-type energy dissipators, flared and submerged outlets, and using adverse hydraulic gradients at the culvert exit. Results have been favorable according to the Bureau of Reclamation. Erosion studies[20] have also been made for culverts with a cantilevered outlet, and the effect of riprapping the pool into which the outlet discharges. The energy was effectively dissipated by means of the armor-plated stilling basin shown in Fig. 4-35. Flared outlets similar to a typical inlet shape are reported not effective in reducing erosion at submerged outlets. See Chapter 8, Culvert Grades.

Three conditions of get-away flow are shown in Fig. 4-36—submerged, controlled and free. If get-away is good, the outlet will be free and high velocity will be maintained in the transition. This may require protecting the bed and the banks against scour and eddy action.

Section V—HYDRAULICS OF SEWERS

INTRODUCTION

A sewer is defined as a pipe or conduit, generally closed, but normally not flowing full, for carrying storm water, sewage and other waste liquids. The contents generally flow by gravity, but in some instances are pumped.[22]

Sewers may be classified as sanitary, storm, or combined (receiving both surface runoff and sewage). Variations include such classifications as storm overflow sewer, and relief or auxiliary sewer. The use dictates the basis of design as to capacity.

DESIGN FLOW OF SANITARY SEWERS

The flow rates of sewage for which sewer capacity should be provided are based on present and probable future quantities of domestic, commercial and industrial wastes, along with ground water infiltration. Flow may fluctuate from an extreme minimum, or a daily average, to a peak. A sanitary sewer should have adequate capacity for peak flow, and it should move suspended solids so that deposits in the sewer are kept at a minimum.

The design discharge is based on water-use habits of present and anticipated future population. Increases in per capita sewage flows may be expected because of more industries, more household appliances, and increased availability of sewers as against septic tanks and other means of disposal. Sewage flows for various types of businesses or institutions are given in Table 4-13.

Cooling water for air conditioning or industrial processes should be kept out of sanitary sewers by enforced regulations.

Storm water and ground water infiltration into sanitary sewers should be kept within justifiable limits by good design. No commonly accepted rates

Fig. 4-37. Transition from open ditch to corrugated steel pipe sewer.

Table 4-13   Quantity of Sewage Flow[*22]

Type of Operation	Average Flow in Gals. per Capita per day
Stores, offices, and small business	12 to 25 gals.
Hotels and motels	50 to 150
Schools (without or with showers)	8 to 35
Recreational and summer camps	20 to 25

*Measured or estimated domestic sewage.

Table 4-14   Sewage Flows Used for Design[*22]
Year of data varies from 1943-1949

City	Population in Thousands	Water Consumption	Sewage Flow	Sewer Design Basis	Remarks
		in Gals. per Capita per Day			
Baltimore, Md.	1,300	160	100	135 x (4 to 2)	
Berkeley, Calif.	113	76	60	92	
Boston, Mass.	801	145	140	150	Flowing half full
Dallas, Texas	...	...	150	575	Including storm water and infiltration
Grand Rapids, Mich.	...	178	189.5	200	
Las Vegas, Nev.	45	410	209	250	
Little Rock, Ark.	100	50	50	100	
Los Angeles, Calif.	2,680	165	95	...	
Memphis, Tenn.	450	125	100	100	
Orlando, Fla.	75	150	70	190	
Painesville, Ohio	...	...	125	600	Includes infiltration and roof water
Shreveport, La.	160	135	120	150	

*Measured or estimated domestic sewage.

of infiltration to be used in design have been developed. Excessive amounts of infiltration can make it necessary to increase sewer pipe sizes and increase pumping and treating costs. Faulty joints are the cause of most infiltration, and can also result in in-washing of backfill around a sewer, sometimes with serious settlement of street surfaces and clogging of the sewer itself.

DESIGN FLOW OF STORM WATER

The "rational method," introduced in 1889, recognizes the direct relationship between rainfall and runoff of storm water. A large majority of engineering offices in the United States report the use of this method with satisfactory results for urban drainage.

Improved methods in the science of hydrology deal with the application of a definite design storm pattern to the drainage area and the determination of a runoff hydrograph from total rainfall.

The rainfall frequency used in design of storm sewers in residential areas ranges from 2 to 10 years, with 5 most common. For storm sewers in commercial and high-value districts, the frequency is 10 to 15 years, depending upon economic justification. For flood protection works, 50 years or more.

Time of concentration is discussed on page 88.

Runoff coefficients are given in Tables 4-4, 4-15 and 4-16.

There are other methods of determining runoff, including actual sewer and inlet gagings, principally used in several large cities. Some methods consider such influences as infiltration capacity of pervious areas, depression storage, overland flow detention (such as on airports, where ponding is permitted temporarily), and detention in gutters, catch basins and lateral sewers.

Table 4-15   Runoff Coefficients for Storm Sewers[22]

Description of Area	Runoff Coefficients
Business:	
Downtown areas	0.70 to 0.95
Neighborhood areas	0.50 to 0.70
Residential:	
Single-family areas	0.30 to 0.50
Multi units, detached	0.40 to 0.60
Multi units, attached	0.60 to 0.75
Residential (suburban)	0.25 to 0.40
Apartment dwelling areas	0.50 to 0.70
Industrial:	
Light areas	0.50 to 0.80
Heavy areas	0.60 to 0.90
Parks, cemeteries	0.10 to 0.25
Playgrounds	0.20 to 0.35
Railroad yards	0.20 to 0.40
Unimproved areas	0.10 to 0.30

Tables 4-15 and 4-16 are applicable for storms of 5- to 10-year frequencies. Less frequent higher intensity storms require higher coefficients. Coefficients are based on assumption that the design storm does not occur when ground surface is frozen.

Table 4-16   Runoff Coefficients for Various Surfaces[22]

Character of Surface	Average Runoff Coefficients
Streets:	
Asphaltic	0.70 to 0.95
Concrete	0.80 to 0.95
Drives and walks	0.75 to 0.85
Roofs	0.75 to 0.95
Lawns; Sandy Soil:	
Flat, 2%	0.05 to 0.10
Average, 2 to 7%	0.10 to 0.15
Steep, 7%	0.15 to 0.20
Lawns; Heavy Soil:	
Flat, 2%	0.13 to 0.17
Average, 2 to 7%	0.18 to 0.22
Steep, 7%	0.25 to 0.35

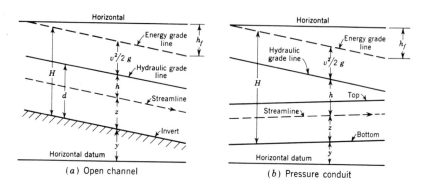

Fig. 4-38. Hydraulic profiles for uniform flow.

HYDRAULIC CONSIDERATIONS FOR SEWERS

Estimated design flows in sewers are based on assumptions, the accuracy of which is variable. The hydraulic computations for size should be carefully made, but with a factor of allowance for reasonable variations and for anticipated changes in contributing areas.

A number of inter-related factors are involved in sewer hydraulics, including: variation of flow; slope of hydraulic grade line or the invert (which is not parallel to the energy grade line except for uniform flow in an open channel); pipe friction; critical depth, critical flow and critical velocity; drawdown and backwater depths.

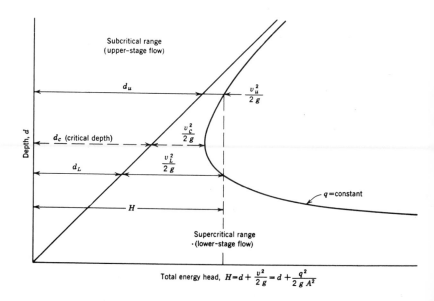

Fig. 4-39. Depth of flow versus total energy head.

TRANSITIONS, BENDS, JUNCTIONS

Common practice in the design of sewers and storm drains is to use a straight line and grade and a single conduit size for a reach, or section, at either end of which is a break in grade, a bend, a junction, or a change in size or shape of conduit. However, large conduits may be laid on gentle curves. At changes in grade, junctions, sharp bends, and points where large increments of flow are received, and for conduit changes in shape or size, special transition structures may be designed.

PIPE FRICTION FORMULAS

Manning's formula, simpler than Kutter's, has come into general use in solving problems of open-channel flow in sewers (applying to flow with a free water surface whether or not the conduit is covered). It has an *n*-value substantially equal to Kutter's *n* for types of pipe commonly used in sewer construction, including corrugated metal pipe with part or full bituminous linings.

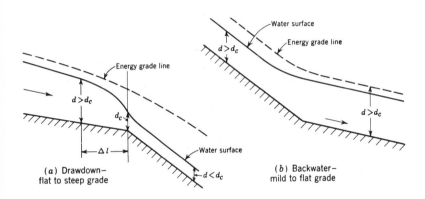

Fig 4-40. Hydraulic profiles for non-uniform flow.

The Manning equation is:

$$V = \frac{1.486}{n} R^{\frac{2}{3}} S^{\frac{1}{2}} \tag{6}$$

in which:

V = mean velocity of flow, in fps
R = hydraulic radius in ft, equal to area/wetted perimeter
S = slope of hydraulic grade line, in ft per ft
n = coefficient of roughness of conduit interior

Graphs commonly available for the solution of both the Kutter and Manning formula are applicable to full conduits only. Other graphs are necessary to determine the depth and mean velocity at other than full flows. Fig. 4-41 is an alignment chart prepared by T. R. Camp for the solution of the Manning equation for circular pipes flowing full. See also Figs. 4-42 and 4-46.

VALUES OF *n*

According to the ASCE Manual of Practice, tests on pipe for friction factors "have generally been conducted under ideal laboratory conditions—for example, with clear water in long straight lines with controlled velocities. The designer is faced with the problem of assuming a coefficient of roughness con-

servative enough to allow for anticipated future conditions in actual construction. Sewers are seldom installed under ideal conditions. Some of the
disturbance factors which influence the loss of head and therefore the friction
coefficient are as follows:

   a. Rough, opened, or offset joints

   b. Poor alignment and grade due to settlement or lateral soil movement

   c. Deposits in sewer

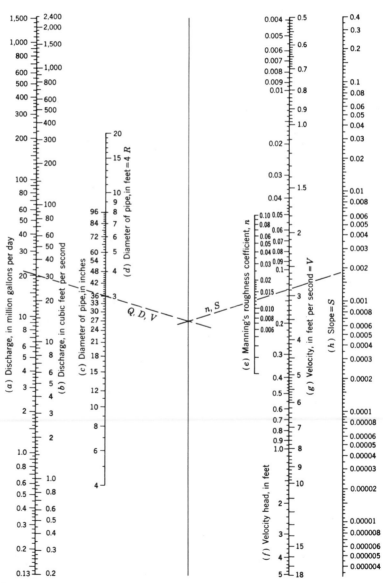

Fig. 4-41. Alignment chart for flow in pipes, for Manning's formula.

Table 4-17   Solution of Manning's Formula—Pipe Running Full

Diam. in Inches	Area in Square Feet	Hydraulic Radius	$R^{2/3}$	$AR^{2/3}$	$\dfrac{1.486}{n} \times R^{2/3} \times A$ for various values of n				
					$n=.012$	$n=.015$	$n=.019$	$n=.021$	$n=.024$
6	.196	.125	.250	.049	6.068	4.854	3.832	3.467	3.034
8	.349	.167	.303	.106	13.13	10.50	8.290	7.501	6.563
10	.545	.208	.351	.191	23.65	18.92	14.94	13.52	11.83
12	.785	.250	.397	.312	38.64	30.91	24.40	22.08	19.32
15	1.227	.3125	.461	.566	70.09	56.07	44.27	40.05	35.04
18	1.767	.375	.520	.919	113.8	91.04	71.88	65.03	56.90
21	2.405	.437	.576	1.385	171.5	137.2	108.3	98.01	85.75
24	3.142	.50	.630	1.979	245.1	196.1	154.8	140.0	122.5
30	4.909	.625	.731	3.588	444.3	355.5	280.6	253.9	222.2
36	7.069	.75	.825	5.832	722.2	577.8	456.1	412.7	361.1
42	9.621	.875	.915	8.803	1090	872.1	688.5	622.9	545.0
48	12.566	1.00	1.00	12.566	1556	1245	982.8	889.2	778.0
54	15.904	1.125	1.082	17.208	2131	1705	1346	1218	1065
60	19.635	1.25	1.16	22.777	2821	2256	1781	1612	1410
66	23.758	1.375	1.236	29.365	3636	2909	2297	2078	1818
72	28.274	1.50	1.310	37.039	4587	3669	2897	2621	2293
78	33.183	1.625	1.382	45.859	5679	4543	3587	3245	2839
84	38.485	1.75	1.452	55.880	6920	5536	4370	3954	3460
90	44.179	1.875	1.521	67.196	8321	6657	5255	4755	4161
96	50.266	2.00	1.587	79.772	9878	7903	6239	5645	4939
108	63.617	2.25	1.717	109.230	13526	10820	8543	7729	6763
114	70.882	2.375	1.780	126.170	15624	12500	9868	8928	7812
120	78.54	2.5	1.842	144.671	17915	14330	11320	10240	8957

$Q = AV$

$Q = A \times \dfrac{1.486}{n} \times R^{2/3} \times S^{1/2} \quad V = \dfrac{1.486}{n} \times R^{2/3} \times S^{1/2}$

V = Velocity in fps R = Hydraulic Radius. S = Hydraulic slope = fall in ft divided by length in feet.

Q = Capacity in cfs A = Area of pipe in square ft. n = Coefficient of Roughness.

Note: To obtain Q for any diameter pipe, multiply the figure shown in the column under the proper value of n by the sq root of the slope.

Table 4-18   Values of *n* for Manning's Formula for Sewer Design[22]

Kind of Pipe	Use in Designing[a]	
	From	To
Cement-lined cast iron pipe	0.012	0.015
Dirty or tuberculated cast-iron pipe	0.015	0.035
Concrete pipe	0.012	0.015
Asbestos-cement pipe	0.012	0.015
Vitrified sewer pipe	0.012	0.015
Corrugated steel pipe:		
Uncoated, ½-in. corrugations[b]	0.024	0.026
Asphalt coated and 25% paved	0.021	0.023
Smooth asphaltic lining	0.012	0.015

[a]Suggested ranges of values are for sewage. The lower values (left column) are for clear water.
[b]For research data for 1-in. and 2-in. deep corrugations (for clear water) see Table 4-12.

d. Coatings of grease or other matter on interior of sewer

e. Eddying and deposits of solids caused by enlargements at manholes and junction chambers

f. Tree roots, joint compounds, and mortar dams resulting from careless jointing and other protrusions

g. Flow from laterals disrupting flow calculations

"In giving weight to these factors, the designer should consider among other things the type of pipe and joint, the anticipated quality of construction, and the degree of inspection during construction.

"Suggested *n*-values for use in the Manning formula for various types of sewer pipe are given in Table 4-18. These values may also be used in the Kutter formula, except for corrugated pipe. The Kutter values for corrugated pipe are lower than the values for Manning's *n*. If the interior of a pipe or conduit consists of two different surfaces, common practice is to use a weighted value of *n* based on the percentage of the periphery covered by each material."[22]

DETERMINING STORM SEWER SIZES

The following charts, Figs. 4-42 to 4-46 are based on Manning's formula and show the discharge for circular pipe sewers flowing full on various slopes, for values of $n = .012, .015, .019, .021,$ and $.024$.

Table 4-17, is a solution of Manning's formula for the discharge of circular pipes flowing full, for value of $n = (.012$ to $.024)$. It is necessary to multiply the values in the table by the square root of the (hydraulic) slope to obtain the discharge.

The charts and table apply only when flow has reached a constant velocity.

Example

Assume a 48-in. pipe sewer with a value of *n* of 0.015 on a slope of .006 ft per ft. (Submerged outlet condition.) What is the discharge capacity?

Solution:

Entering the left hand column of Table 4-17 at the 48-in. diameter and reading horizontally to the value of $n = .015$, we get a value of 1245. Multiplying this value by the square root of the slope—.006 (Table G-8, p. 362), we get 1245 × .07746 = 96 cfs.

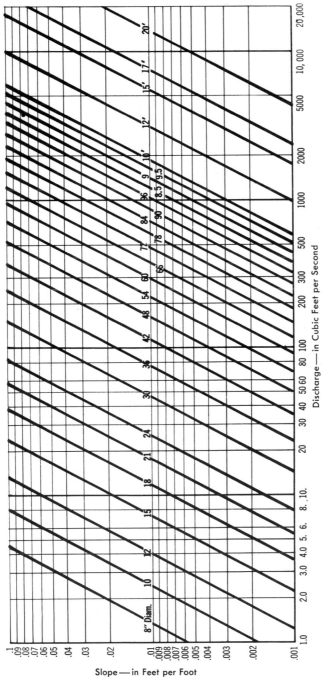

Slope — in Feet per Foot

Fig. 4-42. Discharge of Pipe Based on Manning's Formula.

Pipe* Flowing Full $n = .012$

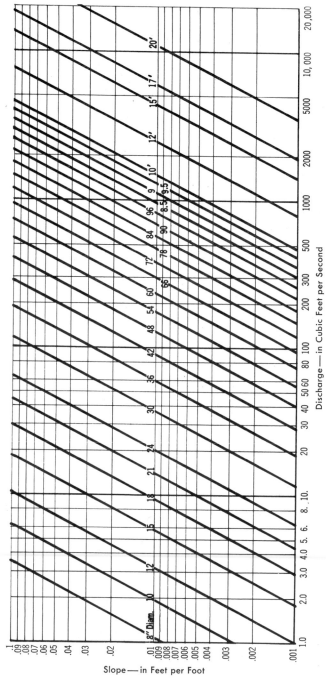

Fig. 4-43. Discharge of Pipe Based on Manning's Formula.

Pipe* Flowing Full   **n = .015**

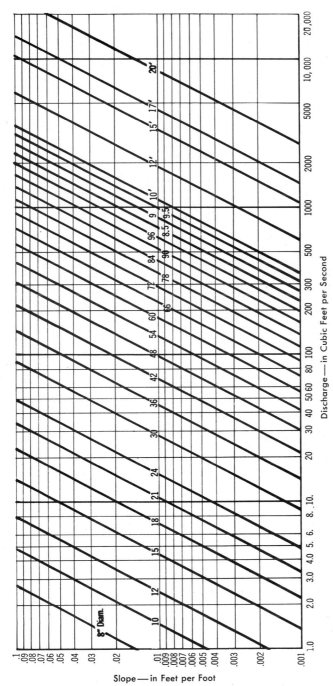

Slope — in Feet per Foot

Fig. 4-44. Discharge of Pipe Based on Manning's Formula.

Pipe* Flowing Full $n = .019$

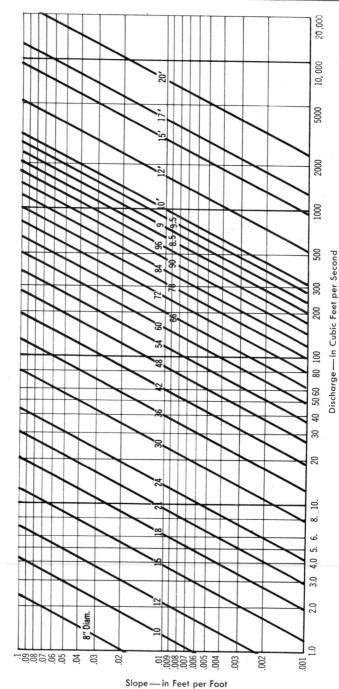

Fig. 4-45. Discharge of Pipe Based on Manning's Formula.

Pipe* Flowing Full   **n = .021**

Slope — in Feet per Foot

Discharge — in Cubic Feet per Second

*Note: A pipe-arch flowing full has 84% of the capacity of a round pipe flowing full when periphery, "n" and slope are equal.

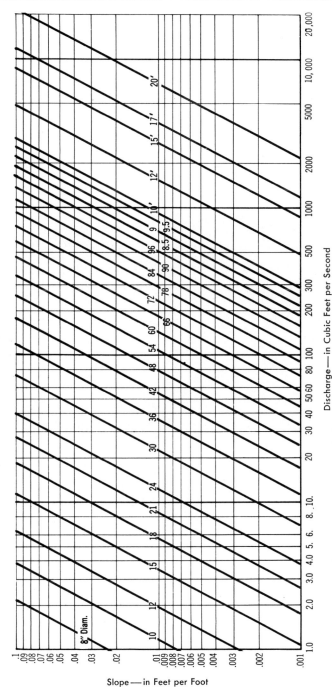

Slope — in Feet per Foot

Fig. 4-46. Discharge of Pipe Based on Manning's Formula.

Pipe* Flowing Full   **n = .024**

HYDRAULICS OF SUBDRAINS

The computation of runoff for ground water is described in Chapter 10 Sub-drainage. Selection of suitable size underdrain pipe is also suggested in that chapter.

If a pipe is to carry both storm water and ground water, as is sometimes the case on airports, the latter can be usually handled without any increase in size because of the lag between the time of a storm and the time of concentration for the ground water to seep to the subdrainage pipe.

MISCELLANEOUS

The hydraulics of various appurtenances such as catch basins, manholes, fittings, tunnel liner plate, end sections and others are either described under the references to those products or are left for other publications.

Fig. 4-47. Large pipe-arch culvert flowing under *inlet control* and *free outlet* conditions. (See page 111.)

REFERENCES AND BIBLIOGRAPHY

1. Herr, L. A., *Tools for Use in the Hydraulic Design of Culverts*, U.S. Bureau of Public Roads, 10th Annual Georgia Highway Conference, Atlanta, Feb. 1961.
2. Chow, V. T., *Hydrologic Design of Culverts*, Univ. of Ill., Proc. ASCE, Vol. 88, HY2, Mar. 1962.
3. Searcy, J. K., *Design of Roadside Drainage Channels*, U. S. Bureau of Public Roads, Hydraulic Design Series No. 4, U. S. Gvmt. Printing Office, Washington, D. C., 1965, 56 pp. (Contains a list of 55 helpful references.)
4. ASCE, *Hydrology Handbook*, American Society of Civil Engineers. Manual No. 28, 1949, 184 pp.
5. U. S. Weather Bureau, *Rainfall-Frequency Atlas of the United States*, Tech. Paper 40, U. S. Gvmt. Printing Office, Washington, D. C., 1961.
6. U. S. Weather Bureau, *Rainfall Intensity—Duration—Frequency Curves for Selected Stations in the U. S.* Tech. Paper 25, U. S. Gvmt. Printing Office, Washington, D. C., 1955, 53 pp.
7. King, H. W., *Handbook of Hydraulics*, McGraw-Hill Book Co., Inc., New York, 4th ed., 1954.
8. Department of Defense, U. S. Corps of Engineers, *Hydraulic Tables*, U. S. Gvmt. Printing Office, Washington, D. C., 1944, 565 pp.
9. U. S. Bureau of Reclamation, *Hydraulic and Excavation Tables*, U. S. Gvmt. Printing Office, Washington, D. C., 10th ed., 1950, 173 pp.
10. Jones, C. W., *Design of Culverts*, Supv. Bridge Engineer, Calif. Div. of Highways and Chairman of ASCE Task Force, 1961.
11. U. S. Bureau of Reclamation, *Culvert Hydraulics—A Library Study*, Hydraulics Branch Report No. Hyd-489, U. S. Gvmt. Printing Office, Denver, Colo., 1962, 24 pp.
12. Herr, L. A. and Bossy, H. G., *Hydraulic Charts for the Selection of Highway Culverts*, U. S. Bureau of Public Roads, Hydraulic Eng. Circular No. 5, U. S. Gvmt. Printing Office, Washington, D. C., 1964, 54 pp.
13. Herr, L. A. and Bossy, H. G., *Capacity Charts for the Hydraulic Design of Culverts*, Bureau of Public Roads, Hydraulic Eng. Circular No. 10, U. S. Gvmt. Printing Office, Washington, D. C. 1965, 90 pp.
14. Grace, J. L., Jr., Department of Defense, U. S. Corps of Engineers, *Friction Factors for Hydraulic Design of Corrugated Metal Pipe*, U. S. Waterways Exp. Sta., Vicksburg, Miss., Highway Research Board, Proc. Vol. 44, 1965.
15. Tomb, A. M., *How to Figure Culvert Capacity*, Rural and Urban Roads, Chicago, Feb. 1964.
16. U. S. Bureau of Public Roads, *Debris Control Structures*, Hydraulic Eng. Circular No. 9, Washington, D. C., Feb., 1964, 37 pp.
17. Calif. Div. of Highways, *California Culvert Practice*, Sacramento, Bulletin, 1944, 119 pp.
18. French, John L., *Tapered Inlets for Pipe Culverts*, ASCE, Proc. Paper 3845, Vol. 90, No. HY2, March, 1964, pp. 255-299.
19. Highway Research Board, *New Developments for Erosion Control at Culvert Outlets*, Bull. 286, 1960.
20. U. S. Bureau of Reclamation, *Progress Report on Results of Studies on Design of Stable Channels*, Report No. Hyd-352, U. S. Gvmt. Printing Office, Denver, Colo., 1952, 60 pp.
21. U. S. Bureau of Public Roads, *Design Charts for Open Channel Flow*, Hydr. Design Series No. 3, 1961.
22. American Society of Civil Engineers; Water Pollution Control Federation, New York, N. Y., *Design and Construction of Sanitary and Storm Sewers*, Manuals of Engineering Practice, Nos. 37 and 9, respectively, 1960, 283 pp.

Fig. 5-1. Assembly of 21 plates is partially done on the bank, then lowered into place for joining onto the completed portion.

CHAPTER 5 Cost Factors

Through the joint efforts of engineers, contractors and manufacturers, construction methods and materials are being constantly improved. Especially significant is the increase of pre-engineered and prefabricated structures, with consequent reduction of on-the-job labor. This has a three-way effect. (1) It affords factory-controlled quality under more ideal working conditions. (2) In reducing design and inspection time, it permits the engineer to concentrate on the job as a whole, rather than its details. And (3) although product cost may be higher, installed cost is usually less. Fig. 5-1.

SCOPE

Costs will vary not only in different locales, but even from job to job, depending on soil, water, weather, labor efficiency, wage scales, topography, design standards and construction practices. Therefore, even when costs are given in machine and man hours, they hold meaning only when accompanied by a description of the conditions applying to that particular job.

Average costs, of value in general comparisons, are likely to mislead if applied to a specific job. Unit prices bid on past work likewise are a poor basis for bidding future work unless tempered by judgment, experience and some knowledge of the circumstances applicable in each case.

In view of these limitations, this chapter is devoted principally to a general analysis of the various cost factors that collectively make up the total installed cost of the products described in this handbook. By relating these factors to the materials or structures involved and also to current local prices and practices, their relative importance can be generally determined.

PRICE VS. COST

The contractor is interested in how quickly and profitably he can install a culvert, conduit, subdrain or other structure. In other words, installed cost.

The engineer's concern, on the other hand, is the total cost of various alternates that would meet the minimum requirements for the planned service life of the project. Will the structure perform its intended purpose with a minimum of repairs, upkeep, and inconvenience of replacement? What is the initial cost?

Salvage value is related to future market and usage conditions. Unless these factors are predictable, they should not be used in this economic study.

Therefore, a logical selection is based on only those costs incurred during the design life of the project.

In the case of the Interstate Highway System, the federal government pays 90 per cent of construction costs with taxpayers' money, and the states pay 10 per cent. But the states are faced with maintenance costs that limit their construction outlays. At state level, construction that reduces maintenance costs reasonably is worthy of serious investigation in the selection of materials. Price and cost are not necessarily the same.

COST ITEMS INCLUDED

True *first cost* of a structure is made up of all or part of the following items:
1. Material cost
2. Hauling and handling
3. Excavation and backfill

lowered into the stream bed

Fig. 5-2. Nested helically corrugated pipe is stored on a freeway job, and occupies a minimum of space.

4. Installation
5. Replacing traffic surface
6. Detours, slow orders, delays to equipment on the job
7. Supervision, overhead, contingencies, insurance
8. Engineering design and inspection
9. Miscellaneous

1. MATERIAL COST

A material is not a structure until installed and ready to serve. On this basis, a material could well have the lowest purchase price and yet the highest installed cost, and vice versa.

Recent improvements in the methods of manufacturing corrugated steel pipe, plus new methods of design (see Chapter 2), are changing the cost picture for drainage conduits. For example, savings of up to 40 per cent have been achieved in the material cost of steel culverts in the western part of the United States. These savings have arisen in part from reduced gages, in turn the outcome of better understanding of soil-and-steel interaction. Note that structural adequacy is in no way sacrificed, and rational durability is increased through criteria to result in sound economic design.

2. HAULING AND HANDLING

Cost of getting materials to the job site is controlled principally by weight, bulk, distance, methods of transportation, and accessibility of the job site.

Transportation costs are a factor even when prices are quoted *f.o.b.* destination, because the manufacturer must include this cost in his price. Steel pipe of various sizes, structural plates and other products can generally be nested into bundles to enable hauling greater footage on a single truck trailer or railroad car. Fig. 5-2.

Handling pipe on the job, generally done by powered equipment, is simplified if lighter weight permits some manual handling and maneuvering. Steel pipe is relatively light in weight compared with other, rigid materials. See Table 5-1. This leads directly to installing longer lengths with fewer joints.

Table 5-1 WEIGHTS OF VARIOUS PIPES

Pounds per Lineal Foot—Approximate

Diameter in Inches	Corr.[1] Steel Pipe Helical Galvanized	Gage	Corr.[2] Structural Steel Plate Pipe	Concrete[3] Culvert Pipe	Aluminum[4]	
					Weight	Thickness in Inches
12	10	16		93	3.3	.060
15	12	16		127	4	.060
18	15	16		168	5	.060
24	19	16		264	6.3	.060
30	30	14		384	10	.075
36	36	14		524	16.4	.105
42	42	14		686	25	.135
48	65	12		867	35	.164
54	73	12		1068		
60	81	12	112	1295		
72	123	10	165	1811		
84	173	8	228	2409		
96	198	8	268	3090		
108		5	374	3865		
120		1	522			

Sources:
[1] Armco Cat. HC-4564
[2] Republic Handbook, G-152, 1965.
[3] Concrete Pipe Handbook, American Concrete Pipe Assn., Arlington, Virginia, 1966, p. 236, ASTM C76, Wall B.
[4] Reynolds Aluminum Highway Products, Reynolds Metal Co., 1963.

Assembled on the bank

Fig. 5-3. Assembled on the bank, this structural plate steel culvert is lowered into the stream bed.

Table 5-2   Trench Excavation and Backfill Quantities
for Corrugated Steel Pipe
All Quantities in Cubic Yards per Foot of Trench

Trench Depth to Flow Line in Feet	Nominal Inside Diameter									
	18 in.		24 in.		30 in.		36 in.		48 in.	
	Excava.	Backfill	Excava.	Backfill	Excava.	Backfill	Excava.	Backfill	Excava.	Backfill
5	0.6	0.6	0.7	0.6	0.8	0.7	0.9	0.7	1.1	0.6
10	1.3	1.2	1.5	1.4	1.7	1.5	1.9	1.6	2.2	1.8
15	2.0	1.9	2.2	2.1	2.5	2.3	2.8	2.5	3.3	2.9
20	2.6	2.9	3.0	2.8	3.3	3.1	3.7	3.5	4.4	4.0
25	3.3	3.2	3.7	3.6	4.2	4.0	4.7	4.4	5.6	5.1
30	3.9	3.8	4.4	4.3	5.0	4.8	5.6	5.3	6.7	6.2

Excavation based on nominal inside diameter plus 24 in.

Figs. 5-3, 5-4. Long lengths are particularly advantageous for subdrainage construction.

3. EXCAVATION AND BACKFILL

Pipe with relatively thin walls and simple joints obviously requires less excavation, and in the case of sewers, requires less backfilling. Local conditions will determine whether the difference is of consequence. Accompanying Tables 5-2 and 5-3 demonstrate the savings.

> *Example:* Excavation for a 48-in. corrugated steel sewer pipe in a trench 20 ft deep is approximately 4.4 cu yds per ft of trench. A 48-in. rigid sectional pipe requires 4.9 cu yds of excavation, or 0.5 cu yd more than for steel pipe.

Backfilling figures are slightly less because of the space occupied by the pipe, but the total difference for excavation plus backfill in the above example is approximately 0.8 cu yd per ft of trench. Multiply the difference by the local cost of handling earth to determine the savings per lineal foot of pipe.

4. INSTALLATION

The economic advantages of shop-fabricated corrugated steel pipe are generally recognized. However, it is in the area of the larger field-assembled plate pipe *versus* monolithic boxes and arches that important savings of time and money are possible.

Field assembly of steel plate structures can proceed so rapidly that in a matter of days the grading operations can be carried on unhindered. This is in contrast to weeks, possibly months, required for formwork, pouring concrete, stripping forms and curing—operations that delay grading spreads and increase grading costs.

In some cases, pipe can be pre-assembled into longer lengths on the stream bank or trench site and lowered into place. This may be advantageous where it is difficult or costly to dewater the installation site. Where pipe must be installed with water in the trench, special couplings are available for making quick, positive connections.

Table 5-3 Trench Excavation and Backfill Quantities for Concrete Pipe
All Quantities in Cubic Yards per Foot of Trench

Trench Depth to Flow+Shell Thickness in Feet	Nominal Inside Diameters and Outside Diameters (OD)									
	18 in. ID (22 in. OD)		24 in. ID (29 in. OD)		30 in. ID (35½ in. OD)		36 in. ID (42 in. OD)		48 in. ID (56 in. OD)	
	Excava.	Backfill	Excava.	Backfill	Excava.	Backfill	Excava.	Backfill	Excava.	Backfill
5	0.7	0.6	0.8	0.6	0.9	0.7	1.0	0.7	1.2	0.6
10	1.4	1.3	1.6	1.5	1.8	1.6	2.0	1.7	2.5	1.8
15	2.1	2.0	2.5	2.3	2.8	2.5	3.1	2.7	3.7	3.1
20	2.8	2.7	3.3	3.1	3.7	3.4	4.1	3.7	4.9	4.3
25	3.6	3.5	4.1	3.9	4.6	4.3	5.1	4.7	6.1	5.5
30	4.3	4.2	4.9	4.8	5.5	5.5	6.1	5.8	7.4	6.8

Excavation based on nominal outside diameter plus 24 in. Extra excavation for bell and spigot type not included. Backfill costs per cu yd are usually considerably higher than for excavation.

5. REPLACING TRAFFIC SURFACE

Where installation of culverts or drains requires removal of street, road or track surfaces, the cost of replacement is an important item to be included in total cost. Such costs, together with such less tangible items as inconvenience to traffic and possible loss of trade or business, should be considered. Alternative installation methods such as tunneling, boring or jacking would not require disturbing the surface nor require future maintenance.

6. DETOURS, SLOW ORDERS

Interruption of today's heavy traffic is obviously expensive and undesirable. Detours other than the runaround type increase mileage, time, hazards and inconvenience.

In some cases a structure can be placed one half at a time, and thereby permit one lane or one-way traffic. However, in replacing single drainage structures or adding water or sewer lines under busy thoroughfares, jacking, boring, tunneling or threading are the means to net saving to the traveling public.

Where detours or slow orders are necessary, this expense is a definite part of the first cost of the structure. Hence comparative materials which facilitate rapid installation should be considered by the engineer and contractor.

7. SUPERVISION, OVERHEAD, CONTINGENCIES, INSURANCE

Other factors being equal, materials simple to place or install will require least supervision. Shortened construction time also reduces overhead—a major item on any construction job. Contingencies and insurance are also factors in installation costs.

8. ENGINEERING COSTS

Design and inspection costs are less for prefabricated steel construction than for other designs. Prefabricated design requires a minimum of calculations and engineering drawings. Most materials are produced and fabrication is controlled under mill and factory conditions where adverse weather has no

Fig. 5-4. Laying, lining and joining 84-in. diam. corrugated steel sewer during winter weather at Shea Stadium, New York City.

effect on the quality of the product. Testing and inspection are simple. With pre-fabricated steel design, construction joints are few and are openly inspected. Fast progress on assembly and installation means less of the field inspector's time and attention.

OTHER FACTORS

Weather can be an important factor influencing costs. Some materials require protection from freezing weather. If so, include such protective measures in total cost. Floods and other emergencies can cause additional expense through loss of form work or other damage. Pipes may be subject to flotation and require extra precautions.

A choice of materials capable of quick installation and prompt backfill will reduce such hazards.

Tunneling, boring or jacking pipe have been mentioned in connection with detours. These operations are conducted largely underground, so are well suited to winter scheduling and offer work for crews released from operations of more seasonable nature.

UNSTABLE FOUNDATION CONDITIONS

Where unstable foundation soils are encountered, the engineer is confronted with (1) relocation of the route, (2) replacement with stable soils, (3) special bedding, piling, cradles, or (4) specifying corrugated steel pipe on an exclusive basis. Solution 4 is particularly pertinent under high fills where rigid structures are not only unsuitable but also costly to maintain.

COST OF END TREATMENT

Total cost of a culvert installation should include the cost of headwalls or other end treatment. Headwalls are necessary with some culvert materials to prevent progressive undermining (due to scour at the outlet end) or to prevent separation of pipe sections because of transverse pressures. Steel end sections, Fig. 5-5, eliminate the need for headwalls and are designed for locations where some form of end finish is necessary with corrugated pipe. Normally factory assembled, in larger sizes they may be supplied for bolting together on the job. They are economical in first cost and require no maintenance. Table 5-4 lists the savings in pipe length to be anticipated through use of steel end sections on pipe or pipe-arches.

Fig. 5-5. County construction crew installing 72-in. diameter steel end section. Total elapsed time was one hour—lifting from truck, excavating and full attachment of end section.

Table 5-4   Savings in Pipe Length Through Use of Steel End Sections

Pipe Diameter in Inches	Savings in Pipe Length		Pipe-Arch Size	Savings in P-A Length	
	Per End L in Inches	Per 2 Ends L x 2 in Feet	Span x Rise in Inches	Per End L in Inches	Per 2 Ends L x 2 in Feet
12	21	3.5	18 x 11	19	3.2
15	26	4.3	22 x 13	23	3.8
18	31	5.1	25 x 16	28	4.5
21	36	6.0	29 x 18	32	5.3
24	41	6.8	36 x 22	39	6.5
30	51	8.5	43 x 27	46	7.6
36	60	10.0	50 x 31	53	8.8
42	69	11.5	58 x 36	63	10.5
48	78	13.0	65 x 40	70	11.6
54	84	14.0	72 x 44	77	12.8
60	87	14.5	79 x 49	77	12.8
66	87	14.5	85 x 54	77	12.8
72	87	14.5			
78	87	14.5			
84	87	14.5			

Note: L = Savings in length of pipe and pipe-arch in inches and in feet, when using steel end sections. These savings may more than offset cost of end sections.

SUMMARY

First cost is made up of many items that require careful judgment of both engineer and contractor. Cost per year of service depends on durability, maintenance, ease of replacement and many other factors as influenced by local conditions. Economy is a worthy goal on every construction project.

REFERENCES AND BIBLIOGRAPHY

1. Manufacturers catalogs and handbooks:
   1. Metal Products Div., Armco Steel Corp., Cat. HC-4564, 1964.
   2. Republic Steel Corp. Handbook G-152, 1965, 103 pp.

3. American Concrete Pipe Assn. Handbook, 1966, 500 pp., (ASTM C76, Wall B).

4. Reynolds Metal Co., Aluminum Highway Prod., 1963.

CHAPTER 6 Couplings and Fittings

Shop-fabricated corrugated steel pipe and pipe-arches are supplied in lengths convenient for shipping and handling on the job. For longer installed lengths, standard connecting bands or special field joints are used. Among joint selection criteria are strength, joint tightness, simplicity and economy of installation.

Strength. Job conditions influencing strength requirements include type and stability of soil; whether in trench or embankment; under high fill or shallow cover; or wherever alignment and grade are critical and must be maintained.

Tightness. Varying degrees of resistance to infiltration or exfiltration are needed for soil, water or air. Couplings need be only as tight as conditions require and cost can be controlled accordingly.

Simplicity and Convenience. Under favorable or average conditions, the simplest of connections can best serve the purpose, at a saving in time and money. Under the adverse conditions of a water-filled trench, an unstable foundation or sloughing trench walls, select that type of joint which does the job quickly although possibly at greater direct cost. Fig. 6-2.

Economy. That coupling which satisfactorily meets the requirements of strength, tightness and convenience is usually most economical whether it be low or high in initial cost.

Purpose of Structure. Type of coupling may vary according to the purpose of the structure.

Culverts, storm drains and spillways require average strength and tightness of coupling. Where continuous beam strength is needed, a wider or more positive type of band should be selected.

Fig. 6-1. King-size wye or lateral for large storm sewer was shop-assembled, then dismantled and shipped to the job for final erection.

151

Fig. 6-2. When the trench for a sewer or culvert cannot be dewatered, simple but effective couplings are a "must".

Fig. 6-3. Interior of a 36-in. and 42-in. short-sectional pipe sewer troubled with infiltration throughout much of its 3-mile length.

Fig. 6-4. Corrugated steel expanding bands placed in sewer of Fig. 6-3. Sand and silt were removed before the sewer was restored to service.

Sanitary sewers and levee culverts call principally for practical watertightness, along with strength.

Low pressure water lines and air ducts will require joints sufficiently tight to meet specifications.

Subdrainage joints need not be watertight as infiltration of water is to be expected. However, infiltration of soil and escape of water in some instances must be prevented.

Repairs of short-sectional rigid pipe joints, in distress and leaking or allowing soil infiltration, may be accomplished by a special type of internal corrugated coupling band. Where a continuous line of corrugated steel pipe is threaded into a failing drain, special internal expanding or external contracting joints are available. Figs. 6-3 and 6-4.

Jacking. Where a corrugated steel structure is jacked through an embankment (or is threaded through an existing structure), the pipe may be coupled by means of field bolting or riveting through pre-punched holes, or welding.

DESIGN FEATURES OF COUPLINGS

· **Corrugated Bands** connect annularly corrugated and helically corrugated lock seam pipe from 6 to 96 in., diam. and pipe-arches from 18 x 11 in. to 85 x 54 in. Corrugated connecting bands vary from 3 corrugations (7 in. ±), to 5 corrugations (12 in. ±) to 9 corrugations (24 in. ± nominal). Figs. 6-5 and 6-6.

· **Smooth** sleeve joints are for lock seam pipe 6 to 12 in. nominal diameter and, in special cases, larger. Fig. 6-7.

· **Two-piece** joining bands with integrally formed flanges which may be fastened with bolts are available for helically corrugated pipe in diameters 6 in. through 24 in.

· **Gain in Length.** Where *helically corrugated* pipe is joined with connecting bands, the gain may be 0 to 2 in. per joint. With commonly used connecting bands for *annular corrugations*, there is a gain in length at each joint equal to one corrugation ($2^2/_3$ in. or 3 in.). Where pipe with annular corrugations is lapped for field connections by riveting or bolting, there is no gain or loss in nominal length.

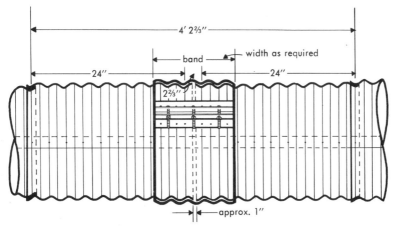

Fig. 6-5. Standard angle-and-bolt connecting band, as used on annular or helically-corrugated steel pipe and pipe-arches.

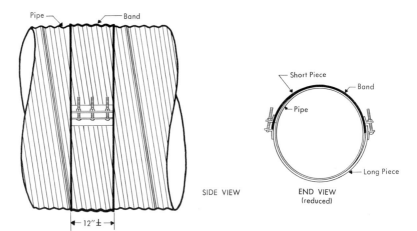

Fig. 6-6. Available as a one-, two-, or three-piece connecting band is that shown here for helically corrugated pipe.

Fig. 6-7. Snug-fitting, rugged sleeve joint holds corrugated steel pipe together, resists shearing forces of soil settlement. No bolting is necessary.

- **Gage.** For couplings, 16 gage is generally satisfactory unless specified otherwise. Material and coating are the same as pipe.
- **Number of Pieces.** Couplings may be of one or more pieces, depending on type, size and needs of installation conditions. When two-piece bands are used, one-half band can be attached to the bottom half of one pipe with the other half band left free for positioning in the field. Fig. 6-8.
- **Fasteners.** Couplings may be fastened or tightened by (1) bolts through slots in the coupling band or collar, (2) bolts through steel angle lugs, (3) bolts through turned-out integral flanges, (4) "hairpins" and wedges,

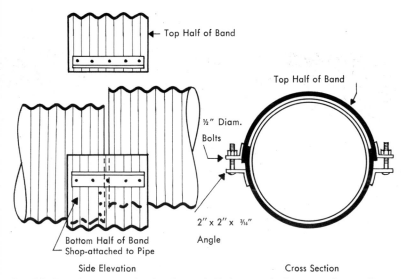

Fig. 6-8. Two-piece connecting band—one half shop-attached to preceding section—second half bolted on the job. This joint is effective in deep trenches or other inconvenient locations.

(5) U-bolt and bar, (6) silo lugs, threaded rods and nuts.

- **Tightness.** Couplings may be supplied with suitable gasket or other sealant where practical water-tightness or air-tightness is required. Fig. 6-9.
- **Special Bands.** Special bands are available for asphalt smooth-lined pipe and, when the bolting must be done from the inside, for lining failing rigid pipes with corrugated steel pipe.

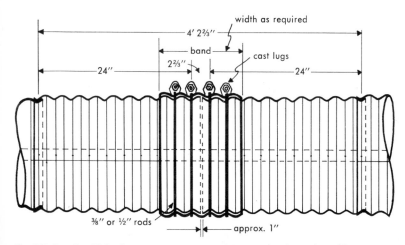

Fig. 6-9. Details of joint for levee culverts or aerial sewers, using rods and lugs.

Fig. 6-10. Camber or vertical curvature in a pipe under a high fill—or horizontal curvature in a culvert or sewer line—is possible with ordinary couplings. Greater changes
in alignment require fabricated fittings.

Fig. 6-11. Standard fittings for corrugated steel pipe and pipe-arches are available
shop-fabricated for a wide variety of conditions.

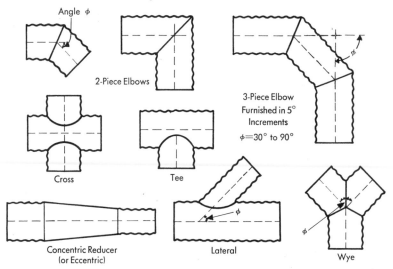

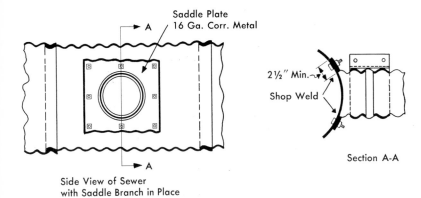

Saddle Plate
16 Ga. Corr. Metal

2½" Min.

Shop Weld

Section A-A

Side View of Sewer
with Saddle Branch in Place

Fig. 6-12. Saddle branch, bolted to main sewer on the job, or at the plant, enables laterals and house connections to join the sewer.

FITTINGS: STANDARD AND SPECIAL

Flexibility exists in most metal conduits sufficient for several degrees of curvature to the pipe itself during installation. Camber in a pipe under a high fill is one example of such need. Field joints or couplings permit further curvature. Fig. 6-10.

More than these moderate changes in alignment, and where two or more pipes (or pipe-arches) are joined, will call for a junction made with a shop fabricated fitting or a manhole. Shop·fabricated manholes are popular and economical. Fig. 6-15. Other shop fabricated fittings include "standard" elbows, tee or saddle branches, wyes, crosses, reducers, risers, and catchbasins. Standards usually include angles of 30°, 45°, 60° and 90°, and in some cases increments of 5°. See Figs. 6-11, 6-12, 6-13, 6-14.

Cut ends such as skews, bevels, step-bevels and skew bevels (mostly for larger structures) are considered specials, although widely used.

Fig. 6-13. Complicated junctions and fittings are possible with corrugated steel.

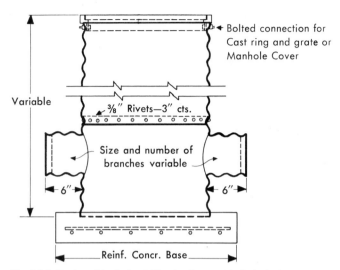

Variable

¾" Rivets—3" cts.

Size and number of
branches variable

6"   6"

Bolted connection for
Cast ring and grate or
Manhole Cover

Reinf. Concr. Base

Fig. 6-14. Design of typical catchbasin of corrugated steel pipe.

FABRICATION NOTES

For small pipes (6, 8 and 10-in. diameter), standard fittings of smooth galvanized steel are available in many areas. These include 45° and 90° elbows, tees, 45° laterals or wyes, and reducers.

Larger fittings, up to 96-in. diameter, are shop-fabricated of corrugated sheets or pipe. All parts are shop welded. All fittings are furnished in lengths as short as possible but sufficient to attach standard connecting bands.

Fig. 6-15. Corrugated steel manhole, shop-fabricated, is quickly fitted into the line to expedite completion of the sewer.

Fig. 6-16. Special fitting of galvanized steel for lake water intake of power station. Sealant ribbons were used on all seams. Divers made underwater bolted connection between sections.

Structural Plate fittings are shop cut from curved corrugated plates and welded together. Such structures are usually assembled and bolted in the shop in a trial fit to assure that all parts mate properly, then are marked clearly for field assembly. Fig. 6-16.

FIELD INSTALLATION OF FITTINGS

Steel fittings can be specified and installed to the same strength and tightness values as the remainder of the lines. The couplings described on preceding pages are generally suitable for this purpose.

With smaller fittings, the sleeve joint or stab joint is integral with the fittings. No bolting is necessary but gaskets may be added as required.

Medium size fittings usually require bolted couplings of adequate strength, with or without gaskets for watertightness and to keep out surrounding soil.

Aerial sewers demand a little extra care to insure adequate strength and tightness. Structural plate fittings are assembled and bolted together on the job. Where watertightness is needed, seam sealants or possibly welding may be specified.

Fig. 7-0. Reasonable care in locating and installing drainage structures pays dividends in long, satisfactory service.

CHAPTER 7 **Installation Instructions**

Section I—CORRUGATED STEEL
DRAINAGE STRUCTURES

IMPORTANCE OF GOOD INSTALLATION[1]

A well situated, properly bedded, accurately assembled and carefully backfilled galvanized steel drainage structure will function properly and efficiently for a long period of time. Smaller structures demand less care in the details of proper installation than larger ones. But in both instances, reasonable precautions in handling, base preparation, assembling and backfilling, will pay handsome dividends in satisfactory service. Fig. 7-1.

Corrugated steel structures because of their strength with light weight and their resistance to fracture can be installed quickly, easily and with the least expensive equipment. The flexible steel shell is designed to distribute external loads around its structure and into the backfill. Such flexibility permits unequal settlement and dimensional changes that would—and sometimes do—cause failure in rigid structures. This clear advantage of corrugated steel structures is further strengthened by a well prepared foundation and a well tamped backfill of stable material, for these best satisfy the design assumptions and insure the most satisfactory installation. Reasonable care during installation is assumed, and selection of steel gages and associated design criteria are based on that assumption. Just as with drainage structures of concrete or other materials, careless installation of corrugated steel structures can quickly undo the work of the designer.

Fig. 7-1. Installing multiple corrugated steel culvert under a Missouri River levee. Beveled ends were protected with a slope pavement.

161

PREPARATION OF BASE

Excavation to Line and Grade

When excavating with a bulldozer or heavy earth-moving equipment for a corrugated steel structure, it is often economical to dig a wide flat base. This is satisfactory if the backfill is tamped carefully under the lower portions of the structure. See Fig. 7-2. For hand excavation, guide lines should be strung to denote excavation boundaries; string at least one line parallel to the grade line to assist in maintaining line and grade.

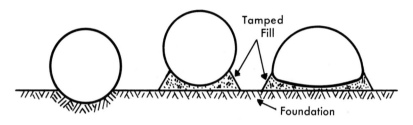

Fig. 7-2. Methods of bedding corrugated steel structures on wide flat base.

In trench installation, keep the trench as narrow as possible but sufficiently wide to permit tamping under the haunches. Generally, trench width will range from 12 to 24 in. greater than the outside diameter of the galvanized pipe structure. Above 60-in. diameter or where mechanical tamping equipment is used, more trench width is required. Wide trenches require more excavation, more backfill, and also tend to increase the load on the structure. Side walls should be as vertical as practical, at least to an elevation above the top of the pipe.

In natural streambeds, make sure the structure base is as uniform and stable as possible for its full length. Often a slight change in location can improve foundation conditions without affecting flow. Frequently it will be necessary to stabilize the foundation as described later.

Uniform Foundation

Corrugated steel drainage structures can settle unevenly without disjointing or breaking. Best performance and appearance, however, results from a firm, uniform foundation evenly distributing the load.

All pipe culverts or sewers should be installed with the lower quarter of the circumference firmly supported. Bed shaping of the natural foundation—still required with rigid pipe—demands careful workmanship to accurately fit the entire length of the structure. Corrugated steel structures can be bedded satisfactorily by excavating to a flat surface and carefully tamping the fill under the haunches. See Figs. 7-2 and 7-3.

All pipe and pipe-arch structures should be placed on a stable earth or fine granular foundation. Never install them on sod, frozen earth or on a bed which contains boulders, rock or stumps. When granular materials are used for bedding, the fill at the ends of the structure should be sealed against infiltration of water. This often can be done by bedding the ends in well tamped clay or by using a steel headwall or end section.

Fig. 7-3. Use of granular base to overcome wet soft foundation.

Unstable Foundation Soils

Especially when the excavated grade line for the structure traverses both soft and hard spots, the foundation should be made as uniform as practical. Hard spots can be excavated below grade and replaced with softer material. In any case, abrupt changes from hard to soft foundation should be avoided.

Soft, unstable material at foundation level should be excavated below the flow line grade and replaced with sand, gravel, crushed stone or other suitable material. Make the width of the base at least twice the diameter of the pipe and as deep as the foundation conditions require. See Fig. 7-4.

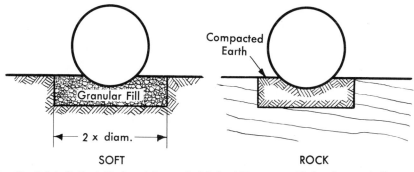

Fig. 7-4. *Left:* Unstable foundation material should be removed below flow grade line and replaced with sand, gravel, crushed stone or other suitable material. *Right:* When rock is encountered in the foundation, it should be excavated to at least 8 in. below the bottom of the structure.

Frequently a relatively thin mat (6 to 12 in.) of granular material, well graded, will provide satisfactory support, but it may be necessary to replace very soft foundations to a depth of 3 ft. Diameter of pipe and height of fill will be controlling factors.

In swampy locations, especially along shore lines or adjacent to large rivers, deep unstable foundations are frequent problems. If they cannot be readily stabilized with granular material, brush or timber mats may be used to spread the load.

When placing large diameter culverts, particularly beneath high fill, it is generally good practice to install galvanized steel perforated pipe subdrainage on each side, parallel to the culvert, to prevent subsequent saturation of the foundation and of the fill around the pipe. In hilly country, foundation damage from seepage zones in the slopes adjacent to the fill can be similarly controlled. Details concerning proper installation of subdrains are given in Chapter 10, *Subdrainage*.

Cambered Grade Line for High Fill

Cambering the center part of the foundation will compensate for unequal settlement beneath the weight of heavy fills. This prevents the structure from sagging in the middle as the foundation consolidates.

Sufficient camber generally can be obtained by installing the upstream half of the pipe on a flat grade, and then using a steeper grade on the downstream half. If camber is necessary, it should be no less than ½ of 1 per cent of the total length of the structure. The maximum amount of camber should be determined by the field engineer from evaluation of foundation soil conditions. See Fig. 7-5. Be careful not to elevate the pipe center above its inlet, as this will pocket water in the pipe.

Rock Foundations

Rock encountered in the foundation should be removed to at least 8 in. below the bottom of the structure; excavate wide enough to avoid any possibility of the pipe resting on the rock. The excavated area is backfilled with compacted earth to cushion the pipe, generally 8 to 12 in. thick. (See Fig. 7-4.)

Fig. 7-5. Cambering or arching long lines of pipe under a high fill is a means of providing a grade line without low, pocketing areas.

Fig. 7-6. Standard angle and bolt connecting band. For larger sizes the band can be provided in two or three pieces.

ASSEMBLY OF PIPE CULVERTS AND SEWERS

Unloading and Handling

Corrugated steel drainage products will withstand rough handling without cracking or breaking, but should be unloaded and handled with reasonable care. Lifting or rolling will protect the galvanized or bituminous coating—avoid dragging over gravel or rocky surfaces. Paved pipe sections stockpiled in hot climates should be placed to prevent flow of the asphaltic pavements.

Corrugated metal structures can be lowered down embankments or into deep trenches with the aid of ropes or slings. Lifting lugs with hookhole can be attached at the fabricating plant to avoid damaging any bituminous coating or lining.

Shop Fabricated Pipe and Pipe-Arch

Helically corrugated steel pipe will require no positioning precautions unless the invert is paved. Longitudinal laps of riveted or welded corrugated steel pipe should be located at the sides or the quarter points, not in the bottom.

Riveted or spot welded pipe is supplied in multiples of 2 ft or 4 ft, with maximum individual lengths governed by shop, transportation or field handling facilities. Culverts 20 to 30 ft long are generally supplied in a single section.

Connecting Bands

Corrugated connecting bands of galvanized steel are used to join sections of corrugated steel pipe. "Standard" bands are used for most installations on all sizes of pipe. Fig. 7-6. "Two-piece" bands are used on the larger sizes under difficult installation conditions. "Rod and lug" bands are used on special work where maximum watertightness is essential—as in levees, aerial sewers and similar installations.

Width of the connecting band varies with the pipe diameter, ranging from 7 to 24 in.

Especially fabricated or bolted connections can be supplied for jacking, boring, threading or other special installation. See Chapter 6 *Couplings and Fittings*.

For helically corrugated and spun-lined pipe, the adjacent ends may butt together.

In installing corrugated bands on riveted and spot welded pipe, first slip the band into position over the end of one pipe section with the band open to receive the next section. The adjoining length is brought to within about 1 in. of the first section, and the band is tightened with the corrugations of the band matching the corrugations of the pipe sections. For every band used, the rated length of pipe will increase $2^2/_3$ or 3 in.—equal to the length of one corrugation.

Keep dirt and gravel out of the joint, so that corrugations fit snugly. As the plain galvanized band is tightened, tap it with a mallet or hammer to take up slack and to insure a tight joint. Mere torqueing of bolts will not produce a tight joint on large diameter culverts.

To speed the coupling operation, especially for large diameter structures, a chain or cable-cinching device will help draw the band tight.

A special clamping device exists that fits over coupling band angles and draws them together. Advantage of such devices is that they permit faster handtightening of the bolts so that a wrench is needed only for final tightening. Corrugated steel pipe-arch structures are installed in much the same way as round pipe.

Bituminous Coated and Paved Pipe

Asphalt pavement is employed to protect the corrugated steel pipe against erosion from abrasive materials, and so prolong the drainage structure life. With invert paved pipe, asphalt covers about 25 per cent of the circumference and fills the corrugations in the flow line. To be effective, paved pipe must be installed with the smooth, thick pavement placed and centered on the bottom.

On coated pipe, the surface between coupler and pipe may need lubrication with fuel oil or soapstone solution. This will allow the band to slip around the pipe more easily and to draw into place more firmly, particularly in cold weather. Lubricating and tapping the bands so they can be drawn to proper register will assure a strong joint.

Where damage to the bituminous coating exposes the metal, repair by patching before the structure is backfilled. Use a coating similar to that covering the pipe. Suitable materials include asphalt mastic with asbestos fibers and coal tar cutback.

Helically Corrugated Pipe

Helically corrugated pipe is installed in the same manner as riveted or spot welded corrugated steel pipe. The connecting bands may consist of a smooth collar or sleeve joint, or may be helically corrugated to fit the pipe. To assemble, place the band (or first half, if not of one-piece construction) around or under the first pipe section. Then lay the second pipe section with the corrugations matching. Complete the band around the pipe and fasten tightly.

With perforated pipe make sure to rotate each section so that perforations face the bottom. Any gap left between pipe sections, upon proper positioning of perforations, will be effectively closed by the coupling band.

Fig. 7-7. Using a minimum number of bolts until the structure is assembled makes for greater flexibility in erecting.

Structural Plate Pipe and Pipe-Arches—Field Erected

Excavations for structural plate structures are prepared and backfilled as for shop-fabricated steel structures.

Such structures are shipped complete with all plates, bolts and nuts necessary for erection. Inside one package or keg of bolts, clearly marked, are detailed erection instructions showing the order of assembly and position of each plate. Bolt heads are color coded for different lengths.

Structures should be temporarily assembled with as few bolts as possible. Three or four untightened bolts near the center of each plate, along longitudinal and circumferential seams, are sufficient. This procedure gives maximum flexibility until all plates are fitted into place. See Figs. 7-7 and 7-8.

After part of the structure has been assembled into shape by partial bolting, the remaining bolts can be inserted and hand tightened. Always work from the center of a seam toward the plate corner. Do not insert corner bolts until all others are in place and tightened.

Alignment of bolt holes is easiest when bolts are loose. Drifting with a drift pin is best done when adjacent bolts are tight.

It is essential that bolts be well tightened. Progressively and uniformly tighten nuts, starting at one end of the structure, *after all plates* are in place. See Fig. 7–7. The operation should be repeated to be sure all bolts are tight. Maximum torque with power wrenches should be 300 ft-lb, plus or minus 50. Bolts should not be overtightened.

Structural Plate Arches

Structural plate arches are generally erected on a masonry foundation. The arch rests in a groove or unbalanced channel, which must be accurately built to line and grade for easy assembly of the plates. When the arch is set on a

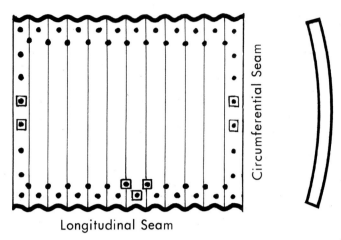

Longitudinal Seam

Fig. 7-8. Details of curved corrugated structural plate.

skew, holes in unbalanced channels must line up with those in the plates. Layout for channel installation is shown on special plate assembly drawings furnished with each skewed structural plate arch. For straight-end arches on which headwalls are to be built, allowance should be made in design for a lip (approx. 2 in.) at each end.

Diaphragms

Steel diaphragms or cutoff walls reduce danger of water seepage that might cause a washout along the outside of the structure. Typical of such installa-

Fig. 7-9. Use of square, steel diaphragms on levee culvert discourages seepage.

tions are pipes through levees or dams where the pipe may be subjected to a hydraulic head. Fig. 7-9.

Diaphragms should be located midway between two adjacent riveted circumferential seams, as near the center of a pipe length as possible, and at least 4 ft from a field joint. In multiple line installations, space the diaphragms to assure at least 12-in. clearance between the faces of diaphragms on adjacent pipes for working room in backfilling.

The bottom half of the diaphragm is placed after excavating for the pipe and before laying and joining the pipe. Generally a narrow trench is excavated for the diaphragm, although it may be driven or jetted into place under some soil conditions. The diaphragm must be lined up to mesh with the corrugations of the pipe. The top half of the diaphragm is placed as soon as the pipe has been placed. The cross trench for the lower half should be backfilled with good fill material and tamped to give maximum compaction.

Multiple Installations

Two or more structures laid parallel in the same trench or streambed should be separated (as indicated in Fig. 7-13) sufficiently for mechanical equipment to operate between them. Such tamping and compaction helps prevent washouts during high water or flood stage.

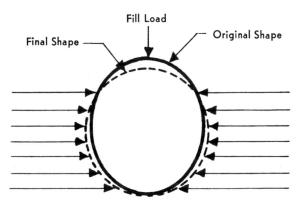

Fig. 7-10. Proper side support enables a flexible steel structure to resist tremendous fill loads.

VERTICAL ELONGATION

As a corrugated steel pipe structure deflects under load, its vertical diameter shortens and the horizontal diameter increases. This spreading in the horizontal dimension compresses the backfill and builds up an increasing side support for the structure. Fig. 7-10, exaggerated for clarity, demonstrates this action. Magnitude of deflection is a measure of backfill compaction, since the better the backfilling, the less the deflection.

It is possible *just by compaction* to elongate the pipe vertically by 2 or 3 per cent. The load, even of a high fill, will then deflect the pipe either to true circular shape or leave some residual vertical elongation.

This composite interaction of steel and earth can usually be obtained by compaction technique at less cost than by factory or field vertical elongation.

Corrugated Steel Pipe. Upon order, riveted, spot welded or helically corrugated steel pipe may be provided by the fabricating plant either (1) formed to a specified 5 per cent vertical elongation; or (2) elongated with tension wires or turnbuckle rods at the horizontal axis.

Structural Plate Pipe. Structural plate pipe can be preformed at the fabricating plant to elliptical shape by the use of short and long radius plates. Vertical elongation by compaction is a simpler method—optionally supplemented by cables or rods and turnbuckles inserted through bolt holes at the horizontal axis.

With any type of vertical elongation, the pipe should be permitted to deflect *slowly* as the fill load is applied. Otherwise the pipe may deflect at points where ties or struts contact the pipe.

All wires, turnbuckles or struts must be removed after the fill has been completed or consolidated. Earlier removal, before the fill has completely settled, may be required if danger exists of impeding flood water.

Do Not Strut Arches or Pipe-Arches

Unlike round corrugated steel structures, arches and pipe-arch structures do *not* appreciably change their horizontal dimension under load. Nothing is gained by strutting, for additional side support is not created.

BACKFILLING

Corrugated steel structures, as discussed previously, build up side support as they deflect under load. To obtain maximum load-bearing capacities, and to prevent washout and settlement, backfill must be good material, properly placed and carefully compacted.

Too much emphasis cannot be placed on the necessity for adequate compaction of backfill. *Faulty compaction has led to more trouble with pipe installations than all other factors combined.*

Backfill Material

The designer ordinarily assumes that backfill surrounding any pipe has a density or strength as great as the undisturbed adjacent soil, or as great as required for a modern roadway embankment. Thus he depends on the installing crew to obtain the expected compaction.

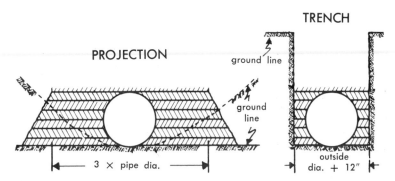

Notes: Place fill in uniform well tamped 6" layers.
Keep fill at same elevation on both sides of pipe.

Fig. 7-11. Backfill should be placed in uniform, well tamped 6-in. layers on both sides of the structure.

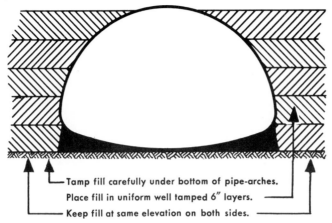

Tamp fill carefully under bottom of pipe-arches.

Place fill in uniform well tamped 6″ layers.

Keep fill at same elevation on both sides.

Fig. 7-12. Compaction under the corners of pipe-arches is important.

Selected, drainable backfill material is preferred. But most local fill material can be used if carefully placed and compacted. It should be free from large rocks, stumps and hard lumps or clods larger than 3-in. diameter. Avoid frozen fill, sod, cinders or earth containing a high percentage of organic material. The ideal backfill is granular material containing a small amount of silt or clay, since it makes a dense, stable fill.

Placing Backfill Around Structure

Fill material under haunches and around the structure should be placed alternately in 6-in. layers on both sides of the pipe to permit thorough tamping. The fill is placed alternately to keep it at the same elevation on both sides of the structure at all times. Figs. 7-11 and 7-12 show how pipe and pipe-arch structures should be backfilled.

Tamping can be done with hand or mechanical equipment, tamping rollers or vibrating compactors, depending upon field conditions. More important than method is that it be done *carefully* to insure a thoroughly tamped backfill.

Compaction of fills by puddling or jetting is not recommended. These methods usually do not produce reliable backfills for corrugated steel structures.

Tamping Equipment

1. *Hand Equipment.* For tamping under the haunches of a structure, a pole or 2 x 4 in. timber is generally needed to work in the small areas. Hand tampers for compacting horizontal layers should weigh not less than 20 lb and have a tamping face not larger than 6 x 6 in. Ordinary "sidewalk" tampers are generally too light.
2. *Mechanical Tampers.* Most types of power tampers are satisfactory and can be used in all save the most confined areas. However, they must be used carefully and completely over the entire area of each layer to obtain the desired compaction. Avoid striking the structure with power tamping tools. Fig. 7-13.
3. *Tamping Rollers.* Where space permits, sheepsfoot, rubber-tired and other types of tamping rollers can be used to compact backfill around the struc-

Fig 7-13. Proper use of vibratory tamper between two pipes. If larger equipment is used, more space must be provided.

ture. If rollers are used, fill adjacent to the structure should be tamped with hand or hand-held power equipment. Be sure to keep the rollers from hitting the structure. Smooth rollers are generally not satisfactory for compacting fills.

4. *Vibrating Compactors.* Vibrating equipment can be used to compact the granular backfills but generally is unsatisfactory for clay or other plastic soils.

Backfill on Arches

Care must be taken in backfilling arches, especially half-circle arches, because they have a tendency to shift sideways or to "peak up" under backfilling loads. The ideal way is to cover an arch in layers—each layer conforming to the shape of the arch. *If one side is backfilled more than the other, the arch will move away from the larger load.* If both sides are backfilled equally and tamped thoroughly, the top of the arch may peak up unless enough fill has been placed over it to resist the upward thrust. See Fig. 7-14.

Arches Without Headwalls

When backfilling arches without headwalls, or with headwalls not sufficiently strong to maintain the shape of the arch, place the first fill midway between the ends of the arch. This fill should be kept in as narrow a strip as possible until the top of the arch is reached. The remainder of the backfill should be placed from the top of the arch, starting at the center and working both ways to the ends. By this means, illustrated in Fig. 7-14, least side pressure is developed until the top is loaded.

Arches With Headwalls

In backfilling arches with headwalls heavy enough to maintain the shape of the arch, it is advisable to place the fill against one head wall until the top of the arch is reached. Continue dumping in layers toward the opposite headwall.

Filling on only one side causes arch to shift. If fill is not placed on top as backfilling proceeds, arch may raise, thereby flattening side radius.

COMMON MISTAKES IN BACKFILLING ARCHES (above)

Place fill on arch by distributing material around and over the structure in uniform layers, tamping thoroughly. Place material from top of arch.

RECOMMENDED BACKFILLING PRACTICE

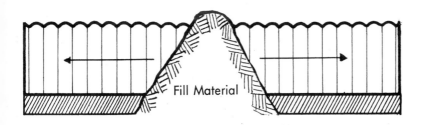

Fill Material

SIDE VIEWS—Without and With Headwalls

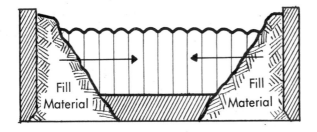

Fill Material   Fill Material

Fig. 7-14. Recommended and poor backfilling practice for corrugated steel arches.

Fig. 7-15. Steel end sections provide efficient end finish.

Completing the Fill Over Structure

Complete the fill over a corrugated steel structure using materials essentially the same as those used for the backfill and placed and compacted in the same manner. Distribute and compact the fill evenly to a depth equal to the height of the structure, or the entire fill, if it is shallow.

In trenches, fill material should be tamped in layers from the top of the structure to the original ground level. This assures thorough compaction and eliminates settlement.

Protection of Structure from Equipment

It is important to protect drainage structures during construction because maximum strength does not develop until fill consolidates. To avoid imposing concentrated loads far in excess of those the structure would normally carry, heavy construction equipment should not cross the structure prematurely. Also, heavy vehicles moving too close to the wall of the structure can create an eccentric loading with harmful results.

More than normal fill is a frequent need to protect the structure during construction, especially if heavy equipment is used. The minimum cover required has been tentatively established as one eighth of the barrel diameter (or span) for highway conduits and one quarter diameter for railway conduits, with a minimum of 1 ft. How much excess protective fill is needed depends upon the wheel loads of equipment used as well as frequency of loading.

Trestle Replacement

Replacement of trestles with culvert structures should receive careful inspection. These generally involve fairly high fills and large diameter steel pipe. Obtaining a good foundation and a well compacted backfill is often difficult when working around the old trestle timbers. A better fill can be made if the timbers can be removed before fill is placed.

Dumping fill from the top of the trestle must be avoided. Dirt must be placed in thin horizontal layers and well compacted to an elevation well above the top of the steel pipe. Vegetation, organic matter, and other loose trash should be stripped from the surface before the fill is started. Steep slopes should be benched or step cut before filling, to avoid wedge action that increases fill pressure.

Experience has shown that water pockets frequently occur in trestle fills. Particular care should be exercised to provide galvanized steel subdrains for all seeps and pockets showing in the base of the fill. Seeps have a tendency to drain toward culvert structures, thus softening the backfills and causing structural difficulties.

End Sections

Steel end sections provide a practical and economical method of finishing metal culverts. They may be installed at the time the culvert is placed or after the backfill around the barrel has been completed. Fig. 7-15.

Cut Ends

By cutting the ends of corrugated metal structures, need for additional end finish can often be eliminated. Ends cut to specified embankment slopes are furnished by the culvert fabricator. They can be beveled (limit 2:1), skewed or a combination of skew and bevel. Ends cut as skews or bevels (or both) are not as strong as square ends, and in the case of large structures may require temporary bracing. Skew angles less than 70° or greater than 110° when combined with bevels, require the addition of full headwalls or ring beams.

The embankment slope around the structure can be protected against erosion by a cutoff wall and by riprapping around the structure end with stone, bags filled with dry sand-cement mixture, Fig. 7-16, or by use of a slope pavement. Cut ends should be reinforced with masonry or concrete headwalls, when the bevel exceeds 2:1 and the skew is greater than 15 degrees.

Fig. 7-16. Bags filled with a sand-cement mixture give erosion protection at the ends of a culvert.

Fig. 7-17. Jacking an 84-in. diameter steel pipe under a highway embankment. Earth is removed at the heading in a wheelbarrow or cart.

Section II—JACKING

New openings for culverts, sewers, conduits, underpasses, etc., are frequently required under existing railroads, highways, runways, levees and other engineering works. Four methods of placing such openings are: open trenching, jacking, tunneling and boring.

Open trenching, most commonly used, is well adapted to new construction and to replacements under shallow fills and areas of light traffic. This method is detailed on preceding pages.

The *jacking method* of installation, in use for the past four decades, offers important advantages. These include protection of the general public, and fast, uninterrupted movement of traffic. In various parts of the country, experienced subcontractors will do this kind of work at predetermined prices. Fig. 7-17.

Diameters

Pipes from 30 to 96-in. diameter have been installed by jacking with no settlement of surface structures and no interruption of traffic. However, 36 to 60-in. are sizes most commonly jacked today. One essential working condition: the structure must be large enough to allow a man to excavate ahead of the pipe without being too cramped. For the average size man, minimum working space seems to be 36-in. diameter. Maximum pipe diameter capable of being jacked depends on several factors; the main ones are: ground conditions, height of cover and safety.

Lengths

Maximum length of pipe capable of being jacked is variable; it depends on the pipe diameter, ground conditions and the pressures required to push the pipe.

Lengths greater than 400 ft have been installed by jacking. In such installations, ground conditions must approach the ideal, and the pipe must be kept in motion continuously to keep it from "freezing" tight.

Where pipe does "freeze up" it is possible, under most conditions, to jack the balance of the pipe from the opposite side of the fill to meet the end already in place. Proper junction of these two pipes is a matter not only of engineering calculation, but also careful control of field crew work to assure that line and grade are accurately met and maintained.

Depth of Cover

Overburden on pipe to be jacked beneath operating railroads should be at least one pipe diameter below base of rail—no less than 3 ft—to get below the ballast line and into stable material. Under reinforced highway slabs, the cover can be the least needed for a cushion between slab bottom and pipe top. Under bituminous type pavements, the cover should equal that beneath railroads.

Acceptance of Jacking

This method of installing new openings has today become standard procedure for most railroads and for numerous highway departments. It saves time, money and material, and supplies a factor of safety all-important to present day movement of traffic. Jacking also avoids the cost and nuisance of repeated maintenance of the fill (due to settlement) usually necessary when open trench installation is used. For levee or dike installations, jacking avoids sacrificing valuable land and the building of new setback levees.

JACKING PROCEDURE[2]

Testing of Soil

Jacking should not be attempted (1) in dry sand, (2) in gravelly soil known to contain large boulders, (3) through fills where logs or stumps are known to exist or (4) where it is impractical or uneconomical to lower the water table below the excavation.

In all questionable soil conditions, test the soil by boring or sampling before deciding upon jacking. Such testing is neither costly nor time-consuming. Effective chemical means now exist to stabilize soils ahead of the jacking face.

Approach Trench

Pipe to be jacked through fills higher than the diameter of the pipe, plus required minimum cover, need no working pit. However, an open jacking face is desirable. Excavate an approach trench into the fill far enough to provide a jacking face of 3 ft or more above the pipe. This open face should be shored securely to prevent slipping or raveling of the embankment. Make provision for a sump in one corner of the approach trench or pit.

Backstop and Guides

A substantial backstop is necessary to take the thrust of the jack. A 60 to 80-ft length jacking job in reasonably good soil often develops 150 to 300 tons of jacking resistance.[3] The backstop is of heavy timbers or steel framing.

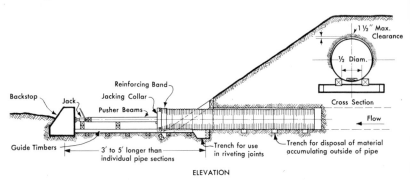

ELEVATION

Fig. 7-18. Set-up for typical jacking operation. There is no interference at traffic level.

Steel rails or timbers that support the pipe as it enters the bore must be accurately placed on line and grade. Both line and grade should be checked at least once per shift as work progresses. Fig. 7-18.

Pipe for Jacking

To jack corrugated pipe, sections are especially prepared for field jointing by riveting or bolting. A jacking band is recommended to reinforce the end receiving the thrust—especially for long lines or large diameters. When jacking through loose or gravelly soils, smooth steel sheets of light gage should be bolted to top and bottom of the pipe sections.

Equipment

Necessary equipment for jacking includes an electric power plant for lights, pumps, excavating tools, muck handling equipment and jacks. A wheelbarrow is economical for pipe 48 in. and larger. For smaller pipe, some type of skip or dolly-mounted dirt box is required.

Jacking Operation

As material is excavated ahead of the pipe, the pipe is jacked in to follow this excavation. The distance dug ahead of the pipe rarely exceeds 12 to 18 in. Some loose soils may reduce this to 3 or 4 in.

Section III—BORING

Boring is another means of installing conduits and culverts without disturbing surface structures or traffic. This method is generally confined to pipe diameters from 10¾ in. through 36 in. Various types of machines on the market are built to perform this operation.

Two basic boring methods exist. In the first, conduit pipe is pushed into the fill as the boring auger drills out the ground. Fig. 7-19. The second method consists of drilling the hole through the fill and pushing the conduit pipe into the hole after the drill auger has completed the bore. Both methods have their advantages. But if there is any doubt concerning ground conditions, the first method is the safer of the two; it offers greater protection to the surface structure under which the conduit is placed.

Location of Holes

Boring installations are generally small diameters, so the prospect of being stopped by boulders, rocks—even utility lines—should be considered and alternate locations provided for the conduit. Rocks and boulders are prevalent in some locations. In other areas, the possibility of encountering such obstacles is remote. The engineer and the contractor must guide their thinking accordingly.

Where obstacles are encountered in fills, it may be necessary to abandon that exact location.

Some machines will bore through rock and coal but it is not often economically practical to adapt these rock cutters to earth augers. Most earth boring augers will penetrate soft rock, wood or brick, but experience and "feel" are required to judge the practicability of going ahead when such obstacles are met. Line and grade may suffer because of these obstacles and even though it is possible to complete the bore, it may not be satisfactory for the purpose intended. Under such circumstances it may be wiser to abandon the bore when the obstacle is encountered and move a few feet to try again.

Fig. 7-19. Boring under an express highway to provide conduit for a sewer or water line. Smooth-wall steel pipe is used for this purpose.

Fig. 7-20. Lining and extending a twin failing masonry arch under a main line railroad, using elliptical shaped 22-ft diameter structural plate pipe. Space between old and new structure was backfilled. New structure has step-bevelled ends and a 3-ft high toe-wall.

Section IV—LINING

There comes a time when tunnels, stone arches, conduits and culverts begin to deteriorate and lose strength. The decision to rehabilitate or replace is usually based on available methods, safety and economics. Also, due to changing conditions, some old structures must be strengthened to accommodate present and future loads greater than those for which the structures were originally designed.

Discussion here is confined to some of the economical methods used to rehabilitate and strengthen drainage openings, small bridges, sewers, etc.

Masonry and Concrete Arches: These structures begin to deteriorate from natural causes after being in service for a limited period of years. Mortar comes out of the joints, the stones loosen; alternate freezing and thawing causes trouble. Concrete begins to crack and spall off or heavy loads cause foundation settlement, resulting in cracking and spalling. Consequently, the structure needs to be strengthened or must be replaced. Rehabilitation in numerous cases is the most economical and can be accomplished with least effort.

Lining such a structure with a structural steel plate or steel liner plate arch takes little space, and conserves a maximum amount of the original waterway capacity. These steel arches can be supported on new concrete side walls or on original bench walls where feasible. Fig. 7-20. Small arches, 6 ft or less, can be lined with riveted corrugated steel sections.

Over the past 30 years, many hundreds of lineal feet of masonry arches have been given renewed life by this lining method. Results have been very satisfactory.

Pressure Grouting

Pressure grouting the space between the old and new structures, prevents further collapse of the old structure and avoids concentrated pressures on the new lining. Two-inch grout couplings welded into the liner plates can be furnished at proper intervals for convenience in grouting. A mixture of 1 part cement to 3 parts sand, plus an additive for lubrication, has been found satisfactory.

Grouting should be carefully done. Inspect frequently to see that voids are being thoroughly filled. In fact, due to shrinkage of the grout after "set up", the top row of grout holes should be "check grouted" after grout placement is completed to be sure any voids due to shrinkage have been filled.

Other Shapes of Structures

This same relining method can be applied to full round, elliptical or other structural shapes that have begun to show signs of deterioration or collapse. New corrugated steel pipe, structural steel plate or liner plate can be threaded inside an old structure to give it new life for long trouble-free service. Frequently, due to excessive deflection or joint settlement, the diameter of the new lining will necessarily be much smaller in order to have clearance for threading. In such cases it sometimes is necessary to jack or tunnel a supplementary opening alongside the present structure to restore the waterway capacity lost from the old culvert. See Chapter 14 *Tunnels*.

It also happens that changes in runoff conditions may no longer require as large an opening as originally. In these cases, any reduction in waterway area due to "threading" is not serious. These changing conditions should be investigated before the engineer defines his requirements.

Rehabilitation through relining can also be applied to storm or sanitary sewers which are beginning to show signs of weakening. Fig. 7-21. Methods of installation of liners for sewers will vary with sewer size and the liner type, but the basic principles here would be the same as those used in "threading" or lining any relatively short culvert open at both ends.

Fig. 7-21. Lining a failing sewer by threading with corrugated steel pipe, asphalt coated and paved.

Section V—BRIDGE FILLING

On railroads and highways are innumerable small bridges—built of timber, concrete and steel, or a combination of these materials—larger than the drainage area truly demands. Maintenance on these bridges becomes quite costly as the structure ages. Eventually, arrangements must be made for major repairs or complete replacement. At that time a complete investigation should be made of the actual waterway opening required, the importance of the structure from a traffic standpoint, consideration of fire hazard, elimination of maintenance and the most economical material to be used.

Economics of materials does not necessarily mean low first cost. Reduced maintenance cost, long trouble-free life, ease of installation without traffic interruptions and capital investment should be considered along with the cost of retiring the old structure and/or rerouting traffic.

Structural plate and corrugated steel pipe have been used quite extensively over the past 30 years for filling and replacing timber trestles on railroads, and small steel, wood or concrete spans on county and state highway systems. The success of these metal structures is evidenced by the growing acceptance of their use. In some instances one opening will take care of the waterway; while in other cases a whole battery of pipes may be necessary. Drainage area and available headroom will determine the size and number of pipes required. Fig. 7-22.

Fig. 7-22. Providing a creek crossing with eight 14-ft diameter 7 gage structural plate pipes with the beveled ends pre-assembled and lifted into place.

Backfill Method Important

Proper foundation and tamping of the backfill are very significant and these operations are of sufficient importance to warrant repeating. At those spots where the pipe or pipes are close to existing pile bents and cross bracing, a good job of backfilling and tamping is mandatory. Preferably, surround the pipe with pit run gravel or other types of pervious material (except cinders or slag) rather than clay. Precautions should be taken to seal the upstream end against seepage under and alongside the pipe—a cause of failures.

Impervious materials can be used on top of the pervious material to build up the fill; but since water will follow the line of piling and cross bracing (and could cause soft spots around the pipes), it would be better for such water to collect on the outside and seep into the culvert before it can do harm to the fill. This is particularly true where structural plate is used. After the fill has consolidated, this pervious material will gradually cease to function as a water collector. However, it should be there at the time of installation to help eliminate soft spots alongside the pipe that tend to form from rainfall during the fill build up.

In case of replacement of railroad trestles, the caps and stringers should remain in place to handle traffic until the fill has become consolidated. Otherwise the railroad should be willing to raise track that settles with the fill. In case of highway bridge replacements, a temporary surface should be placed on the new fill until consolidation is final.

REFERENCES AND BIBLIOGRAPHY

1. National Corr. Steel Pipe Assn., *Installation Manual for Corrugated Metal Structures*, Manual CMPA-1165, Chicago, Ill., 1965, 54 pp.
2. Colvin, C. M., *Jacking Culverts Through Fills*, Western Construction, San Francisco, Calif., April, 1953.
3. Feld, Jacob, Highway Research Board, Bulletin No. 14, 1948.

Fig. 8-1. Carrying runoff from winter's snows is an important function for a culvert.

PART II

Applications

CHAPTER 8 Culverts

Section I—APPLICATIONS

DEFINITION

A culvert is a conduit to convey water by gravity through an embankment. It is a "grade separation" for water and the traffic above it. Fig. 8-1.

Distinction is made between culverts and *storm drains* or sewers, mostly on the basis of length. *Subdrains* or underdrains carry ground water. *Conduit*, *underpass* and *service tunnel* are general terms for a pipe that carries other kinds of traffic.

Required size and shape have been discussed under Chapter 4 *Hydraulics* and Chapter 1 *Product Details*. The distinction between a highway culvert and a bridge is that the top of the culvert does not ordinarily act as the roadway surface. A bridge, on the other hand, is a physical link in a roadway. In administration of Federal Aid highway funds, structures 20 ft or less between abutments are classified as culverts. Some states and railroads, however, do consider smaller structures as bridges.

Structural plate pipe culverts as large as 24 ft in diameter have been installed beneath a main line railroad. Steel pipe-arch culverts with a span of over 20 ft have been successfully employed. Steel arch culverts in service range to 30 ft in span.

SCOPE OF APPLICATIONS

Highway, and railway culverts are intended primarily to convey surface water from one side of the road to the other. The surface water may be a stream intersecting the roadway, water accumulated on the right of way, or seepage intercepted by the slopes or side ditches.

These culverts may be classified as cross drains, side road or entrance culverts, and relief culverts (on long grades). Median drains on "dual lane" or divided highways may be classified either as culverts or storm drains. Spillways down cut or embankment slopes may qualify as culvert extensions. Fig. 8-2.

Municipal culverts are generally situated in suburban areas, parks, recreation areas and cemeteries. They may also be used at street and driveway intersections lacking storm sewers and catchbasins. Part circle culverts or arches with low clearance also serve the latter purpose.

Industrial culverts are generally the same as on highways and railways. They find special use where overburden or waste developed from industrial or mining operations must be disposed of in ravines or other waterway areas. Public utility companies can require large culverts for intake or discharge of water where a thermal power plant is located on a stream or lake. See Fig. 8-3.

Flood protection by means of levees usually requires culverts at intersected streams or where storm sewer outfalls discharge. Such culverts are supplied with steel gate structures to protect against backwater from floods and to permit outflow by gravity at other times. They are equipped with corrugated steel diaphragms to counteract seepage.

Fig. 8-2. Extending a culvert down an embankment eliminates erosion and excessive maintenance.

NEW CONSTRUCTION OR REPLACEMENT

Culverts may also be classified as to whether they are new construction on a new alignment or whether they are supplementary, repair, replacement, or relocation.

Supplementary. An existing culvert may be supplemented by an extension because of road widening or erosion troubles. Inadequate capacity is one reason for adding another culvert alongside an existing one. In installing the supplementary culvert, adequate space should be provided so fill around the new culvert can be well tamped. Under suitable conditions, the new culvert can be jacked or tunneled through the fill without disrupting traffic.

Repairs. Repairs to an existing culvert are aimed at perpetuating its service life. Repairs may consist of re-paving the invert, threading a corrugated steel pipe through and grouting the annular space, or using expanding collars and gaskets to seal leaking joints in short-sectional rigid pipe.

For such repairs, corrugated steel pipe reduces the waterway area least of any available methods.

Replacement–Emergencies. Culvert replacement may be routine or emergencies created by floods, washouts, slides, collapsed structures, or other "acts of God" that require prompt replacement and return to service. Corrugated steel structures are particularly adapted to these emergencies. Where an existing bridge or trestle is being replaced with a culvert (large or small, single or multiple) the open trench and fill method can generally be used.

Proper foundation and tamping of the backfill are highly important for any type of culvert structure. Where the pipe is close to existing pile bents and cross bracing, a good job of tamping is mandatory. It is preferable to surround the pipe with pit run gravel or other well-graded material (except cinders or slag) rather than clay.

Smaller structures can be replaced by open-trenching and installing half at a time or by the well-tried jacking method or tunneling.

Salvage. On many construction jobs, corrugated steel pipe is highly suitable because it will withstand considerable rough handling. It can thus be used repeatedly in different locations. Temporary uses on construction projects include culverts on by-pass or run-around detours and on access or construction roads.

On abandoned roads or relocations, for example, corrugated steel pipe frequently can be removed and re-used with only reasonable care needed in removal of the old structure.

Maintenance. One does not put on a pair of shoes and wear them without any attention until they are worn out. Maintenance, especially of preventive character, helps prolong the service life of any culvert and keep it in good working condition.

Good construction of a culvert, as well as properly prepared up-and-downstream areas, will help to keep maintenance at a minimum. Even so, flood damage can result from driftwood or soil erosion. There can be silting, or collection of debris within a culvert and at its ends. Icing in northern climates can reduce the waterway opening. These call for immediate attention by maintenance personnel if the safety of roadway and traffic are to be preserved.

Periodic inspection and proper maintenance will save premature replacement of any type of culvert.

Fig. 8-3. Three structural plate pipes serve to carry lake water to power station.

Section II—CULVERT LOCATION AND LENGTH

PRINCIPLES OF CULVERT LOCATION

By culvert location is meant alignment and grade with respect to both roadway and stream. Proper location is important because it influences adequacy of the opening, maintenance of the culvert, and possible washout of the roadway. Although every culvert installation is a separate problem, the few principles set forth here apply in most cases.

A culvert is an enclosed channel serving as a continuation of and a substitute for an open stream where that stream meets an artificial barrier such as a roadway, embankment, or levee. It is necessary to consider abutting property, both as to ponding upstream and as to safe exit velocities in order to avoid undue scour or silting downstream.

An open stream is not always stable. It may be changing its channel—straightening itself in some places, and becoming more sinuous in others. It may be scouring itself deeper in some places, silting in others. Change of land use upstream by clearing, deforestation or real estate development can change both stability and flood flow of a stream.

Because a culvert is a *fixed* line in a stream, engineering judgment is necessary in properly locating the structure.

ALIGNMENT

The *first* principle of culvert location is to provide the stream with a direct entrance and a direct exit. Any abrupt change in direction at either end will retard the flow and make necessary a larger structure.

A direct inlet and outlet, if not already existing, can be secured in one of three ways—by means of a channel change, a skewed alignment, or both. The cost of a channel change may be partly offset by a saving in culvert length or decrease in size. A skewed alignment requires a greater length of culvert, but is usually justified by improving the hydraulic condition and the safety of the roadbed. See *skew angles*, page 192, and method of specifying same.

The *second* principle of culvert location is to use reasonable precautions to prevent the stream from changing its course near the ends of the culvert. Otherwise the culvert may become inadequate, cause excessive ponding, and possibly wash out,—any one of which can lead to expensive maintenance of the roadway. Steel end sections, riprap, sod, or paving will help protect the banks from eroding and changing the channel.

Culvert alignment may also be influenced by choice of a grade line. Methods of selecting proper alignment are illustrated in Fig. 8-4.

At roadway intersections and private entrances, culverts should be placed in the direct line of the roadway ditch, especially where ditches are required to carry any considerable amount of storm water.

Culverts for drainage of cut-and-fill sections on long descending grades should be placed on a skew of about 45 degrees across the roadway. Thus the flow of water will not be retarded at the inlet.

Broken alignment under a roadway may be advisable on long culverts. Consideration should be given to entrance and exit conditions, and to increasing the size of the structure to handle or to cleaning out debris the stream may carry during flood periods.

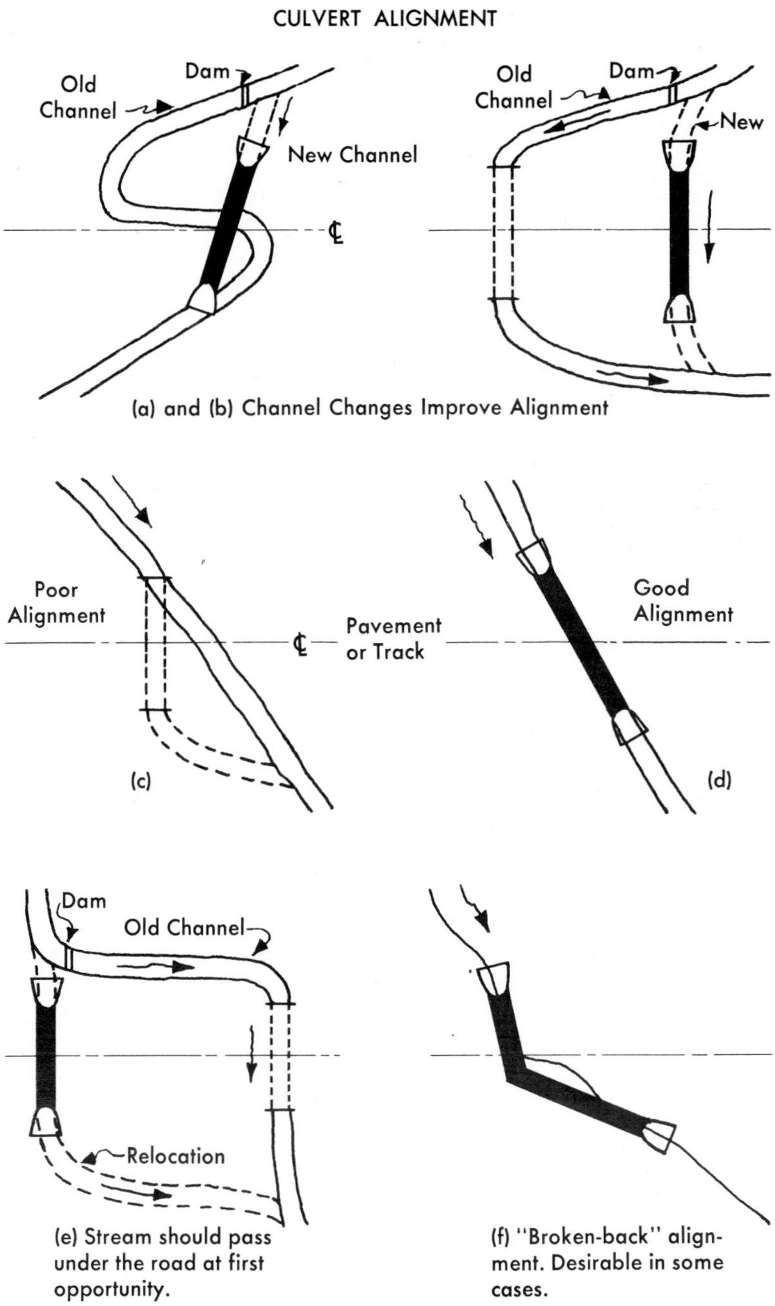
CULVERT ALIGNMENT
Old Channel
Dam
New Channel
℄
Old Channel
Dam
New
(a) and (b) Channel Changes Improve Alignment
Poor Alignment
℄
Pavement or Track
Good Alignment
(c)
(d)
Dam
Old Channel
Relocation
(e) Stream should pass under the road at first opportunity.
(f) "Broken-back" alignment. Desirable in some cases.

Fig. 8-4. Various methods of securing correct culvert alignment.

GRADE

The ideal grade line for a culvert is one that produces neither silting nor excessive velocities and scour, one that gives the shortest length, and one that makes replacement simplest.

Velocities as great as 10 ft per second cause destructive scour downstream and to the culvert structure itself unless protected. Safe streambed velocities are given in Table 4–9, page 100. The silt carrying capacity of a stream varies as the square of the velocity.

Capacity of a culvert with a free outlet (not submerged) is not increased by

CULVERT GRADES

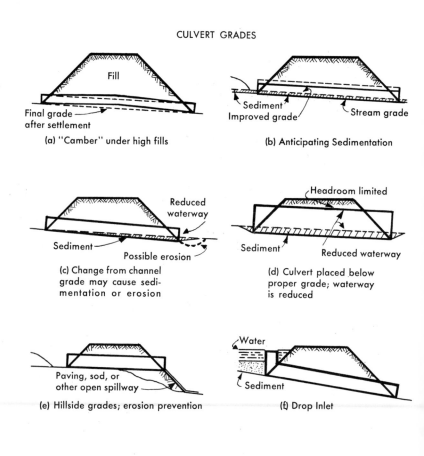

(a) "Camber" under high fills

(b) Anticipating Sedimentation

(c) Change from channel grade may cause sedimentation or erosion

(d) Culvert placed below proper grade; waterway is reduced

(e) Hillside grades; erosion prevention

(f) Drop Inlet

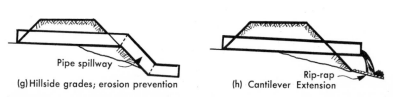

(g) Hillside grades; erosion prevention

(h) Cantilever Extension

Fig. 8-5. Proper culvert grades are essential to safe functioning of the structure.

placing on a slope steeper than its "critical slope." (About 1 per cent for a 96-in. pipe.) The capacity is controlled by the amount of water that can get through the inlet.

On the other hand, the capacity of a pipe on a very slight gradient and with a *submerged* outlet is influenced by the head (difference in elevation of water surface at both ends). In this case, the roughness of the culvert interior, in addition to the velocity head and entrance loss, is a factor.

A slope of 1 to 2 per cent is advisable to give a gradient equal to or greater than the critical slope, provided the velocity falls within permissible limits. In general, a minimum slope of 0.5 ft in 100 ft will avoid sedimentation.

In ordinary practice the grade line coincides with the average streambed above and below the culvert. However, deviation for a good purpose is permissible as follows:

1. In *freshly graded areas*, on relatively flat gradients, expect sedimentation to occur. Set the culvert invert several inches higher than the streambed, but on the same slope (see Fig. 8-5).

2. Where *headroom is limited*, setting a culvert below streambed grade will likely result in sedimentation and reduced waterway area. Either use a low, wide culvert such as a pipe-arch, or raise the road grade.

3. Under *high fills*, anticipate greater settlement of the culvert beneath the center of the fill than at the sides. Give the culvert *camber* by laying the upstream half nearly level and putting all the fall in the downstream half.

4. Under *high fills*, it may not be necessary to place the culvert at streambed level. If some ponding is permissible, the culvert can sometimes be placed in firm ground at a higher level, thus reducing the length.

5. In *steeply sloping areas*, as on hillsides, the culvert need not always be placed on the same steep grade. The culvert can be put on the "critical" slope with a spillway or cutoff wall at the outlet to prevent undermining. This keeps the culvert shorter and under shallower cover.

6. On *steep slopes*, it is also possible to use a broken-back grade line under the fill, although this is less desirable. Or a drop inlet or catch-basin will help give the culvert a suitable slope.

Remember, the ideal grade line avoids silting and also avoids high velocities and scour. (See Chapter 4 *Hydraulics* and Chapter 12 *Erosion Prevention*, including riprap, end sections, ditch checks, spillways and other means of controlling scour.)

CULVERT LENGTH

The required length of a culvert depends on the width of the roadway or roadbed, the height of fill, the slope of the embankment, the slope and skew of the culvert, and the type of end finish such as end section, headwall, beveled end, drop inlet or spillway.

A culvert should be amply long so that its ends do not clog with sediment or become covered with a settling, spreading embankment. Either results in impaired efficiency and increased maintenance. On the other hand, culvert ends should not be wastefully exposed.

A cross-sectional sketch of the embankment and a profile of the streambed will perhaps best determine the length of culvert needed. Lacking such a sketch, the length of a simple culvert under an embankment can be determined as follows:

To the width of the roadway (and shoulders), add twice the slope ratio times the height of fill at the center of the road. The height of fill should be

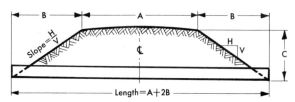

Fig. 8-6. Computation of culvert length when flow line is on a flat grade.

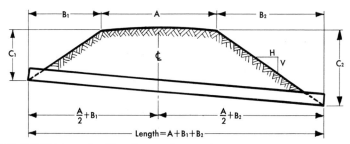

Fig. 8-7. Determining culvert length on a steep grade.

measured to the flow line if headwalls are not to be used, and to the top of the culvert if headwalls or end sections are to be installed.

Example: A roadway is 40 ft wide on top, two to one side slopes, and at the center of the road the height of fill to flow line is 7 ft: 40 + (4 x 7) = 68 ft length at flow line. See example in Fig. 8-6.

If the culvert is on a slope of 5 per cent or more, it may be advisable to compute the sloped length in the manner shown in Fig. 8-7, bottom drawing. However, as fill slopes usually vary from the established grade stakes, any refinement in computing culvert length may not be necessary.

For dual-lane divided highways, the width of the median strip should be added to the lengths of the two individual culverts, unless the roadways are widely spaced with an open channel between.

PIPE LENGTH FOR SKEW ANGLES

Where a culvert crosses the roadway at other than a right angle, the increased bottom center line length should be computed as follows:

First determine the length at right angles to the roadway, as in Fig. 8-6. Then divide by the cosine of the angle between the normal and skewed direction.

Example: Assume a normal length of 62 ft and an angle of 14 degrees skewed from the normal.

$$\text{Skew length} = \frac{62}{.970} = 63.8 \text{ ft (Fig. 8-8)}.$$

The bottom center line length is specified to the nearest 2-ft length.

The ends of the structure may be cut to make them parallel to the center line of the road. For correct fabrication of corrugated steel culverts it is

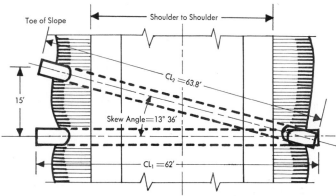

Fig. 8-8. Skew-length computation for example on opposite page.

essential to specify the *direction of flow* as well as the *skew angle* or skew number. (See following paragraph.) This is particularly true not only for pipes and pipe-arches with the invert paved, but also for structural plate pipe, pipe-arches and arches.

SKEW DIAGRAMS

To insure proper shop fabrication, a skew diagram should always be furnished with each order. One method is to state the "skew number" as the azimuth (angle) between the bottom of the circle shown in Fig. 8-9 and the "left end" of the culvert. (The direction of flow is shown by an arrow.)

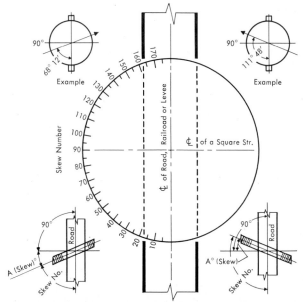

Fig. 8-9. Diagram for method of properly specifying skewed culverts. The direction of flow should also be indicated for fabrication as a left or right.

Table 8-1 Part Circle Corrugated Steel Culverts—Minimum Gages, Weights, Dimensions[1]

Gage	Weight Per Foot, in Pounds																															
12	5.4	5.7	6.0	6.4	6.7	7.1	7.4	8.1	8.5	9.2	9.9	10.7	10.8	11.3	11.6	11.9	12.5	12.7	13.4	13.8	14.2	14.5	14.9	15.4	16.2	17.0	18.9	19.9	21.3	21.9	22.6	25.4
10	6.9	7.2	7.6	8.1	8.5	9.1	9.5	10.3	10.8	11.8	12.7	13.6	13.8	14.4	14.8	15.2	16.0	16.2	17.1	17.6	18.1	18.4	19.0	19.6	20.7	21.6	24.2	25.3	27.2	27.9	28.8	32.4
8	8.4	8.8	9.2	9.9	10.3	11.0	11.6	12.5	13.2	14.3	15.4	16.5	16.8	17.5	18.0	18.5	19.4	19.7	20.8	21.4	22.0	22.4	23.1	23.9	25.2	26.3	29.4	30.8	33.1	34.0	35.1	39.5
Base in In.	Rise, in Inches																															
12	2	2¾	3½	4⅛	4⅝	5⅛	5⅝																									
14	...	...	...	2¼	3¼	4⅛	4¾	5¾	6¼	7																						
16			...	...	...	...	3⅛	4¾	5⅜	6½	7⅜								12 Ga. Min.													
18				...	...	...	...	2½	3¾	5½	6⅝	7½	7¾	8¼	8¾																	
20						...	...	...	...	2⅝	5½	6¾	7	7⅝	8	8⅜	9⅛	9⅜														
22							...	...	...	...	3¼	5⅜	5⅞	6⅝	7⅛	7⅝	8⅜	8¾	9½	10	10½	10¾										
24									...	...	...	...	3⅝	5	5¾	6⅜	7⅜	7¾	8¾	9¼	9¾	10⅛	10⅝	11¼								
26											...	...	...	...	3¼	4¼	6	6½	7⅝	8¼	9	9¼	9⅞	10½	11⅝	12⅜						
28												...	...	...	...	...	3½	4¼	6⅛	7	7⅞	8¼	9	9⅝	10⅞	11¾				10 Ga. Min.		
30														...	...	...	...	...	3⅝	5	6¼	6⅞	7¾	8½	10	11	13½	14⅝				
32															...	...	...	...	...	8 Ga. Min.		4½	5⅞	7⅛	8⅞	10	12¾	13⅞				
34																	...	...	...			...	...	5	7½	8¾	11⅞	13⅛	15	15¼		
36																			...	...	...	...	...	...	5	7⅛	10⅞	12¼	14⅜	15⅜	16⅝	
42																				...	...	...	...	...	...	...	5⅝	8½	11¼	12¼	13¼	17⅝
48																					...	...	...	...	...	...	...	...	...	6⅝	9⅝	14½

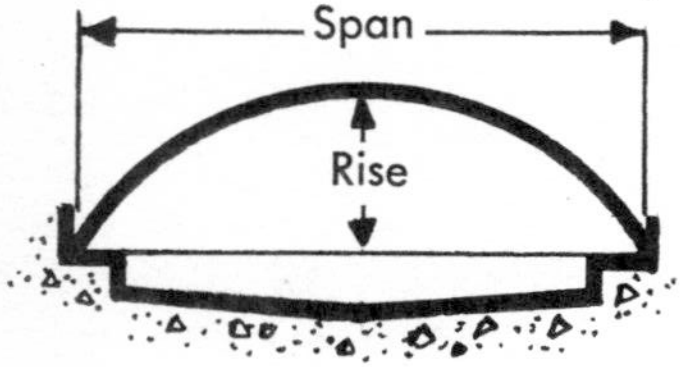

Note: Minimum gages shown on chart are for traffic conditions. 12 gage corrugated may be used under sidewalk areas for all sizes.

PART CIRCLE CULVERTS

Storm water in larger towns and cities is controlled mostly by curbs and gutters, from which the water discharges into storm sewers. In the smaller towns and boroughs and in outlying districts of larger cities, street water is carried away in surface ditches and may not be connected to a sewer system.

A popular and economical solution to the problem, where excessive water is not a factor, consists of corrugated steel part circle culverts built within the depression and covered with pavement. Part circle edges rest on small steel angles set in a concrete or masonry base, or on a corrugated or flat metal base. The intake and outlet may be in the gutter, or the construction may be such that it does not restrict the width of the street.

With as little as 2 in. of cover over them, they develop strength sufficient to withstand traffic loads and impact quite well. With rigid type pavement, a thickness of 3 or 4 in. will minimize pavement cracking.

PART CIRCLE CULVERT SIZES

Part circles are made up in standard lengths of 25½ in., which, when lapped, make a length of 2 ft even. Lengths are not bolted; the pavement holds them in place. See Table 8-1 for sizes.

SPECIAL CULVERT PROBLEMS

Many other uses or variations of culverts exist beyond the ordinary across-the-road structure. Although mentioned or illustrated elsewhere in the text, in summary:

Equalizer culverts

Levee culverts and diaphragms

Outlet spillways for small farm pond dams

Intakes and outlets for public utility power stations

Paved fords

Side road culverts and private entrances

Siphons (inverted) conduct irrigation water beneath a road

Median drains

Spillways

Fig. 8-10. Culvert crossing under roadbed on a skew is properly protected with a half headwall.

Section III—END FINISH

PURPOSES

Wide differences of engineering opinion exist on need for end finish of pipe culverts and about the design and materials to use for that purpose. End treatment may vary from simple riprap to elaborate retaining walls and energy dissipators.

Among the principal needs for end finishes are: (1) to prevent scour at the inlet end and undermining at the outlet, (2) to increase hydraulic efficiency, (3) to prevent seepage and burrowing of rodents, (4) to retain the fill, (5) anchorage for pipe, and (6) appearance.

1. *Preventing Scour and Undermining.* At the inlet end it may be necessary to protect the embankment against scour and eddying or vortex action. If the culvert is designed to *avoid ponding* above the crown, erosion can be controlled more easily and presumably at less cost. Treatment may consist of a headwall or a flared steel end section, either of which can be supplemented by paving, riprap or sod situated well above the channel level.

   The *outlet* end may require a velocity control in the form of an endwall, pipe spillway, flume or apron for discharging the water into a stilling basin or to retard its velocity so that it does not undermine the culvert or embankment. The use of a cutoff wall at the outlet will give added protection against undermining.

2. *Increasing Hydraulic Efficiency.* Several highway organizations (see Chapt. 4) have published considerable research on methods of improving inlet flow conditions with a view toward increasing carrying capacity. Flared or warped headwalls were found to increase the capacity of a corrugated metal culvert from 1 to 10 per cent over that with a straight end wall. The same sources report that a headwall increases the efficiency over no headwall.

Fig. 8-11. Cost of headwalls or other end finish is properly a part of the total cost. Maintenance and ease of culvert extension are also factors.

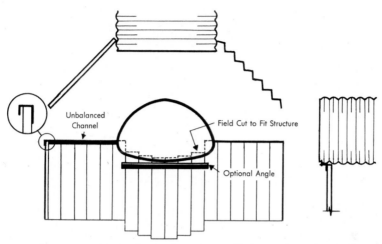

Fig. 8-12. How a steel sheeting headwall can be provided on a pipe-arch culvert.

3. *Preventing Seepage and Burrowing.* Porous, granular fills around a culvert may encourage seepage unless sealed at the upstream end by clay or other impervious material. A small headwall or curtain wall also helps prevent seepage.

   Where rodents burrow along the barrel of a culvert, dangers of wash-out can be reduced by the use of diaphragms at intermediate points along the barrel. See Fig. 7-9.

4 *Retaining the Fill.* Ordinarily, lengthening a culvert is more economical than building a big headwall, endwall or retaining wall. Instances do exist, however, where it is impossible to procure sufficient right of way or where physical conditions make it inadvisable to extend the culvert to the toe of the fill. For these or other cases a retaining type of headwall of steel or concrete may be the most satisfactory answer.

5. *Anchorage for Pipe.* Short-sectional rigid pipe cannot offer positive pro-tection against pulling apart at the joints. Where intermediate joints do pull apart, progressive undermining may occur as well as honeycombing of the fill. Heavy headwalls will tend to prevent such disjointing.

   With any prospect of buoyancy at the square inlet end of corrugated metal structures that project from the fill, corrective measures should be applied. Beveling or step-beveling the pipe ends, or building concrete headwalls is one solution. Such a headwall serves to eliminate pipe pro-jection, furnishes weight to the pipe end and improves the entrance con-dition.

6. *Appearance.* Along mowed roadsides, if the ends of the culvert are visible, a simple unobtrusive end finish adds to the general attractiveness of the roadway. While this consideration is of special moment on expressways and parkways, it also is generally true of state highways, principal county roads, and where railroads parallel highways. Where the ends of the cul-vert are not visible, of course, the expense of end treatment is not justified for appearance.

Table 8-2   Dimensions of Galvanized Steel End Sections for Round Pipe

Pipe Diam. in Inches	Gage	Dimensions in Inches					Approximate Slope	Body
		A ± 1	B (max.)	H ± 1	L±1½	W ± 2		
12	16	6	6	6	21	24	2½	1 Pc.
15	16	7	8	6	26	30	2½	1 Pc.
18	16	8	10	6	31	36	2½	1 Pc.
21	16	9	12	6	36	42	2½	1 Pc.
24	16	10	13	6	41	48	2½	1 Pc.
30	14	12	16	8	51	60	2½	1 Pc.
36	14	14	19	9	60	72	2½	2 Pc.
42	12	16	22	11	69	84	2½	2 Pc.
48	12	18	27	12	78	90	2¼	2 Pc.
54	12	18	30	12	84	102	2	2 Pc.
60	12	18	33	12	87	114	1¾	3 Pc.
66	12	18	36	12	87	120	1½	3 Pc.
72	12	18	39	12	87	126	1⅓	3 Pc.
78	12	18	42	12	87	132	1¼	3 Pc.
84	12	18	45	12	87	138	1⅙	3 Pc.

1. All 3-piece bodies to have 12 gage sides and 10 ga. center panels. Width of center panels to be greater than 20 per cent of the pipe periphery. Multiple panel bodies to have lap seams which are to be tightly joined by ⅜ in. diam. galvanized rivets or bolts.
2. For 60 in. thru 84 in. sizes, reinforced edges to be supplemented with galvanized stiffener angles. The angles will be 2 in. by 2 in. by ¼ in. for 60 in. thru 72 in. diameter and 2½ in. by 2½ in. by ¼ in. for 78 in. and 84 in. diameter. The angles to be attached by ⅜ in. diam. galvanized nuts and bolts. (Notes continued under Table 8-3 on facing page.)

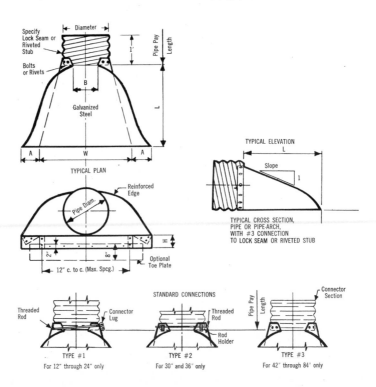

Fig. 8-13. Details of steel end sections and connections for circular steel pipe.[2]

Table 8-3 Dimensions of Galvanized Steel End Sections for Pipe-Arch

Pipe-Arch in Inches		Dimensions in Inches						Approxi-mate	
Span	Rise	Gage	A ± 1	B (max.)	H ± 1	L±1½	W ± 2	Slope	Body
18	11	16	7	9	6	19	30	2½	1 Pc.
22	13	16	7	10	6	23	36	2½	1 Pc.
25	16	16	8	12	6	28	42	2½	1 Pc.
29	18	16	9	14	6	32	48	2½	1 Pc.
36	22	14	10	16	6	39	60	2½	1 Pc.
43	27	14	12	18	8	46	75	2½	1 Pc.
50	31	12	13	21	9	53	85	2½	2 Pc.
58	36	12	18	26	12	63	90	2½	2 Pc.
65	40	12	18	30	12	70	102	2¼	2 Pc.
72	44	12	18	33	12	77	114	2¼	3 Pc.
79	49	12	18	36	12	77	126	2	3 Pc.
85	54	12	18	39	12	77	138	2	3 Pc.

3. For the 79 in. by 49 in. and 85 in. by 54 in. sizes, reinforced edge to be supplemented by 2 in. by 2 in. by ¼ in. galvanized angles.
4. Angle reinforcement will be placed under the center panel seams on the 79 in. by 49 in. and 85 in. by 54 in. sizes.
5. Galvanized toe plate to be available as an accessory, when specified.

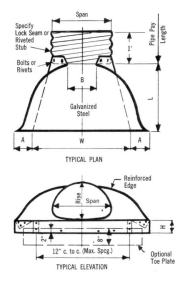

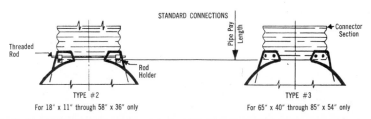

Fig. 8-14. Details of steel end sections and connections for steel pipe-arches.[2]

DESIGN CONSIDERATIONS

Beyond the foregoing reasons for end finish, there are other design considerations. Headwalls should neither be employed to mark the end of a culvert nor as a safety measure to keep a highway vehicle from veering off into a stream. A simple inexpensive marker can serve the first purpose, and a steel guardrail the second.

From a maintenance standpoint, a protruding headwall interferes with power mowing of weeds or grass, and at roadway level, with snow removal. If painted, a headwall calls for continual maintenance to keep it looking neat.

Other design features of end treatment considered desirable include reasonable first cost, ease of removal in case of extensions (salvability) and resistance to damage.

Cost of headwalls or other end finish is properly a part of total culvert cost, and should be so considered in comparative designs. Fig. 8-11. If increased capacity is the goal, the question may properly be asked whether selecting a larger size is less costly than building elaborate control works.

MATERIALS AVAILABLE

Materials commonly used for end treatment on culverts and pipe spillways include concrete, steel, rubble masonry, riprap and vegetation. Several are here described.

Sheeting. One practical form of end protection consists of driving corrugated steel sheeting as a cutoff wall and low height headwall or endwall. It is cut to receive the last section of the culvert barrel, and capped at about mid-diameter with an unbalanced steel channel, as shown in Fig. 8-12. This type of end finish is particularly appropriate for large culverts which may have the ends *beveled* or step beveled. Length of the sheeting below the flow line should be one-half to one diameter of the culvert, with a minimum of 3 ft.

End Sections. Steel end sections are shop fabricated for assembly in the field by attachment to corrugated metal culverts from 12 to 84 in. in diameter

Fig. 8-15. Fitted to the end of this pipe-arch, a steel end section provides an attractive all-steel structure.

Fig. 8-16. A steel end section gives a finished look to a culvert and, in case of extension, can be re-used.

or pipe-arches from 18 by 11 in. to 85 by 54 in. Dimensions and other data are given in Tables 8-2 and 8-3, and in Figs. 8-13 and -14.

These end sections are listed in standard specifications of state highway departments, county road departments, railroads and others. They meet the requirements for efficient and attractive end finish on culverts, conduits, spillways and sewer outfalls. They attach to the culvert ends by simple bolted connections of various designs, and so can be completely salvaged if lengthening or relocation is necessary.

Riprap and Others. The slope at the end of a culvert (mitered or square cut) can be economically protected against erosion by riprap. Stone riprap should preferably be sealed by portland cement grout or asphaltic concrete.

Sand bags filled with a dry sand-cement mixture (1 part cement to 4 parts sand) make a neat and satisfactory end treatment. These can be stacked vertically or sloped to fit the end of the culvert.

Additional references to *culverts:*

Chapter 1—Product Details
Chapter 3—Service Life
Chapter 4—Hydraulics
Chapter 5—Cost Factors
Chapter 6—Couplings and Fittings
Chapter 7—Installation
Chapter 12—Erosion Prevention
Chapter 13—Dam and Levee Drainage

REFERENCES AND BIBLIOGRAPHY

1. *Handbook of Drainage and Construction Products.* Armco Drainage & Metal Products, Inc. Middletown, Ohio, 1955.

2. *End Sections and Culvert End Treatment Designs.* Armco Metal Products Div., Middletown, Ohio Fldr. ES-13165, 8 pp.

Fig. 9-1. Inspecting an 84-in. bituminous-coated steel sewer pipe 33 years after it was installed across a peat bog. Same structure is shown in Fig. 9-2.

Fig. 9-2. The pipe was in good structural and material condition.

DEFINITIONS

Sewer. A pipe or conduit, generally closed, for carrying sewage and other waste liquids but normally not flowing full.
Sewage. Largely the water supply of a community after it has been fouled by various uses. From the standpoint of source, it may combine the liquid or water-carried wastes from residences, business buildings, and institutions, together with those from industrial firms and with such ground water, surface water, and storm water as may be present.

—From "Glossary—Water and Sewage Control Engineering," APHA, ASCE, AWWA and FSIWA

SEWER SERVICE CONDITIONS

Sewers may be classified as separate or combined, depending on whether storm water and sanitary sewage are carried in the same conduit or separately.

A *storm sewer* carries storm and surface water and street wash, exclusive of domestic and industrial wastes. Such water is little if any more corrosive than rural watershed runoff. Erosion by the hydraulic traffic may be a factor.

A *sanitary sewer* is designed to carry domestic sewage and the discharge from commercial and light industrial plants. Fresh sanitary sewage is usually neutral or slightly alkaline and usually well-diluted.[1] Hence, corrosion will be minimal in any well designed and normally maintained sanitary sewer system if the velocity of flow is sufficient to carry the sewage to its point of disposal before putrefaction processes begin.

Putrescible organic material may accumulate in older sewers where flow is sluggish or stagnant due to incorrect design or because of low points created by settlement in grade. Sufficiently high temperature and concentration of sewage, in the presence of an atmosphere deficient in free oxygen, encourages growth of anerobic bacteria; "sewer gases" will be released as a consequence. If bacterial action takes place in the presence of high sulphate waters, hydrogen sulphide gas (H_2S) evolves.

Hydrogen sulphide gas, in sufficient quantities, can be fatal to humans. It readily combines with moisture and oxygen in the atmosphere of the sewer to form dilute sulphurous or sulphuric acid, both of which are quite corrosive. Corrosive attack of this nature will occur above the water line of the sewer. The most effective measure, in preventing onset of such corrosion, is design of sanitary sewers with velocities adequate to avoid deposits of any solids.

Combined sewers, common in many communities, have the special advantage of dilution and flushing by occasional storm waters. Some sanitary sewers are designed for periodic flushings.

Industrial wastes may be handled in sanitary or combined sewers; in some cases sewers are built especially to cope with highly corrosive wastes. While hydrogen-ion concentration (*pH*) determinations of domestic sanitary sewage have little significance, they prove helpful in studying the corrosive nature of tannery, pickling, plating, refinery or other industrial wastes.[1] Many governmental agencies have in recent years adopted ordinances calling for regulation of minimum and maximum *pH* of industrial wastes to prevent damage to sewer installations. Control of the *pH* values is also important to the efficient operation of sewage treatment plants.

Sewers are subject to the same structural forces, loading conditions, and

Fig. 9-3. Installing a twin 85 x 53-in. helically corrugated steel pipe-arch sewer with a total length of 7800 ft.

material or chemical conditions that can cause deterioration of culverts. In addition, they may be subject to attack by the "hydraulic traffic" they carry.

Sewers may be further classified as to overflow, relief, intercepting, main, branch, outfall, and other descriptive terms based on function.

DESIGN OF SEWER SYSTEMS

The detailed surveys and the designing and planning of sewer projects are beyond the scope of this handbook. For a comprehensive summary of engineering practice on this subject, consult *Design and Construction of Sanitary and Storm Sewers*. Extracts from this text on quantity of sanitary sewage, quantity of storm water, and hydraulics of sewers appear in Chapter 4 *Hydraulics* of this handbook. This chapter deals primarily with the general considerations and suitability of steel pipe and other appurtenances for sewer construction. See Fig. 9-3. Other chapters in this handbook refer in detail to such factors as strength, durability, installation and economics of sewer materials.

CORRUGATED STEEL SEWERS

Corrugated steel sewers have long been used for the types of service just described. The strength, flexibility, positive joints, and installation economics of flexible steel sewers are enhanced by the use of special coatings and linings capable of resisting practically all of the destructive service conditions listed earlier. These same linings give corrugated steel sewers the same hydraulic efficiency and flow capacity that is accorded other smooth-bore pipes. See Table of Coefficients, page 134.

Steel sewers not only find substantial use in new construction, but are also adaptable to replacing failing sewers of all kinds. They are employed extensively to reline sewers of all sizes and shapes with a minimum reduction in waterway area.

STORM SEWER INLETS

Various means exist for admitting or diverting storm water into sewers and stream enclosures. Curb or gutter openings, usually located at street intersections, intercept storm water before it reaches pedestrian crossings. Steel gratings or bars prevent entrance of large objects but allow passage of leaves, silt or debris during storms.

For ends of highway bridges and overpasses, for low places in paved ditches or curb-and-gutter sections, various types of inlets are used—generally attached to a pipe spillway.

Large flat expanses—such as railroad yards and single or multiple tracks in long cuts—may require grate inlets at intervals to drain storm water from the surface. These frequently consist of corrugated steel "risers" varying in diameter from 8 to 36 in. Standard grates of cast iron or cast steel are used.

Catchbasins are sometimes inserted into the system to entrap solids. The base may be concrete or a steel plate welded to the bottom. Catchbasins must be cleaned out frequently and therefore involve a maintenance problem. If drainage lines are laid on self-cleaning grades, no need will generally exist for catchbasins.

On airports, the structures are generally grate-covered inlets, manholes, combination manholes and inlets, occasional catchbasins and lamp holes. Lined ditches and pipe spillways are also employed.

STANDARD AND SPECIAL FITTINGS

Standard fittings such as tees, saddle branches, wyes, elbows and reducers are available for all types of corrugated steel sewers. See Chapter 6 *Couplings and Fittings*.

Special fittings with various outlets and connections can readily be shop-fabricated from corrugated steel.[3]

Saddle branches for house connections to sanitary sewers, or junctions with inlets or other sewers, may be welded-assembled at the plant or may be prefabricated and attached at the job site.

MANHOLES

Manholes serve primarily to give access to the sewer from the street, for cleaning or inspection. They are usually installed at street intersections, at changes in alignment or grade, and at intermediate points of 300 to 500 ft.

Fig. 9-4A, B. Two different types of prefabricated steel manholes with transition and lateral connections.

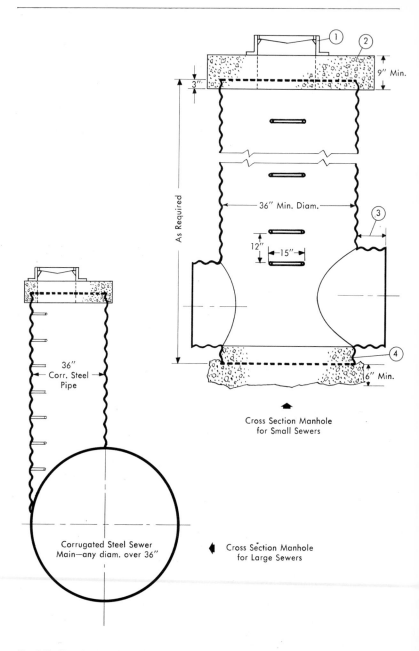

9″ Min.

3″

As Required

36″ Min. Diam.

12″

15″

36″
Corr. Steel
Pipe

6″ Min.

Cross Section Manhole
for Small Sewers

Corrugated Steel Sewer
Main—any diam. over 36″

Cross Section Manhole
for Large Sewers

Fig. 9-5. Two designs for corrugated steel manholes.

Manholes (or junction chambers) may be round or rectangular. They are commonly constructed of corrugated steel, brick, concrete block or reinforced concrete. Steel manholes are usually prefabricated and can be quickly set in place by means of any lifting equipment. Fig. 9-4A, 9-4B.

Inside diameters range from 3 to 5 ft but may be varied to suit conditions. Suggested designs are shown in the accompanying photographs and drawings. The riser may be welded to a section of the main line sewer, as in Fig. 9-5.

If the sewer is carried through the manhole, this is done with a half circle pipe. A floor at the springing line serves as a platform for workmen.

SEWER JOINTS

Various types of joints and couplings are described in Chapter 6 *Couplings and Fittings*. The amount of infiltration or exfiltration is determined by the type of coupling chosen and the care taken in installation. With silty or fine sandy soils, it may be more important to prevent surrounding soil from being sucked into the sewer and creating voids and cave-ins than to restrain water from escaping from the sewer. Lock-seam (helical) corrugated steel pipe or welded seam pipe is effective in reducing infiltration and exfiltration to a practical minimum.

A typical standard of permissible infiltration is 150 gallons per in. of diameter per mile per day. Local specifications may deviate from this figure.

SEWER OUTFALLS

Storm sewers and outlets from sewage treatment plants generally discharge into streams, lakes or bays. If the line extends across swampy, unstable soils or is subject to the direct impact of flooded streams, special anchorage or support is necessary to avoid lateral movement or disastrous settlement of the outfall. An aerial sewer on pile bents is a possible solution. Fig. 9-6.

Fig. 9-6. Aerial sewer of corrugated steel pipe has ample strength.

Fig. 9-7. Installing 6500 ft of 84-in. spun-lined corrugated steel pipe as subaqueous outfall sewer into Raritan Bay along New Jersey seacoast.

Steel sheeting, retards or other devices will protect against floating debris, drifting beach sands and ice. Heavy monolithic headwall structures, if used, are expensive and must be designed to resist undermining or settlement.

Subaqueous outfalls may have to be tied down or weighted with heavy concrete blocks to prevent movement. Fig. 9-7. Sewers passing through wet, unstable soils can sometimes be stabilized by subdrain pipe placed below or beside the sewer to lower the ground water level. If there is a choice of backfill material available, granular is preferred.

SEWAGE TREATMENT PLANTS

The modern sewage treatment plant requires several thousand feet of sewer pipe as well as many control gates. Asbestos-protected corrugated steel pipe is extensively used. Welded steel pipe is generally chosen for force mains or pressure sewers. Modern fabrication methods for corrugated steel sewer pipe include spot welding of seams and helical lock-seam construction, with improved resistance to exfiltration.

Oxidation of sewage is generally obtained during effluent passage from primary treatment through a trickling filter bed. Such filters consist of a bed of broken stone, slag or other coarse material 3 to 10 ft deep, and from 40 to 60 ft and larger in diameter, partly buried. Both riveted corrugated steel sheets and (since 1936) corrugated structural steel plates have been used satisfactorily in building such filters. See Fig. 9-8.

Some subsurface filtration processes employ perforated corrugated steel pipe.

Where no public sewerage system and treatment plant exists, as for some industries, golf courses, institutions, motels and shopping centers, it is possible to purchase small "packaged" sewage treatment plants.

SEPTIC TANKS

For isolated dwellings beyond corporation limits, the septic tank is still considered "an efficient, economical and wholly satisfactory method of sewage disposal."[4] Septic tanks of steel sheet have been used for decades and found satisfactory and economical. The service life of steel septic tanks is prolonged by asbestos protection.

House connections of bituminous-coated corrugated steel pipe are successful and economical. For the drain field assembly, perforated corrugated metal pipe may be used.

SEWAGE LAGOONS

The sewage lagoon or pond is a comparatively new and economical way for some small communities to treat limited amounts of sewage. No chemicals, no machinery and practically no maintenance is required. Instead, the natural biological processes are permitted to stabilize human and industrial wastes. With an upper limit of 400 people per acre, this treatment method requires inexpensive, relatively flat and isolated land. Lagoons can be built for 40 to 60 per cent less than conventional plants, making them well suited for small communities.

Sewage lagoons have only two major maintenance requirements. First, to prevent mosquito propagation, grass and weeds should be cut around interior banks; alternatively, larvae-eating fish may be planted in the lagoon. Secondly, lagoon dikes should be protected against damage by erosion or by rodents undermining the banks. Steel sheeting will prevent rodent damage to dikes. Corrugated steel manhole units equipped with water control gates make efficient water level control structures for lagoons.

WATER CONTROL GATES

Sewage pumping and treatment plants require control and transfer of sewage in its various stages of treatment. This may be in channels and bypasses or between reservoirs, wet wells, tanks, beds, chambers and various other structures.

Fig. 9-8. Corrugated steel sheets are used in building tanks for holding aggregates for trickling filters at sewage disposal plants. Cost here was 70 per cent of alternate designs.

Gates control the flow of sewage by gravity. These gates may be of the slide type or the flap type which open and close by means of the pressure or back pressure of the water. Flush bottom-closure is a desirable feature for complete drainage.

SEWER MAINTENANCE AND REPAIRS

Sanitary sewers are a relatively modern development. Many were first built around the beginning of the Twentieth Century, as were also storm sewers. These have deteriorated to such an extent that repairs or replacements are the problem of many communities. Regular inspections will detect incipient troubles and enable preventive repair. Where sewers are large and safe enough to walk through, first-hand observations can be made. Photographic surveys can now be made with closed-circuit TV cameras. These last reveal on-the-spot condition of sewers of almost any size from the smallest to the largest.

Here are ways to renew failing or inadequate sewers:

1. *Cleaning.* This is a temporary and continual job, particularly if cracks or broken and open joints continue to admit surrounding fill.

2. *Repairs at Joints.* Caulking or grouting of joints is of questionable value. Effective use has been made of corrugated internal expanding bands and gaskets to prevent infiltration.

3. *Half-Soling.* Where the invert has worn through but the remainder of the structure continues in good condition, it may be possible to "half-sole" the invert by using curved sheets or plates with a bituminous pavement topping.

4. *Top Repairs.* Large arch and pipe sewers can be repaired by attaching

Fig. 9-9. Full spun lining in sewer being installed on a large military base.

base channels at the sides and then relining with a corrugated steel arch, filling the space between the two structures by pumping in weak cement grout.

5. *Threading.* Where the cross-sectional area is not greatly reduced by failures in the sewer structure, lengths of corrugated steel pipe can be pulled into the distressed section. Successive lengths are joined with internal expanding or external contracting bands.

6. *Tunneling.* Where the existing sewer is inadequate, it may be possible to enlarge or replace it by tunneling with corrugated steel liner plates. Such a tunnel can either serve as a conduit or as the finished sewer. A pavement or full lining may be added.

Sewers can be renewed almost perpetually by these means.

Additional references:
  Chapter 2—Strength
  Chapter 3—Service Life
  Chapter 4—Hydraulics
  Chapter 5—Cost Factors
  Chapter 6—Couplings & Fittings
  Chapter 7—Installation

REFERENCES AND BIBLIOGRAPHY

1. Hardenbergh, W. A., and Rodie, E., *Water Supply and Waste Disposal*, International Textbook Co., Scranton, Pa., 1963.
2. Water Pollution Control Federation, New York, N. Y.; *Design and Construction of Sanitary and Storm Sewers*, Manual of Engineering Practice No. 9, 1960.
3. *Sewer Structures*, Metal Products Div., Armco Steel Corp., Middletown, Ohio. Catalog CSS-7465, 1965, 44 pp.
4. University of Illinois, *An Investigation of the Performance of Small Septic Tanks*, Eng. Experiment Sta. Bull. Series 409, Feb. 1953.

Fig. 10-1. Soil moisture and unstable soils are a challenge to the soils engineer.

CHAPTER 10

Subdrainage

Section I—SOIL PLUS GROUND WATER

Subdrainage is the control of ground water—in contrast to surface water or storm drainage.

Subdrainage is a practical, economical way of maintaining firm, stable subgrades and foundations; eliminating wet cuts and frost heaving; preventing sloughing of fill and cut slopes; keeping recreational areas dry; reducing saturation of backfill behind retaining walls; and doing many other important jobs. Fig. 10-1.

The engineer relies on soils as an engineering material of construction in such works as foundations, backfills, embankments, cut sections and channels. He therefore is interested in some of the basic characteristics of soils, the presence of ground water, and whether subdrainage is practical for the soils on or available for his jobs.

With a little study and experience, many soil and ground water problems can be recognized and resolved. For the more difficult cases, the soils engineer and laboratory are indispensable.

SOIL CLASSIFICATION

Soils are generally classified in three groups according to grain size—sands-gravels, silts and clays. (See Table 10-1.)

Soils are generally a mixture of these three groups, with descriptions such as sandy loam, silty clay loam, etc., as classified in Table 10-2.

Table 10-1   Grain Size of Soil Constituents

Classification	Diameter of Particles in Millimeters	U. S. Standard Sieve	
		Passing	Retained on
Gravel	Larger than 2.0		No. 10
Coarse sand	2.0 to 0.42	No. 10	No. 40
Fine sand	0.42 to 0.05	No. 40	No. 270
Silt-size	0.05 to 0.005		
Clay-size	Smaller than 0.005	Cannot be separated by sieving. Size is determined by settling velocity in a soil-water suspension.	
Colloidal size	Smaller than 0.001		

Table 10-2   Textural Classification of Soils

Textural Class	Composition in Per Cent		
	Sand	Silt-size	Clay-size
Sand	80–100	0–20	0–20
Sandy Loam	50–80	0–50	0–20
Loam	30–50	30–50	0–20
Silt Loam	0–50	50–100	0–20
Sandy Clay Loam	50–80	0–30	20–30
Clay Loam	20–50	20–50	20–30
Silty Clay Loam	0–30	50–80	20–30
Sandy Clay	55–70	0–15	30–45
Silty Clay	0–15	55–70	30–45
Clay	0–55	0–55	30–100

Fig. 10-2. Standing water contributes to soft foundations. Practical drainage helps to reduce maintenance and early replacement problems.

Various governmental agencies have their own classifications or typical names for soils which differ somewhat from the preceding. The U. S. Bureau of Public Roads has seven general classifications (Table 10-3) with the granular materials rating as "excellent to good for subgrade" and silty-clay materials as "fair to poor."

The Corps of Engineers has five major classifications (Table 10-4) and rates the various named soils according to value for embankments, compaction characteristics, dry weight, value for foundations, and requirements for seepage control. Gravelly and sandy soils rate from "very stable" to "fairly stable" for embankments, "good" for foundations, and because of permeability require either a cutoff, and/or "upstream blanket and toe drainage or wells." The silty and clay soils fall at the "poor" end of the scale for embankments, compaction and foundations. However, they do not need seepage control.

SOIL MOISTURE

Soil moisture is of three kinds: gravitational, capillary and hygroscopic. Gravitational or "free" water moves under the influence of gravity; it is the only kind that can be removed by drainage. Capillary moisture is not affected by gravity, but the removal of free water and lowering of the water table practically eliminates capillary action. Capillarity frequently results in *frost heaving* or the formation and feeding of ice lenses in some silty-clay soils. Hygroscopic moisture is of little or no practical concern.

(*Continued on page 218*)

Table 10-3 Classification of Highway Subgrade Materials

U. S. Bureau of Public Roads with 1945 Highway Research Board Modification

General Classification	Granular Materials (35 Per Cent or Less Passing No. 200)							Silt-Clay Materials (More Than 35 Per Cent Passing No. 200)			
Group Classification	A-1-a	A-1-b	A-3	A-2-4	A-2-5	A-2-6	A-2-7	A-4	A-5	A-6	A-7 (A-7-5, A-7-6)
Sieve analysis per cent passing:											
No. 10	50 max										
No. 40	30 max	50 max	51 min								
No. 200	15 max	25 max	10 max	35 max	35 max	35 max	35 max	36 min	36 min	36 min	36 min
Characteristics of fraction passing No. 40:											
Liquid limit				40 max	41 min	40 max	41 min	40 max	41 min	40 max	41 min
Plasticity index	6 max		Nonplastic	10 max	10 max	11 min	11 min	10 max	10 max	11 min	11 min
Group index	0		0	0		4 max		8 max	12 max	16 max	20 max
Usual types of significant constituent materials	Stone fragments—gravel and sand		Fine sand	Silty or clayey gravel and sand				Silty soils		Clayey soils	
General rating as subgrade	Excellent to good							Fair to poor			

Classification procedure: With required test data in mind, proceed from left to right in chart; correct group will be found by process of elimination. The first group from the left consistent with the test data is the correct classification. The A-7 group is subdivided into A-7-5 or A-7-6 depending on the plastic limit. For $P_w < 30$, the classification is A-7-6; for $P_w \geqq 30$, A-7-5.

Table 10-4   Soil Characteristics Pertinent to Embankments and Foundations (Corps of Engineers)

Coarse Grained Soils

Major Divisions (2)	Name (3)	Value for Embankments (4)	Compaction Characteristics (5)	Std AASHO Max Unit Dry Weight Lb Per Cu Ft (6)	Value for Foundations (7)	Requirements for Seepage Control (8)
Gravel and gravelly soils	Well-graded gravels or gravel-sand mixtures, little or no fines	Very stable, pervious shells of dikes and dams	Good, tractor, rubber-tired, steel-wheeled roller	125–135	Good bearing value	Positive cutoff
	Poorly-graded gravels or gravel-sand mixtures, little or no fines	Reasonably stable, pervious shells of dikes and dams	Good, tractor, rubber-tired, steel-wheeled roller	115–125	Good bearing value	Positive cutoff
	Silty gravels, gravel-sand-silt mixtures	Reasonably stable, not particularly suited to shells, but may be used for impervious cores or blankets	Good, with close control, rubber-tired, sheepsfoot roller	120–135	Good bearing value	Toe trench to none
	Clayey gravels, gravel-sand-clay mixtures	Fairly stable, may be used for impervious core	Fair, rubber-tired, sheepsfoot roller	115–130	Good bearing value	None
Sand and sandy soils	Well-graded sands or gravelly sands, little or no fines	Very stable, pervious sections, slope protection required	Good, tractor	110–130	Good bearing value	Upstream blanket and toe drainage or wells
	Poorly-graded sands or gravelly sands, little or no fines	Reasonably stable, may be used in dike section with flat slopes	Good, tractor	100–120	Good to poor bearing value depending on density	Upstream blanket and toe drainage or wells
	Silty sands, sand-silt mixtures	Fairly stable, not particularly suited to shells, but may be used for impervious cores or dikes	Good, with close control, rubber-tired, sheepsfoot roller	110–125	Good to poor bearing value depending on density	Upstream blanket and toe drainage or wells
	Clayey sands, sand-silt-clay mixtures	Fairly stable, use for impervious core for flood control structures	Fair, sheepsfoot roller, rubber-tired	105–125	Good to poor bearing value	None

Major Divisions (2)	Name (3)	Value for Embankments (4)	Compaction Characteristics (5)	Std AASHO Max Unit Dry Weight Lb Per Cu Ft (6)	Value for Foundations (7)	Requirements for Seepage Control (8)
Silts and clays LL < 50	Inorganic silts and very fine sands, rock flour, silty or clayey fine sands or clayey silts with slight plasticity	Poor stability, may be used for embankments with proper control	Good to poor, close control essential, rubber-tired, roller, sheepsfoot roller	95–120	Very poor, susceptible to liquefaction	Toe trench to none
	Inorganic clays of low to medium plasticity, gravelly clays, sandy clays, silty clays, lean clays	Stable, impervious cores and blankets	Fair to good, sheepsfoot roller, rubber-tired	95–120	Good to poor bearing	None
	Organic silts and organic silt-clays of low plasticity	Not suitable for embankments	Fair to poor, sheepsfoot roller	80–100	Fair to poor bearing, may have excessive settlements	None
Silts and clays LL > 50	Inorganic silts, micaceous or diatomaceous fine sandy or silty soils, elastic silts	Poor stability, core of hydraulic fill dam, not desirable in rolled fill construction	Poor to very poor, sheepsfoot roller	70–95	Poor bearing	None
	Inorganic clays of high plasticity, fat clays	Fair stability with flat slopes, thin cores, blankets and dike sections	Fair to poor, sheepsfoot roller	75–105	Fair to poor bearing	None
	Organic clays of medium to high plasticity, organic silts	Not suitable for embankments	Poor to very poor, sheepsfoot roller	65–100	Very poor bearing	None
Highly organic soils	Peat and other highly organic soils	Not used for construction	Compaction not practical		Remove from foundations	

Notes:
  1. Values in columns 4 and 7 are for guidance only. Design should be based on test results.
  2. In column 5, the equipment listed will usually produce the desired densities with a reasonable number of passes when moisture conditions and thickness of lift are properly controlled.
  3. Column 6, unit dry weights are for compacted soil at optimum moisture content for Standard AASHO (Standard Proctor) compactive effort.

(Continued from page 214)

FREE WATER

Ground water may consist of an underground reservoir (perched) or it may be flowing through a thick seam of pervious material like an underground river, i. e., a well field. Likewise, it may be seeping or percolating through a thin seam between impervious strata, or be concentrated in the form of a spring.

Free water enters or leaves a subgrade by gravity. It may consist of storm water seeping through cracks in the pavement or along the edges. Or it may be ground water percolating from a higher water-bearing stratum, as in a cut or sidehill excavation. (See Section II, Subdrainage Problems.)

Especially noticeable in springtime, this seepage is also visible shortly after rains when the remainder of the road has dried off. Passing traffic also serves to "pump" some of this water plus subgrade soil up through the cracks or joints onto the road surface. Fig. 10-2.

This water is harmful not only because it lowers the bearing power and stability of the subgrade, but because it may freeze on the surface and become an unexpected traffic hazard. It can and should be removed to establish a stable subgrade and prevent possible trouble.

Free water then is not only of greatest importance, but also fortunately is most susceptible to control by subdrainage.

TESTS FOR SOIL AND WATER TABLE

A simple soil auger can be used to locate the free-water table, direction of flow and obtain soil samples down to the impervious stratum. Fig. 10-3. Such tests should generally be made in spring or whenever ground water conditions are at their worst.

Making observations in advance of construction, during construction and afterwards is recommended for getting additional first-hand information. This also helps to make the work of the soils engineer and laboratory more effective.

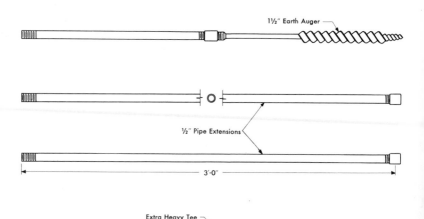

Fig. 10-3. A simple soil auger may be adequate for a soil survey.

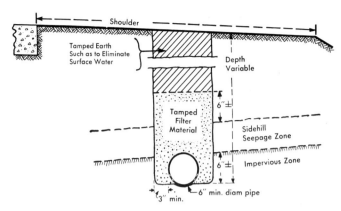

Fig. 10-4. An intercepting drain placed in the impervious zone is effective for keeping free water out of the roadway and subgrade.

SUBSURFACE RUNOFF COMPUTATION

The amount of subsurface runoff in general equals that which soaks into the ground from surface applications, less that lost by evaporation or used by plants. The nature of the terrain, its size, shape and slopes, as well as the character and slopes of the substrata are contributing factors.

A practical way to determine flow is to dig a trench or test pit. This is especially helpful where an *intercepting* drain (Fig. 10-4) is to be placed across a seepage zone to divert the flow.

Table 10-5 Constants for Subsurface Runoff for Various Soil Permeability Types

Depths of Water Removed in 24 Hours

Soil Permeability Type	Depth in Inches		Quantity of Water Per Lateral (cubic feet per second per acre)
	Fraction	Decimal	Constant C
Slow to Moderate	1/16	0.0625	0.0026
Slow to Moderate	1/8	0.1250	0.0052
Slow to Moderate	3/16	0.1875	0.0079
Slow to Moderate	1/4	0.2500	0.0105
Moderate	5/16	0.3125	0.0131
Moderate	3/8	0.3750	0.0157
Moderate	7/16	0.4375	0.0184
Moderate	1/2	0.5000	0.0210
Moderate	9/16	0.5625	0.0236
Moderate to Fast	5/8	0.6250	0.0262
Moderate to Fast	11/16	0.6875	0.0289
Moderate to Fast	3/4	0.7500	0.0315
Moderate to Fast	13/16	0.8125	0.0341
Moderate to Fast	7/8	0.8750	0.0367
Moderate to Fast	15/16	0.9375	0.0394
Moderate to Fast	1	1.0000	0.0420

Determining correct size for subdrainage pipe requires an indirect approach. First, the problem should be studied as set forth in Section II of this chapter —according to highway, railway or other application. For problems other than those involving large flat areas, size determination becomes almost a matter of personal judgment or local experience. The following procedure applies mostly to flat areas.

Example: Rate of runoff for average agricultural soils has been determined by agricultural engineering experiment stations as about ⅜ in. in 24 hours. For areas of heavy rainfall or more pervious soils, this factor may be increased to ¾ or 1 in. Such runoff is converted to cubic feet per second per acre. See conversion table (Table 10-5).[1] The following simple formula is given:

$$Q = CA \qquad\qquad (1)$$

in which Q = discharge or required capacity, in cu ft per sec.

   A = area to be subdrained, in acres

   C = subsurface runoff factor, converted to cu ft per sec. per acre

Assuming a drainage coefficient of ⅜ in. in 24 hrs. (C = .0157) and laterals 600 ft long, spaced on 50-ft centers, the following result is obtained:

$$Q = .0157 \times \frac{600 \times 50}{43,560} = .0108 \text{ cu ft per sec.}$$

SIZE OF PIPE

The size of pipe can be determined by the use of the Manning Formula, or by the use of a nomograph.[1] For normal subdrainage, approximately 500 ft of 6-in. perforated steel pipe may be used before increasing to the next size.

Where possible, a minimum slope of 0.15 ft per 100 ft should be used for subdrainage lines. It is sometimes permissible to use an even flatter slope where necessary to obtain a free outlet. A steeper slope helps to provide a self-cleansing velocity.

THE TRENCH

The principal parts of a subdrain are: trench, perforated pipe, backfill, or filter, top seal, and outlet.

Proper location of the trench presumes a knowledge of the depth of the

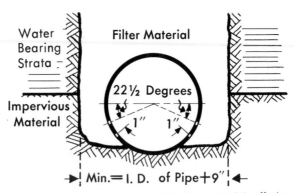

Fig. 10-5. The bottom of a subdrain pipe should be deep enough to effect complete removal of the free water.

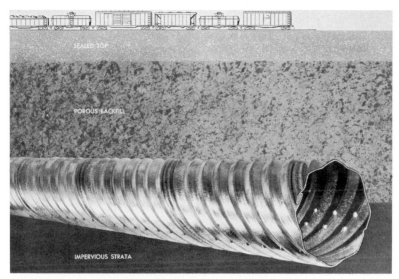

Fig. 10-6. In helically corrugated perforated steel pipe, a blank space in the bottom helps to keep ordinary seepage flow within the pipe.

impervious stratum and the water table, the kind of soil, the source (direction) and the volume of flow, and the depth of frost penetration.

There is no standard depth of trench. It may vary from 2 to 10 ft. It should be about 2 ft below average frost penetration under a bare pavement. The important thing for complete interception is to go deep enough so the pipe can lie in the impervious zone (Fig. 10-5). Width should be 8 to 10 in. more than the pipe diameter.

PERFORATED PIPE

Perforated corrugated steel pipe is used widely to control ground water (Fig. 10-6). Advantages cited are long lengths, light weight, flexibility, strength, simple joints, ample infiltration but with exclusion of many solids.

Diameters range from 6 to 24 in. See Table 10-6.

Table 10-6   Dimensions, Weights, Spacing and Perforations[2,3]

Nominal Perforations		Minimum Width of Unperforated Segment in Inches	Weight per Linear Foot of Pipe Corrugated, Computed			
			Helically Corrugated Pipe Gage Number		Circumferentially Corrugated Pipe Gage Number	
Internal Diameter in Inches	Total Number of Rows		18	16	18	16
6	4	4.5	3.8	4.7	5.0	5.6
8	4	7.0	5.0	6.2	6.3	7.3
10	4	9.0	....	7.6	....	9.0
12	6	9.5	....	9.9	....	10.5
15	6	13.0	....	12.4	....	12.9
18	6	16.5	....	14.8	....	15.3
21	6	20.0	....	17.2	....	17.7
24*	6	....	....	....	....	....

*Interim Fed. Spec. WW-P-00405, Com. PR, 1965.

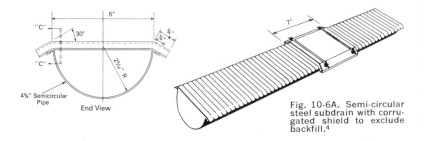

Fig. 10-6A. Semi-circular steel subdrain with corrugated shield to exclude backfill.[4]

BACKFILL MATERIAL: FILTERS

Early subdrains consisted of a trench filled with brush or coarse rock ("french" drains) which quickly silted up. Extensive research by the U. S. Waterways Experiment Station at Vicksburg, Mississippi, shows that a graded material roughly equal to concrete sand (AASHO Specs) has been found most suitable. See Table 10-7 and Fig. 10-7 for a typical analysis. Such material gives better support to the sidewall of the trench and thereby reduces erosion and silting. Filter material should be placed in layers and be tamped.

Tests by the Corps of Engineers showed least clogging occurs with porous or perforated walls rather than through open joints of rigid pipe.[5] Other experiments showed that with the use of finely graded backfill, least clogging occurs when the perforations are in the bottom half of the pipe, at least $22\frac{1}{2}$ degrees below the horizontal axis. A minimum of 16 perforations $\frac{1}{4}$ in.* in diameter, per linear foot of pipe is desirable for all pipe sizes.

Where portions of the line are used as a water conductor rather than interceptor, perforations may be turned up or omitted. Pervious backfill should be eliminated beyond the point where seepage occurs.

---

*AREA Specification 1-4-11 requires $\frac{3}{8}$-in. perforations for railway use.

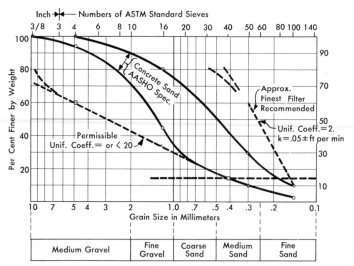

Fig. 10-7. Chart showing range and gradation of granular material for most suitable subdrain backfill. AASHO concrete sand falls within the recommended limits. Maximum size is $\frac{3}{4}$-in. gravel.

Table 10-7 Filter Material Washed Into Test Drains

In Pounds per Foot of Pipe

Types of Pipe	Perforations or Slots			Filter Material Washed in— lb per ft of Pipe
	Size in in.	No. per ft	Loca- tion	
Porous concrete, bevel joints, sec. 2 ft long				0.01
Porous concrete, lap joints, sec. 1 ft long				0.03
Perf. corr. metal pipe, bitu. coated, sec. 10 ft long; split collar couplings, perf. around ⅓ periphery	⅜	40	Down	0.03
	⅜	40	Up	0.2
Perf. concrete pipe, unsealed bell and spigot joints; sec. 2½ ft long, perf. around entire periphery	⅜	24	Down	1.3
	⅜	24	Up	2.3
Perf. clay pipe, unsealed bell and spigot joints; sec. 2 ft long, perf. around en- tire periphery	⅝	30		3.7
Plain concrete pipe, unsealed bell and spigot joints; sec. 3 ft long				7.5
Semi-circular cradle-invert clay pipe, ½ in. open slot on top; unsealed bell and spigot joints; sec. 2 ft long	½		Top	8.4

NOTE: The metal drain pipe was coated with tar which reduced the area of the perforations about 50 per cent.—From U. S. Waterways Experiment Station, Vicksburg, Miss.—Technical Memorandum No. 183-1.[5]

When subdrain pipes with open joints or with perforations turned up are used, it is generally necessary to use two different backfill materials. A coarser filter material (No. 2 in Fig. 10-8) is placed around the pipe to prevent the entrance of fine material into the pipe. Second, the fine filter material must be used to prevent washing of soil fines from the trench walls.

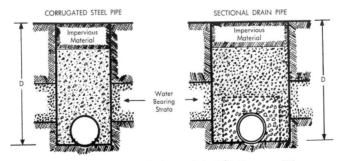

Depth "D" should be varied to suit installation conditions.

Filter Gradation	Percent Passing Std. ASTM Sieve							
	1½	1	⅜	No. 4	No. 8	No. 16	No. 50	No. 100
No. 1	—	—	100	95-100	—	45-80	10-30	0-10
No. 2	100	90-100	25-60	5-40	0-20	—	—	—

Fig. 10-8. Perforated corrugated steel pipe with positively connected joints requires only a single grade of filter material (left). Short sectional pipe with open joints requires two grades of backfill (right) to keep the trench wall fines from clogging the pipe.

FIELD TEST FOR FILTER MATERIAL

A quick field test will determine the suitability of any proposed backfill material.[6] Basically the test measures the time for a standard volume of water to seep through a sample of the backfill. This time is then compared with the known time of a suitable sample (Tables 10-9 and 10-10). The only testing materials required are:

1. A 10-quart water pail with bottom cut out and replaced with a screen or sieve of approximately ⅛ in. mesh
2. Wash tub or tank that can be filled with water to a depth of 8 to 9 in.
3. One-foot ruler graduated in inches
4. Scoop or hand trowel
5. Gravel sample
6. Watch or clock with second hand

Test procedure is illustrated in Fig. 10-9.

Fig. 10-9A. Equipment required and method for field testing backfill for drains. Equipment includes a tub, galvanized pail with bottom replaced with a sieve, ruler, and trowel or small shovel.

Fig. 10-9B. Pail is filled with gravel sample to a depth of 5 in.

Fig. 10-9C. Gravel sample is *slowly* immersed in water until covered by 3 in. of water.

Fig. 10-9D. When gravel sample and bucket is lifted out of the water, the time for the water to drain down 3 in. is noted to give a measure of the permeability of the gravel. *Test method devised by R. C. Thurber & Associates, Ltd., consulting engineers, Victoria, B. C., Canada.*

Table 10-8 Size of Filter Material for Subdrains

Standard ASTM Sieve	Per Cent
Passing a ⅜-in. sieve	100
Passing a No. 4 sieve	95–100
Passing a No. 16 sieve	45–80
Passing a No. 50 sieve	10–30
Passing a No. 100 sieve	2–10

AASHO Spec. M6-51, Gradation limits of concrete sand.

Table 10-9 Filter Times for Suitable Subdrain Samples

Native Material* To Be Drained	Test Time for Field Permeameter (seconds)	Type of Filter (Backfill) Required for Perforated Pipe Subdrains
Well-graded gravel, non-plastic, small percentage of fines. (GW)**	Not applicable	No filter normally required unless unusually large flows of water are encountered. Perforated drains not normally required.
Well-graded sand, non-plastic, small percentage of fines. (SW coarse)	Not applicable	No filter normally required unless unusually large flows of water are encountered. Perforated drains not normally required.
Well-graded sand, non-plastic, small percentage of fines. (SW fine)	Less than 5	Perforated drains helpful here; operate very efficiently. Filter required for best flow is considerably coarser than concrete sand.
Well-graded, silty sandy gravel, low plasticity. (GM)	Less than 5	Perforated drains efficiently drain this material. Filter required for best flow considerably coarser than concrete sand.
Silty gravel-sand mixture with low plasticity (micaceous silt). (SM)	5-40	This filter should contain nothing finer than #200 sieve and less than 5% passing a #100 sieve. Concrete sand suitable.
Sandy silt, low plasticity. (ML)	5-40	This filter should contain nothing finer than #200 sieve and less than 5% passing a #100 sieve. Concrete sand suitable.
Sandy silt, medium plasticity. (MH)	5-40	This filter should contain nothing finer than #200 sieve and less than 5% passing a #100 sieve. Concrete sand suitable.

*For native material other than those listed, the above guide may need some modification.
**Unified Soil Classification System.

Table 10-10 Typical Test Results

Sample Description	Test Time for Field Permeameter (seconds)	Suitability for Backfill for Perforated Pipe Subdrains
Clean, washed and screened concrete aggregate.	5 to 15	Excellent, particularly where large flows into subdrain are expected.
Natural sandy gravel, with 1% or less of silt and clay.	15 to 40	Quite adequate for subdrain backfill.
Natural sandy gravels, with 1% to 5% silt and clay.	40 to 100	Generally unsuitable for subdrain backfill.

TOP SEAL

Use of a sealed trench keeps out surface water which may carry silt and clog the backfill. The material used may be clay or a mixture using asphalt or other binder.

On ordinary construction it is advisable to remove the surface water by means of gutters and catchbasins or drop inlets rather than through the trench backfill. However, if the subdrain is adequate in size and can be cleaned out when necessary, surface water can safely be admitted through the backfill or inlets.

OUTLETS

Pipe outlets should be high enough so they cannot clog with silt or snow. Fig. 10-10. Cantilevering the end of the pipe and deflecting it to enter the stream at an angle will generally protect against undermining. A suitable screen or a flap gate will keep rodents from building their nests in the pipe.

Fig. 10-10. A subdrain outlet should be high enough to prevent clogging. Corrugated steel pipe can be cantilevered over the channel.

INSTALLATION RECOMMENDATIONS

The foregoing pages and those that follow on Subdrainage Problems cover most of the general installation recommendations. Adequate depth of trench and proper backfill are the key to good results. The grade on the perforated pipe should be carefully controlled to prevent low spots which tend to silt up. Actual practice varies in different parts of the country to fit local climate and soil conditions, based on experience.

There is rather complete agreement among all agencies that perforations in the subdrain pipe should be *down*, unless the pipe is used in the outlet section. In other words the rows of perforations are below the middle of the pipe with a 90-degree arc of tight invert. Where the perforations are turned up, it becomes desirable to use a layer of coarse material around the pipe or over the

Fig. 10-11. Fig. 10-12. Two highway projects showing before and after joining 20-ft lengths of perforated steel pipe. Job at left used two-piece bolted couplings; job at right, sleeve couplings.

perforations, with fine material around the coarser material above the pipe.

Most states and other agencies specify that the granular filter material be tamped or rolled. This may be an unnecessary operation for 6 and 8-in. diameter pipe but is helpful on larger sizes and where native soil is used for backfill.

Galvanized perforated pipe is amply durable for most locations. A bituminous coating and paved invert in the blank area between the two groups of perforations can be added where specified.

Couplings and Fittings. Standard two-piece bolted corrugated couplings or sleeve-type joints are used for perforated steel pipe. Standard fittings such as tees, wyes, elbows, reducers, risers and others are available for the drainage layouts. They may be corrugated or smooth and are attached by bolted or sleeve type couplings. Figs. 10-11, 10-12.

Perforated Tubing. Successful use has been made of perforated galvanized smooth tubing (2 or 2½-in. diam.) in tapping water pockets or seams where open-trenching is not practical. This is particularly true for some cut slopes, embankments and landslide areas.

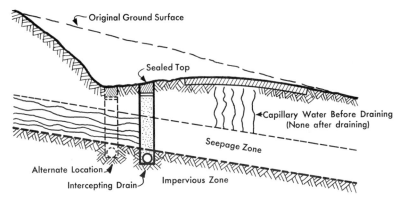

Fig. 10-13. How intercepting drain cuts off the source of supply of harmful capillary water—and free water—under a road surface. Top of trench is sealed to prevent silting.

Section II—SUBDRAINAGE PROBLEMS

Are the problems of soils and ground water different for highways, railways, cities and other engineering works, and are the solutions different? Basically they are the same, but it may be helpful to discuss them at least briefly for the different markets.

A. HIGHWAY SUBDRAINAGE

"All highway surfaces depend upon the underlying earth for their support," reads a booklet published by the Michigan State Highway Department. "If that support is weak, or if it lacks uniformity, it may fail to fulfill its function. Further, if improved surfaces are built upon soils which at certain seasons are subject to extreme changes in volume, not only is support lacking, but destructive counter stresses may be developed which will result in serious heaves, frost boils, excessive pavement cracking and similar troubles. No type or design of surface is capable of successfully resisting these forces. It becomes evident, therefore, that the design of the road should begin with the subgrade, and that effective preventive measures taken in the initial stages of construction will be reflected by ultimate economy in maintenance."

1. Fill Foundation Drainage

An embankment exerts a load or pressure on its foundation. If that foundation soil is wet or compressible, settlement occurs, depending on the fill height. Where seepage strata or springs exist, a subdrain trench and pipe should be placed low enough to intercept the ground water and conduct it to an outlet.

Where a fill is to be built across swampy ground, it may be possible to place a thick blanket of sand over the area, drilling or driving holes into the subsoil, and backfilling with sand. The fill is built over the sand blanket to an extra height for load purposes, and later reduced to finished grade.

Weight of the fill compresses the foundation soil and squeezes the water up through the "sand piles," then laterally through the sand blanket to an outlet. Perforated metal pipe subdrains are used to direct such water to a suitable outlet.

2. Soft, Unstable Fills

Where fills have not been properly made, based on present knowledge of soils and drainage, mudholes, mudpumping and soft spots may develop. Such fills may subside or "go out" entirely at some time.

A more common case even on modern roads is for fills to be supplied with free water through underground strata from an adjacent cut section. If at all possible, the source of water should be located and intercepted. Where the trouble cannot be localized, it may be necessary to use cross drains at various depths and intervals to effectively drain the mass.

3. Sidehill and Through Cuts

For a seepage zone that falls within a cut slope, the remedy may consist of an intercepting drain on top of the bank to prevent the water from reaching the face of the cut.

Where the seepage zone is below the road, an intercepting drain in the shoulder or ditch line will either shut off the water before it enters the subgrade area or, for a deep seam, will reduce the height reached by capillary water. Fig. 10-13.

Lateral drains may extend under the roadway to intercept ground water traveling in the same general direction as the road center line.

4. Rock Cuts

Ledge rock under the side ditches or under the roadway may hold pockets of water and cause the road foundation to become saturated. Frost heaving aggravates the trouble. The remedy consists of making original rock cuts deeper (1 to 4 ft) and backfilling with pervious material drained with a subdrain pipe. One state highway district in New York specifies that undrainable pockets be filled with a fine-grained bituminous mix.

On old construction the ditch can be deepened, but it may be necessary to blast a trench under or along both sides of the road surface.

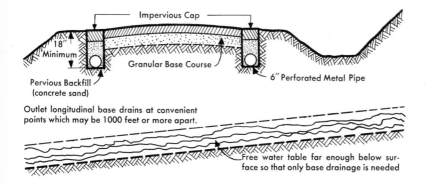

Fig. 10-14. Base drainage removes surface water that may be trapped when a pervious base is laid over a relatively impervious subgrade. On steep slopes laterals may be added under the pavement.

5. Transition From Cut to Fill

The transition from cut to fill section is a frequent source of pavement break-ups, especially where the ground water follows or flows on top of an impervious stratum.

The remedy consists of a subdrain across the roadway in the cut and using a pervious base in the transition area.

6. Base Drainage

A granular base under a pavement is a common way of improving the support for a pavement. However, it may become a trap for surface water entering through cracks or open joints. A subdrain on one or both sides of the roadway will help remove the free water. Fig. 10-14.

B. RAILWAY SUBDRAINAGE

Effects of Soil Measure

Some soils are recognized as making a more stable railroad roadbed and foundations than others, namely granular soils high in internal friction and cohesion, and low in compressibility, capillarity and elasticity. A large clay content is usually adverse. New construction should use only the best available soils. Water is the principal enemy of soil stability.

"Since the stability of most subgrade materials is affected by their moisture content, controlling the amount of water in the roadbed is an important factor in the maintenance of good track. Consequently, adequate drainage of roadbeds is a matter of major importance to every railroad company, more particularly in view of the universal demand for high speed in transportation and the tendency toward greater axle loads."[7]

Long experience has shown that simple drainage measures are effective in removing harmful ground water. Such drainage is long lasting and generally more economical than other measures that treat the symptoms rather than the cause of the trouble. A dry soil is a strong, stable soil.

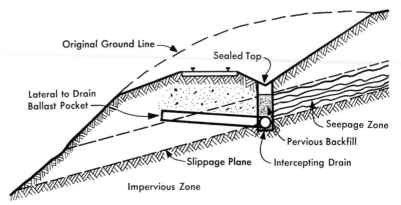

Fig. 10-15. Typical intercepting drain under railroad track with laterals to drain wet ballast pockets.

1. Water Pockets

Railroad roadbeds have somewhat the same drainage problems as highways —namely, soft foundation soils, unstable fills, sidehill and through cuts, rock cuts and transitions from cut to fill—as described on preceding pages. In addition they have several special problems.

One of these is water pockets, which according to the AREA Manual result from ballast being driven into soft subgrade in cut or on fill. These impervious pockets hold water and aggravate the situation.

For old or new construction, a solution is suggested in Fig. 10-15. A cross trench should be dug 6 to 12 in. below the bottom of each located pocket, or at 15 to 30-ft intervals. Perforated steel pipe, 6 or 8-in. diameter, is placed in the trench with a compacted backfill of finely graded filter material.

2. Multiple Tracks

Whether for main lines, passing tracks, yards or stations, longitudinal subdrains can be located between all tracks or every other track, depending on type of soil. Lateral outlets of unperforated corrugated steel pipe should be provided at intervals of 200 to 500 ft, with risers to catch surface drainage. In other words a combination of surface and subsurface drainage may be needed.

Fig. 10-16. Placing perforated steel subdrainage pipe in railroad tunnel for removal of seepage water.

3. Highway Grade Crossings

Wherever railroad tracks cross each other at grade or where railroad tracks cross a highway at grade, the problem is to keep a smooth-riding crossing with minimum maintenance.

Drainage should consist of perforated steel pipe placed in a trench at the ends of the ties on single and double tracks and between pairs of multiple tracks. Fig. 10-17. On two or more tracks, perforated steel cross drains should also be placed at the uphill side of crossings in order to drain the intertrack spaces. Otherwise such spaces may act as subsurface channels and conduct storm water to crossings. Pipe should be on at least a 0.3 per cent grade and at a depth of 3 to 4 ft below the ties if on embankment, or, if in cut, as controlled by the bottom of the side ditches. All trenches should be filled with fine material (similar to AREA concrete sand).

Adequate outlets should be provided to carry away water collected by the subdrain.

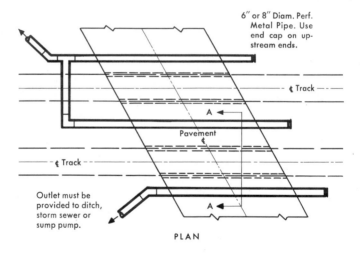

PLAN

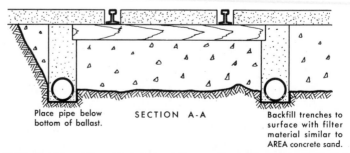

SECTION A-A

Fig. 10-17. Highway grade crossing drainage for normal conditions. A dry stable foundation improves both riding surfaces and reduces maintenance costs.

C. ·MUNICIPAL DRAINAGE

1. Street Subdrains

City streets differ but little from many rural highways when it comes to loads and foundations. The problems of adequate drainage are common to both.

Where free water exists in the subgrade, it is advisable to determine the source, direction and depth. Ground water flow should be intercepted by placing a pipe subdrain in the grass plot behind the curb in residential districts and wherever most convenient in business and industrial districts. Generally such subdrains are parallel to the curb. However, in case of wide streets, laterals may be needed at right angles to or diagonally with the curb.

It is important that the subdrain penetrate well into the impervious zone so that all water will be intercepted. The outlet can generally be a storm sewer manhole. Where a pervious base is needed under a pavement, that base should be provided with a pipe interceptor and outlet. Fig. 10-18.

Fig. 10-18. Streets can be kept smooth longer and with less-frequent pavement repairs where perforated steel subdrains are installed. Here an intercepting drainage system will keep an athletic field and parking area dry.

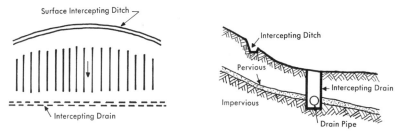

Fig. 10-19. Intercepting drain at toe of slope keeps valley floors and other areas dry and useful.

2. Athletic Fields, Race Tracks

Soft, spongy areas interfere with play and add to maintenance costs.

Prompt removal of surface water should be facilitated, where needed, by the use of subdrainage. Location, spacing and depth of subdrain pipe should depend on the kind of soil and its slope. Drains are usually kept parallel or transverse to the edges of playing areas and at a depth of 3 to 4 ft below the surface. However, the location and slope of an impervious stratum may better control the design.

Of greatest importance is the use of a graded filter material to aid in getting the water to the pipe.

3. Parks, Golf Courses, Open Areas

Large open areas are subject to slightly different handling than are specific playing fields.

The mains should follow the natural drainage in straight lines or long easy curves. This can be handled without elbows or other special fittings, there being enough play in the joints and flexibility in the pipe itself to accommodate easy curvature.

The spacing of laterals depends on the physical composition and texture of the soils. Tables 10-11 and 10-12 may serve as a general guide. Fig. 10-19.

For larger areas such as airports, see Chapter 11.

D. DRAINAGE OF BRIDGES AND RETAINING WALLS

Bridges, underpasses and grade elevations should be protected and stabilized by drainage. An undrained fill behind an abutment or retaining wall can cause bulging, overturning or general disintegration. Fig. 10-20.

Table 10-11   Subdrain Spacings
For depths of 3, 4 and 5 ft

Permeability Class	Permeability Rate In. per Hour	Spacing for Various Depths		
		3 Ft	4 Ft	5 Ft
Very slow.....................	0.0 to 0.05	0 to 15	0 to 20	0 to 25
Slow........................	0.05 to 0.2	15 to 30	20 to 40	25 to 50
Moderately slow..............	0.2 to 0.8	30 to 60	40 to 80	50 to 100
Moderate.....................	0.8 to 2.5	60 to 110	80 to 145	100 to 180
Moderately rapid..............	2.5 to 5.0	110 to 155	145 to 205	180 to 255
Rapid.......................	5.0 to 10.0	155 to 220	205 to 290	255 to 360

Table 10-12 Depth and Spacing of Subdrains Recommended for Various Soil Classes

Soil Classes	Percentage of Soil Separates			Depth of Bottom of Drain in Feet	Distance Between Subdrains in Feet
	Sand	Silt	Clay		
Sand.....................	80–100	0–20	0–20	3–4	150–300
				2–3	100–150
Sandy Loam................	50–80	0–50	0–20	3–4	100–150
				2–3	85–100
Loam......................	30–50	30–50	0–20	3–4	85–100
				2–3	75–85
Silt Loam..................	0–50	50–100	0–20	3–4	75–85
				2–3	65–75
Sandy Clay Loam...........	50–80	0–30	20–30	3–4	65–75
				2–3	55–65
Clay Loam..................	20–50	20–50	20–30	3–4	55–65
				2–3	45–55
Silty Clay Loam.............	0–30	50–80	20–30	3–4	45–55
				2–3	40–45
Sandy Clay.................	50–70	0–20	30–50	3–4	40–45
				2–3	35–40
Silty Clay.................	0–20	50–70	30–50	3–4	35–40
				2–3	30–35
Clay......................	0–50	0–50	30–100	3–4	30–35
				2–3	25–30

1. Surface Water

Water falling on the surface of a long bridge or overpass should be discharged through steel downspouts into a sewer or drainage ditch. At the end of a highway bridge the water should be caught in an inlet and discharged through a spillway to the toe of the slope. Fig. 10-21.

Fig. 10-20. Perforated steel pipe extend through and drain the backfill behind this highway underpass on an interstate highway in Connecticut.

Fig. 10-21. Drainage behind abutments and retaining walls can be efficiently done with perforated steel pipe.

Fig. 10-22. Flat-bottom deck drains on railway overpasses with solid floors are used with a downspout stub to outlet into the wall drainage system and to a sewer.

For a railway bridge with closed deck, the water seeps through the ballast towards a depression in the center of the deck. There a perforated corrugated steel halfcircle deck drain is installed to collect the water and conduct it to an outlet. Fig. 10-22.

2. Subdrainage

Ground water from the fill or backfill against an abutment or retaining wall should lead to an intercepting drain. This consists of a blanket of pervious filter material, 1 ft or more in thickness directly against the wall, with a perforated steel pipe at the lowest point for which an outlet can be obtained.

The pipe should be surrounded with impervious material up to the lowest row of perforations to insure getting all of the water into the pipe. Filter material and other backfill should always be well compacted to minimize future settlement.

E. LANDSLIDE DRAINAGE

Terzaghi defines: "The term landslide refers to a rapid displacement of a mass of rock, residual soil or settlement adjoining a slope . . ." It involves not only mountainsides but cuts, fills, channels and other engineering works. The presence of water is usually an important factor in triggering a slide.

CORRECTIVE MEASURES

Among the control methods suggested[8] are buttresses, cribbing, retaining walls, piling and tie rods—in conjunction with drainage. Drainage falls in the following categories:

(a) Surface
(b) Subsurface
(c) Jacked-in-place or drilled-in-place pipe
(d) Tunneling
(e) Blasting (of impervious barriers)
(f) Sealing joint planes and open fissures

Drainage may not be simple or inexpensive. The geologist who has thoroughly examined the site and has the results of borings can best advise the method.

Interception of surface water may be done by a ditch or impervious gutter. It may be necessary to go deep with a pipe subdrain in a pervious backfilled trench. Or it may be necessary to jack a subdrain pipe or small diameter tubing, Fig. 10-23, or to tunnel. Because of continued soil movements and shrinkage, only steel pipe with its alignment permanently maintained by couplings can be effective. Long lengths of perforated corrugated steel pipe are most satisfactory for this service.

Culverts and sewers in areas subject to sliding should have positive joints. Otherwise they will pull apart and discharge their contents into the mass, thereby aggravating the slide.

Fig. 10-23. Drilling a hole to tap suspected water pockets. After the drill is removed, long sections of 2 or 2½-in. perforated galvanized smooth tubing are inserted into the hole. Note the flow of water from a tube at the center of the picture.

Fig. 10-24. When a landslide occurs, a soils engineer can best locate the source of ground water. Here a subdrain pipe will be backfilled with a pervious filter to trap the water and stabilize the slide. Strong joints are essential.

Fig. 10-25. Perforated steel pipe used to drain around the foundation of a research laboratory.

F. LEVEE SUBDRAINAGE

Toe Drains

The use of perforated steel pipe subdrains for the stream side of levees and the downstream slope of earth and rock dams is accepted as good practice. The purpose is to relieve the ground water pressure from accumulating seepage.

A special type of toe drainage or relief well is shown in Fig. 13-5, for use on major river levees. The bottom portion of the vertical riser is perforated to intercept or collect the ground water. It overflows into a collector pipe and then to an open ditch for downstream disposal.

A levee or dam with long, flat slopes may have a herring-bone system of subdrains.

REFERENCES AND BIBLIOGRAPHY

1. *Solving Drainage Problems*, Bethlehem Steel Corporation, Bethlehem, Pa., Booklet 425-B, 1959, 80 pp.
2. *Perforated Pipe for Controlling Groundwater*, Metal Products Div., Armco Steel Corp., Middletown, Ohio, Catalog HC-8364, 1964, 24 pp.
3. American Railway Engineering Assn., Chicago, Ill. Specification 1-4-11, 1960.
4. Ful-Flo Manual No. FF652, Granco Steel Products Co., St. Louis, Mo. 1965, 12 pp.
5. *Investigation of Filter Requirements for Underdrains*, Technical Memorandum No. 183-1, U. S. Army Engineer Waterways Experiment Station, Vicksburg, Mississippi 39181, Nov. 1941, 48 pp., (out of print, loan copies available).
6. Nasmith, H. W. and MacLean, D. A., *Field Test Simplifies Filter Gravel Quality Control*, Victoria, B. C., Canada, Highway Magazine, Middletown, Ohio, 4th Quarter 1963, pp. 90–93.
7. *AREA* Committee 1, Roadway and Ballast, Roadway Drainage. Manual, American Railway Engineering Association, Chicago.
8. Baker, R. F. and Larew, H. C., *Analysis of Landslides*, Highway Research Board, Bulletin 49, 1952.

Fig. 11-1. Installing helically corrugated perforated steel pipe for subdrainage on O'Hare International Airport, Chicago, Illinois. Inspection holes are of non-perforated pipe attached to metal stubs.

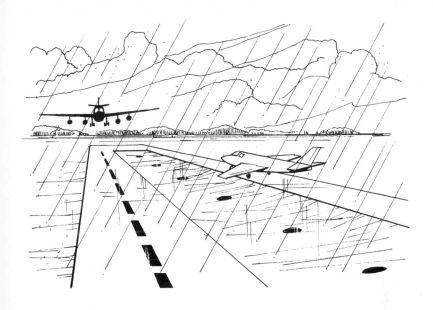

CHAPTER 11 Airport Drainage

PURPOSE OF AIRPORT DRAINAGE[1]

The purpose of airport drainage is to dispose of water which may hinder any activity necessary to the safe and efficient operation of the airport. The drainage system should collect and remove surface runoff from each area, remove excess ground water, lower the water table, and protect all slopes. Natural drainage normally ~~these requirements. Supp~~lementary artificial facilities m~~ust~~ ~~present requirements and any future~~

power of the p~~...~~

CHARACTERISTICS OF AIRPORT DRAINAGE

Airports range in size from an emergency landing strip to a major facility covering several square miles. To handle large planes with heavy, concentrated wheel loads, it is necessary to provide long and wide surfaced runways with comparatively flat longitudinal and transverse grades. Such topography, in combination with various kinds of soils, climate and rainfall conditions, poses real problems to the drainage engineer. He is expected to provide safe movement of aircraft for a maximum of the time, under all weather conditions.

DRAINAGE SURVEYS

Before an efficient drainage system can be designed, certain preliminary information must be obtained, including:

1. Topographic maps of entire site and surrounding areas
2. Soil tests for texture, permeability, horizon and capillarity
3. Determination of water tables
4. Rainfall and other climatological data
5. Drainage from tributary areas
6. Map showing proposed contours of graded site on 1 or 2-ft intervals, along with profiles and cross sections along axis of runways, taxiways, aprons and other paved areas.

After grading, an additional "drainage working drawing" is necessary with contour intervals of 0.2 to 0.5 ft for positioning catchbasins and storm sewers.

RAINFALL

The requirements of airport drainage differ somewhat from those of culverts, storm drains and subdrainage of highways, railways, industrial areas, agricultural, urban and suburban areas. These last were described in some detail in Chapters 4, 8, 9 and 10 and should be reviewed for comparative purposes both as to design principles and the type of drainage structures. For example, it is possible but not economically sound to design a large airport system with capacity to remove the heaviest rainfall within a few minutes after it ends. A more practical way is to determine the maximum intensity on the basis of storms occurring *once in 5 years for a 1-hour duration*. Minor airports may use a frequency as short as 1 or 2 years. General storms (of low intensity but long duration) are given precedence over local storms (of high intensity but short duration) for airport drainage design.

Fig. 11-2. Winter construction of corrugated steel storm sewer on a major airport. This consists of long lines of large diameter pipe, carefully backfilled as shown here.

For rainfall intensity-frequency-duration curves see Chapter 4. As a further guide for local airport sites, the engineer should consult the offices of the local weather bureau, the state highway department, city engineer, state hydrographer and other sources.

SURFACE RUNOFF

Only a portion of the rainfall from any one storm is likely to result in *surface runoff*. The following factors influence the quantity of runoff:

* Intensity and duration of rainfall
* Area of airport and tributary watersheds
* Slope or irregularity of surfaces
* Perviousness of surfaces
* Type and moisture content of soil

The Rational Method, described on page 87, and commonly used by engineers in drainage practice, gives a direct relationship between rainfall and runoff.

The equation is:

$$Q = CiA \tag{1}$$

where Q = peak rate of runoff in cu ft per sec
C = coefficient or ratio of runoff to rainfall (see Table 11-1)
i = the intensity of rainfall in in. per hr
A = the drainage area in acres, tributary to the point under design

The value of i to be selected depends upon the curves for the intensity of rainfall, the assumed period of recurrence and *time of concentration* required for surface runoff to flow from the most distant point in the area to the nearest inlet or point of collection.

Although a frequency or 5-year period of recurrence is generally recommended, the design should be checked for longer periods to determine whether serious damage could result from greater storms.

Subsurface runoff for an airport is generally computed in the same manner as agricultural drainage. See Table 10-5. The figure generally used ranges from ¼ to ½ in. per acre in 24 hours. A runoff of ¼ in. per acre in 24 hours is equal to .0105 cu ft per second from each acre drained. A runoff of ½ in. per acre is .0210 cu ft per second per acre.

Table 11-1   Values of Relative Imperviousness[1]

Type of Service	Factor C
For all watertight roof surfaces	.75 to .95
For asphalt runway pavements	.80 to .95
For concrete runway pavements	.70 to .90
For gravel or macadam pavements	.35 to .70
* For impervious soils (heavy)	.40 to .65
* For impervious soils, with turf	.30 to .55
* For slightly pervious soils (sandy clay loam)	.15 to .40
* For slightly pervious soils, with turf	.10 to .30
* For moderately pervious soils (sandy loam)	.05 to .20
* For moderately pervious soils, with turf	.00 to .10

* For slopes from 1% to 2%.

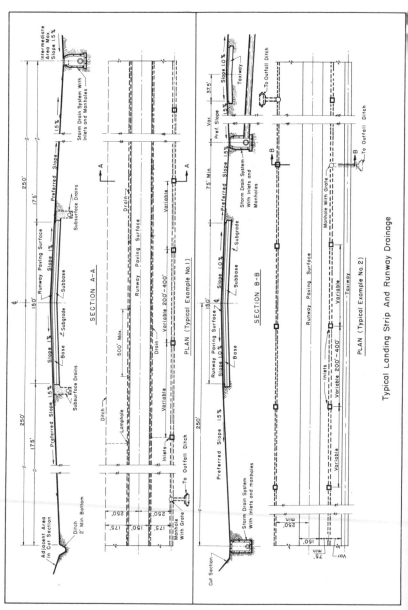

Fig. 11-3. Typical runway drainage layout as designed by Federal Aviation Agency.

Table 11-2 Coefficient of Roughness—
Storm Drains and Open Channels[1]

Pipe	Value of "n" for Manning's
Clay and Concrete	
Good alignment, smooth joints, smooth transitions	0.012
Less favorable flow conditions	0.015
Corrugated Metal	
100% of periphery smoothly lined	0.013
Paved invert, 50% of periphery paved	0.018
Paved invert, 25% of periphery paved	0.021
Unpaved, bituminous coated or non-coated	0.024
Open Channels	
Paved	0.015 to 0.020
Unpaved	
Bare earth, shallow flow	0.020 to 0.025
Bare earth, depth of flow over 1 ft	.015 to .020
Turf, shallow flow	.06 to .08
Turf, depth of flow over 1 ft	.04 to .06

THE DRAINAGE SYSTEM

Before designing the drainage system for an airport, first prepare a topographical map showing contours at 2-ft intervals, and various features of the existing area, including tributary water courses. Next, a detailed layout is needed to show proposed runways, taxiways, aprons and building areas—with the finished contours drawn to intervals of 1 ft or less. Third, the detailed drainage system with finished grades should be shown on the plans. Fig. 11-3.

Four basic types of drainage are used on an airport:

1. Surface water handled by crowned or sloped surfaces, shallow channels, swales, ditches or ponding areas
2. Storm sewers, including inlets, manholes and other appurtenances
3. Base drains for pavements, taxiways and aprons
4. Subdrainage for ground water.

In addition, there may be intercepting or diversion drains or outfall ditches to collect or dispose of water from the airport site and adjoining areas.

The Federal Aviation Agency recommends the following standards for airfields:[1]

* Inlets should be located not less than 75 ft from the edges of the pavement except for apron areas
  Runways and taxiways should be crowned except at pavement intersections
* Use a maximum slope of 5 per cent for a 10-ft width adjacent to paved edges to facilitate rapid runoff
* Provide small ponding areas around inlets (as a factor of safety in capacity design)
* Space inlets so that the flow from the most remote part of the drainage area is not more than 400 ft
* Plan for rapid removal of runoff from the airport area
* Guard against soil erosion
* If porous strata conduct subsurface water into the airport, intercept same and divert

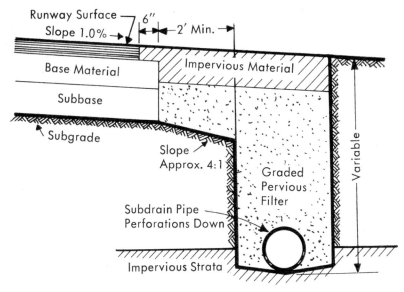

Fig. 11-4. Subdrain and base drain along edge of runway.

* Manholes or combination manholes and inlets should be provided where different pipelines join and at reasonable intervals for cleanout and inspection purposes
* Subdrains should be designed to function as subsurface drains only and should not operate to remove surface waters.

SIZE OF CONDUITS

A ditch when paved is considered to be a "conduit" and should be designed accordingly. See *Hydraulics of Open Channels* (Chap. 4. Sect III) for the use of the Manning equation for determining sizes; also for safe velocities and channel protection.

Storm sewers, stream enclosures and intercepting sewers at the edges of the airport are designed for size as shown in Chapter 4, Sect. V, *Hydraulics of Sewers.*

Subdrains or underdrains, whether for lowering or intercepting ground water, or as an outlet for pavement subbase, are designed for size as in Chapter 10 *Subdrainage.* Fig. 11-4.

SELECTION OF STRUCTURES

The drainage structures used for airports are similar to those used in municipal construction. See Chapter 9 *Sewers.* One principal difference is that the tops of structures in the traffic areas must not extend above the ground level. Possible settlement around the structure should be anticipated and the final grade should facilitate entrance of surface water and avoid any obstruction to equipment.

STORM DRAINS

Uninterrupted functioning of the storm drains on an airport is essential to safety and continuous service of airlines and military operations.

Corrugated steel pipe and pipe-arches have been used extensively as airfield storm drains because of their structural resistance to crushing under impact and vibration. See Chapter 3 for examples. Also, these products come in long lengths that resist disjointing and clogging by entrance of surround fill.

Under pavement areas where exfiltration from storm drains could result in pavement damage, the use of watertight joints is good design practice. See Chapter 6.

Manholes, risers and catch basins are also prefabricated of corrugated steel to provide tighter junction joints and to speed construction. Steel end sections are commonly used on the outfall end of storm drains.

Stream enclosures, small or large, are frequently built of structural steel plates, field-assembled into pipes, pipe-arches or arches.

Subdrains are placed along the edges of the runways to catch any surface water that has gone through pavement joints and edges into the pervious subbase material. In some cases, laterals extend under the runways in order to keep the water table low. In other cases, ground water from areas surrounding the airport must be intercepted.

Perforated corrugated steel pipe in standard diameters 6 to 24 in. and larger has been used on most of the major airports for the past 40 years. The smaller airports also find it economical to use metal subdrains.

Advantages are: single filter around the pipe instead of double filter to keep out silt and backfill fines; more positive joints, and fewer of them needed because of longer lengths, greater structural strength and durability. For comparison of infiltration of solids into subdrain pipes, see Table 10-7.

REFERENCES AND BIBLIOGRAPHY

1. Federal Aviation Agency, *Airport Drainage*, Advisory Circular No. AC 150/5320-5A, Supt. of Documents, Gvmt. Printing Office, Washington, D. C. 20402, 1966, 60 pp.

2. Departments of the Army and the Air Force, *Surface Drainage Facilities for Airfields and Heliports*, Technical Manual No. 5-280-1 /Air Force Manuals No. 88-5, Chapt. 1, Washington, D. C., Aug. 1965. (This and following manual are not distributed generally but are available for reference at many libraries.)

3. Department of the Army, *Drainage and Erosion Control: Subsurface Drainage Facilities for Airfields*, Technical Manual No. 5-820-2, Washington, D. C. (revision of earlier manual, 1959).

4. Department of the Army, *Drainage and Erosion Control Structures for Airfields and Heliports*, Technical Manual No. 5-820-3 (originally designated: Corps of Engineers Manual EM 1110-345-283), Washington, D. C., Aug. 1964, partially revised March 1966.

Fig. 12-1. Median and shoulder spillway drain of curved structural plate steel on an eastern express highway.

CHAPTER 12 Erosion Prevention

One of the most destructive forces that the engineer must combat is soil erosion. It makes unsightly gullies on roadway shoulders, cut slopes, and embankments. It gouges out side ditches and cross streams. It endangers the road foundation and traffic.

Erosion undermines and washes out bridges and smaller drainage structures. It clogs ditches and culverts with sediment. It is a costly nuisance.

PREVENTIVE DESIGN IS IMPORTANT

Proper design can eliminate much of the problem of burdensome maintenance. There are three basic ways of preventing erosion.

The first is to shield the slopes and bald areas with erosion-resistant turf, vines, shrubs or trees. There must be sufficient moisture to start and sustain vegetation.

Second, divert the water into erosion-resistant channels such as (1) paved ditches, (2) corrugated steel flumes, Fig. 12-1, (3) pipe stream-enclosures or storm drains, (4) pipe spillways, (5) stream confinement by steel sheeting or retaining walls.

Third, slow down the velocity of the water by means of ditch checks of steel sheeting plus riprap. A related use, described in the next section, is that of soil-saving dams and ponds to control the flow of water.

CORRUGATED STEEL FLUMES

Steel flumes are essentially part-circle or half-circle "ditches," preferably imbedded for their full depth in the natural ground. They should not run full, so must be designed with a liberal factor of safety or "freeboard." They should discharge into a catchbasin, culvert or stream in a manner to avoid undermining. Figs. 12-3A, 12-3B.

Fig. 12-2. Shoulder spillway with steel end section for an inlet.

Fig. 12-3A. Pipe and flume spillway of structural plate steel. Edges of flume are covered and braced with steel angles.
Fig. 12-3B. *Right:* Cantilevered steel culvert can spill water beyond the slope with little or no danger of undermining the pipe.

Edges of the flume may be reinforced with a steel angle. Horizontal steel struts at intervals will help maintain the designed shape. Steel or concrete anchorages at 10 to 25 ft intervals may be needed to resist frost heaving and other loads. Flume sections are generally connected by field bolting or other means.

STREAM ENCLOSURES

Enclosing storm water in a steel pipe sewer is a sure way of avoiding progressive erosion troubles. Not only is maintenance decreased but eliminating an open ditch—possibly an eyesore—also increases safety, and makes available additional usable land. These last points hold particular merit in real estate developments and along highways.

For suggestions on sizes, connections, fittings, and other design data, see Chapter 4 *Hydraulics*, and Chapter 9 *Sewers*.

On open ditch grades in excess of 5 per cent, stream enclosures will be found more satisfactory than ditch checks or other remedies. Corrugated steel pipe, with its continuous, flexible construction, is most often specified as it resists disjointing and also conforms to shifting or subsiding foundations. Grating inlets can be provided if necessary.

Table 12-1 Cost Comparison of Drop Structures [1]

Type of Structure	Drop		
	4 Ft	6 Ft	10 Ft
Sodded channel	1.00	2.20	7.12
Corr. steel pipe culvert, 5% grade	5.98	9.53	16.30
Corr. steel pipe culvert 20% grade	2.03	2.93	4.70
Reinforced concrete drop	6.50	8.45	15.20
Gravel lined channel	3.43	7.57	24.00

Ratios of costs were based on 1960 bid prices in ten widely dispersed states. (Ratios apply to any units—per lin ft, per structure, etc.) Corrugated pipe culvert had flared inlet without stilling basin.

PIPE SPILLWAYS

The pipe spillway conveys surface water down the face of a cut slope or embankment, on a steep approach to a culvert inlet, or a sharp drop at the outlet. Table 12-1 compares costs of several kinds of drop structures with drops of 4, 6, and 10 ft, designed for a discharge of 10 cu ft per sec. Cost of dissipating water energy at the outlet is not considered. See also Chapter 13 *Dams*.

An alternate means exists to conduct water down a steep slope. The pipe spillway may be placed on a flat slope with its end cantilevered, to discharge the water into an "armored" stilling basin of riprap or other suitable material. Fig. 12-3B.

Fig. 12-4. Spillway of corrugated steel pipe shows method of anchoring with a rod around the pipe attached to pipes driven into cut slope.

DITCH CHECKS

Ditch checks or weirs once were used extensively to control erosion in road-side ditches. Today, they are considered not only a hazard to traffic leaving the roadway, but also a handicap to power mowing. Consequently, give priority to other means of erosion prevention before accepting weirs.

Where a ditch gradient makes the ditch check desirable and economical, it should be designed with capacity ample to prevent possible washout. The drop at successive weirs should generally not exceed 3 ft.

The ditch check may consist of a corrugated steel-sheeting weir with wings sloped to fit the channel, Fig. 12-5, or a series of sodded earth dams with "pipe drops" as shown in Fig. 12-6. For large channels and cross streams above and below a roadway, employ large ditch checks built of corrugated structural plate or bin walls.

Chapter 4 also shows details with erosion control structures at the inlet and outlet of culverts.

WEIR NOTCH CAPACITY

For a sharp-crested weir on ditch spillways, Table 12-2 gives discharge rates in cu ft/sec for various depths and lengths of the weir notch.

SHEETING AND RETAINING WALLS

Along the banks of a stream, or where wave action along a lake shore results in scouring, protection can prevent washout of a roadway or other valuable property.

Wave action can often be retarded by one or more steel-sheeting groins or

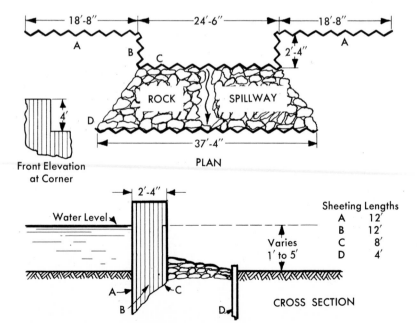

Fig. 12-5. Ditch check of corrugated steel sheeting, with rock spillway apron and sheeting cutoff wall, as built by a reclamation district.

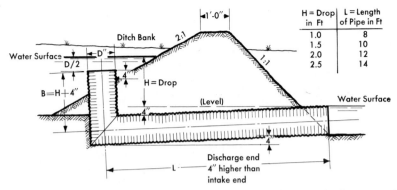

Fig. 12-6. Small ditches with steep slopes can be protected from erosion by means of corrugated steel "pipe drops."

jetties or by means of sheeting-cribs filled with rock. Another practical form of protection is a low wall of sheeting driven along the shore line.

For greater heights, a steel retaining wall is a practical and economical solution. Sheeting and retaining walls are described in detail in Chapters 16 and 17.

Table 12-2   Discharge for Weir Notches in Erosion Check Dams[*2]

(H) Depth of Weir Notch in Feet	Length of Weir Notch in Feet (L)				
	2	4	6	8	10
0.5	2.4	4.8	7.2	9.6	12.0
1.0	6.8	13.6	20.3	27.1	33.9
1.5	12.5	24.9	37.4	49.8	62.3
2.0	19.2	38.3	57.5	76.7	95.9
2.5	26.8	53.6	80.4	107.2	134.0
3.0	35.2	70.5	105.7	140.9	176.1
3.5	44.4	88.8	133.2	177.6	222.0
4.0	54.2	108.5	162.7	217.0	271.2
4.5	64.7	129.4	194.2	258.9	323.6
5.0	75.8	151.6	227.4	303.2	379.0

*Expressed as cu ft/sec as computed from formula $Q = 3.39LH^{3/2}$

REFERENCES

1. Adapted from *Design of Roadside Drainage Channels*, Bureau of Public Roads, Hydraulic Design Series 4, 1965, p. 44.

2. From Iowa Engineering Experiment Station Bulletin 121, Iowa State Univ., Ames, Iowa.

Fig. 13-1. Levee culverts must resist the load of high embankments plus possible unstable foundation soils and hydraulic traffic.

CHAPTER 13 Dam and Levee Drainage

INTRODUCTION

Highway and railway embankments are not ordinarily constructed to impound water or serve as levees along major streams. Inadvertent impounding of water, as for short periods following a storm, is discussed in Chapter 8 *Culverts;* Chapter 11 *Airports;* and Chapter 12 *Erosion.* This chapter describes factors for consideration when the embankment not only performs its normal engineering functions, but also serves as a dam or levee.

Aside from roadways, numerous soil and water conservation projects require building dams and levees, along with proper controls for the water. Included are:

small dams   . . . for water and soil conservation; mosquito elimination
large dams   . . . for water supply, power, recreation, navigation
levees   . . . for flood control, and in connection with dams

Several drainage and related construction products are required for these projects, such as: culverts, diaphragms, end sections, water control gates, toe drains; large intakes and outfall lines for thermal power plants; aggregate bins and air pipes for cooling aggregates; temporary bypass tunnels; pedestrian and vehicular underpasses; shore protection, retaining walls and guardrail.

SOIL-SAVING DAMS

Thousands of small dams are built each year on farms, ranches and other rural areas. Beyond reducing erosion and saving the land, these small dams also help restore the ground water level and supply water for livestock, fishing and recreational purposes. Fig. 13-2.

Size of the dam can vary from a small ditch check, to one large enough to impound a farm pond of several acres, or to an artificial lake of a hundred acres or more. The bigger the dam, the more thorough should be the precautions for handling seepage and overflow. A local or regional Soil Conservation Service office can be helpful in suggesting details based on successful local practice.

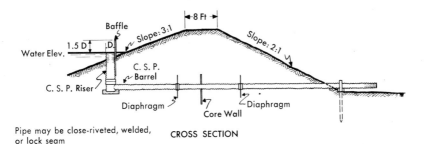

Pipe may be close-riveted, welded, or lock seam   **CROSS SECTION**

Fig. 13-2. Overflow of surplus water from a small farm pond or reservoir is provided by a "mechanical spillway" of corrugated steel pipe.

DRAIN PIPE SPILLWAYS

Even for the smallest of dams, some means should be provided to handle the overflow or to prevent overtopping and possible washout. A turf-covered ditch or corrugated steel flume in the natural ground can safely handle the overflow.

The principal elements of a drain pipe spillway are: (1) drop-inlet or riser with a baffle board or trash screen; (2) junction chamber or manhole; (3) culvert with watertight seams, joints and anti-seep diaphragms, and (4) a slide gate to enable draining the pond for cleaning or other purposes.

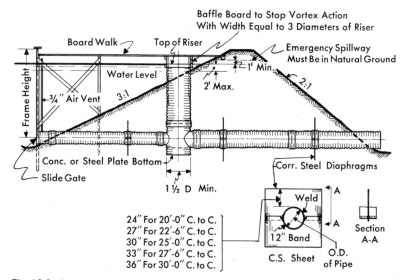

Fig. 13-3. Larger pipe spillway for artificial lake or pond, showing slide headgate for draining all the water from the lake. Size of diaphragms is shown for various spacings between diaphragms.

1. Drop-inlet. Size required to handle excess runoff is determined by the methods given in Chapter 4, *Estimating Runoff from Small Areas, Hydraulics of Open Channels,* or *Hydraulic Design of Culverts.* See Table 13-1 and Fig. 13-3.

Example: A dam with a culvert having an inlet drop of 12 ft of corrugated steel pipe is to serve an ordinary watershed of 25 acres of rolling cultivated land. Interpolating in the second column of Table 13-1, between 20 and 30 acres, the cross-sectional area is 6.8 sq ft. From the footnotes of the same table, a value of 0.66 is obtained for a 12-ft drop through interpolation between values 0.71 and 0.58 for 10 and 15-ft drops. Multiply: 6.8 by 0.66 = 4.49 sq ft as the proper cross-sectional area. The nearest commercial size is a 30-in. diameter pipe with an area of 4.91 sq ft.

Size of the drop-inlet is generally larger than the culvert portion. See Fig. 13-3. The top should be at least 1 ft below the emergency spillway level and 3 or 4 ft below the top of the dam.

Table 13-1   Cross-Sectional Areas for Drop-Inlet Culverts[1]

Watershed Area in Acres	Cross-Sectional Area of Culvert in Square Feet					
	Rolling Land			Hilly Land		
	Cultivated C = 1.0	Pasture 0.6	Woods 0.3	Cultivated 1.4	Pasture 0.8	Woods 0.4
1	1.9	1.1	0.6	2.7	1.5	0.8
2	2.1	1.3	0.6	2.9	1.7	0.8
4	2.5	1.5	0.8	3.5	2.0	1.0
6	2.9	1.7	0.9	4.1	2.3	1.2
8	3.4	2.0	1.0	4.8	2.7	1.4
10	3.8	2.3	1.1	5.3	3.0	1.5
15	4.8	2.9	1.4	6.7	3.8	1.9
20	5.8	3.5	1.7	8.1	4.6	2.3
30	7.8	4.7	2.3	10.9	6.2	3.1
40	9.7	5.8	2.9	13.6	7.8	3.9
50	11.5	6.9	3.5	16.1	9.2	4.6
75	15.9	9.5	4.8	22.3	12.7	6.4
100	20.0	12.0	6.0	28.0	16.0	8.0
125	23.8	14.3	7.1	33.3	19.0	9.5
150	27.3	16.4	8.2	38.2	21.9	10.9
200	33.7	20.2	10.1	47.2	27.0	13.5
250	39.4	23.6	11.8	55.2	31.5	15.8
300	44.4	26.6	13.3	62.2	35.5	17.8
350	48.9	29.3	14.7	68.5	39.1	19.6
400	53.0	31.8	15.9	74.2	42.4	21.2
500	60.0	36.0	18.0	84.0	48.0	24.0
600	65.8	39.5	19.7	92.1	52.6	26.3
700	70.8	42.5	21.2	99.1	56.6	28.3
800	75.0	45.0	22.5	105.0	60.0	30.0

Values computed by Ramser Formula, $a = c \left(130 - \dfrac{77{,}000}{A+600} \right)$ (1)

Where a = cross-sectional area of culvert in sq ft.
A = watershed area in acres, c = coefficient depending on nature and type of watershed.
Formula not recommended for areas larger than given in table.
Use above values for vertical drop through culvert up to 5 ft.
Multiply above values by 0.71 for drop through culvert = 10 ft.
Multiply above values by 0.58 for drop through culvert = 15 ft.
For fan or square shaped watersheds multiply above values by 1.25.
If side spillway of appreciable capacity is provided, reduction of culvert area may be made accordingly.

A baffle board is recommended to stop vortex action. This should be a corrugated steel sheet or a solid timber wall, with a length of three times the diameter of the inlet pipe. This may be supplemented by a coarse steel wire screen to prevent debris from entering the drop-inlet.

2. *Junction Chamber* (manhole). The junction may consist of a simple elbow or tee fabricated of corrugated steel pipe. The bottom may be a steel plate welded to the upright pipe, or be a cast-in-place concrete floor with the bottom of the pipe imbedded. If desired, the slide gate and lift frame may be installed in the junction chamber and riser.

3. *The Culvert.* The size of the horizontal culvert should be capable of accommodating practically any flood flow of the stream above the dam. Size will also control the rapidity of draining the pond for cleaning.

Fig. 13-4. Temporary diversion of stream during construction of a dam can often be handled in large structural plate pipe culverts. The twin pipe shown here was left in place and permanently plugged when the dam went into operation.

Steel pipe with close-riveted, welded, or lock seams and with tight joints should be employed. See Chapter 1 *Seams*. Corrugated steel diaphragms should be included to intercept possible seepage caused by burrowing along the pipe by small animals. Suggested sizes for various spacings of anti-seep rings are shown in Fig. 13-3.

4. Control Gate. Ordinarily the water control gate is situated at the pond end of the culvert and will consist of a hand-operated slide gate, made accessible by means of a walkway from the dam.

LARGE DAMS

Large earth-fill and rock-fill dams often require several years to construct. Various steel products are required in temporary construction and on the completed job. Construction uses include bypass tunnels, culverts (See Fig. 13-4), and underpasses under service roads, steel retaining walls, corrugated pipes for cooling towers, aggregate reclaim tunnels, and conveyor covers.

Permanently installed steel drainage products include culverts under re-located highways and railroads; relief wells and collector pipes (Fig. 13-5); toe subdrains to control seepage through the dam and to relieve ground water pressure behind the dam; retaining walls, steel guardrail, and steel sheeting for shore protection.

Design of these products is described and illustrated under the various products listed. See Index.

LEVEE CULVERTS

The building of levees generally calls for blocking the natural drainage channels. To relieve the water flowing from these tributaries requires levee culverts. These differ from ordinary culverts in that they may be submerged during floods, or longer periods if they continue to serve as equalizers for lakes or reservoirs.

To prevent a stream from backing up through a culvert, a gate is provided to open and close automatically or mechanically. Figs. 13-6 and 13-7.

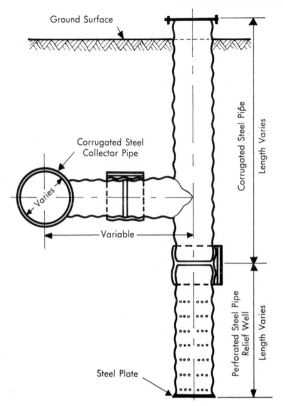

Fig. 13-5. Vertical section of relief well and collector pipe as used on river levees. Perforated corrugated steel pipe is used extensively for toe drainage on dams and levees.

Fig. 13-6. Levee culvert showing (1) diaphragms, (2) flap gate, and riser or manhole.

Fig. 13-7. Slide gate in 48-in. corrugated steel riser on levee culvert.

Design of the levee culvert depends on the size of opening required. Riveted corrugated steel pipe has been used extensively in diameters up to 84 in., either singly or in multiples.

Structural plate pipes are used in diameters up to 10 ft and more.

Saturated and often unstable soil conditions common to levees require that corrugated steel pipe for this service be fabricated differently than ordinary culverts. Seams are made watertight and the coupling bands are selected for both watertightness and extra strength (See Chapt. 6 *Couplings.*)

DIAPHRAGMS

Diaphragms are usually required as cutoff walls to retard leakage alongside the pipe. Such diaphragms or bulkheads should project no less than 2 ft beyond the outside of the pipe, regardless of pipe size, when the diaphragms are spaced 20 ft apart. Spacing greater than 20 ft calls for even larger diaphragms so that the distance the water must travel is at least 20 per cent greater than without the diaphragms. See Fig. 13-6.

Locate diaphragms midway between circumferential riveted seams and at least 4 ft from a field joint. In multiple lines of pipe, space the diaphragms to provide at least 12 in. face-to-face clearance between one another on adjacent pipes.

Steel End Sections in diameters to 84 in. can be used on the ends of levee culverts as shown in Chapter 8.

SERVICE RECORD

Service records of corrugated steel pipe culverts and sewers along the Mississippi, Missouri and many other rivers indicate that: even under flood conditions, they particularly resist disjoining, settlement and infiltration of the surrounding soil. Fig. 13-8. Even under flood conditions, they retain their watertightness. Under levees on the lower Mississippi, the U. S. Corps of Engineers specify and use only coated corrugated steel pipe.

DRAINAGE GATES

Flap and screw lift-operated steel water control gates are two designs used on levees. Screw lift operated gates are used where special control is desired, but they require timely opening and closing.

Both flap and slide gates are available with round or rectangular openings. Flap gates are available from 4-in. diam. to 120 in. Slide gates can be specified from 6 in. by 6 in. through 120 in. by 120 in. and 6 in. to 120 in. diameter. Radial and roller type gates are also available.

Fig. 13-8. Levee culverts and their control gates are subject to periodic inspections because they are expected to be dependable over a long span of years. Most levee culverts are of corrugated steel pipe.

REFERENCES

1. From Iowa Engineering Experiment Station Bulletin 121, Iowa State Univ., Ames, Iowa.

2. *Water Control Gates*, Metal Products Division, Armco Steel Corp., Middletown, Ohio, Catalog G-3204, 1964, 88 pp.

Fig. 14-1. Access shaft for tunnel, 16 ft. in diameter, 30 ft. deep, completed in three working days. Four-flange steel tunnel liner plates were used for the shaft and the tunnel.

CHAPTER 14 Tunnels, Shafts, Caissons

INTRODUCTION

The "open-trench" method of placing underground conduits has in the past been commonly used on new construction of culverts, sewers and underpasses. Interference with traffic, as well as inconvenience to and disruption of business or industry is an undesirable and costly consequence of "open-trench" emplacement. Tunneling is a safe and practical alternative. Fig. 14-1.

More than forty years of field experience with strong, lightweight pressed steel liner plates has popularized the tunneling method of construction. These plates, plus modern excavating and material handling equipment, and increasing knowledge of effective soil stabilization techniques, have led to many thousands of feet of small tunnel jobs completed each year.

Tunneling with steel liner plates means less excavation and less backfilling. Expensive pavements and utilities need not be destroyed and replaced. Future expense caused by street or track settlement can be avoided.

GENERAL APPLICATIONS

Uses of steel liner plates include conduits under railways, highways and streets—for culverts, storm drains, sanitary sewers, and as underpasses for pedestrians, livestock, aggregate conveyors, utility lines, (Fig. 14-2), and freight. Other applications are: lining failing masonry structures such as culverts, sewers (Fig. 14-3); and highway and railway tunnels; mine and sewer entry shafts; steam and utility tunnels and foundation caissons for bridges, buildings, and towers.

Fig. 14-2. Corrugated liner plate tunnel driven under railroad track serves as a conduit to protect a large steel water line.

Liner plates may act as a temporary conduit or skin to be lined by other materials. They also serve alone as the permanent lining or conduit itself. Installation, including bolting, is necessarily from the inside.

Non-tunneling uses of steel liner plates include storage bins and surge tanks.

DESIGN DATA

Steel liner plates are produced in two general designs: (1) four-flange type with abutting end joints, and (2) two-flange type with lapped offset end joints. Offset longitudinal-joint-type liner plate has a relatively deep corrugation continuous through the joint. See Fig. 14-4.

The two-flange plates are supplied with deep corrugations running through the lapped end joints. Four-flange plates are normally supplied with various types of corrugated backs by individual manufacturers, but with no important differences in physical properties or strength. Dimensions, physical properties and gages are given in the accompanying tables as supplied by the manufacturers. Tables 14-1, 14-2, 14-3, and 14-4. Section properties are reproduced from the manufacturers' data.

Liner plates are normally furnished in black steel. They can be galvanized if desired, which is done after fabrication. An additional asphalt coating can be specified for extremely corrosive conditions.

Fig. 14-3. Lining a failed rigid pipe with a 72-in. diameter offset-type steel liner plate.

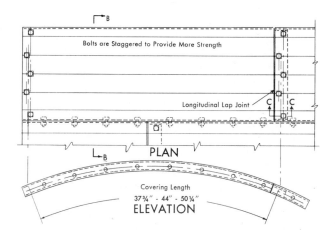

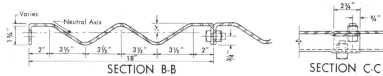

Fig. 14-4. Details of offset type liner plate.

Table 14-1 Sectional Properties and Weights of 2-Flange, Lap-Joint Steel Liner Plates[1]

For 18-inch wide section

Gage	Uncoated Thickness T in In.	Area of Section A in In.^{2}	Moment of Inertia I in In.^{4}	Section Modulus S in In.^{3}	Radius of Gyration r in In.	N. A. to Outer Fiber x in In.	Approx. Plate Weights Including Bolts, in Pounds		
							12 Pi Plate	14 Pi Plate	16 Pi Plate
14	0.0747	1.7237	0.6202	0.5809	0.5998	0.7571	25	28	31
12	0.1046	2.4266	0.8847	0.8229	0.6038	0.7795	33	37	42
10	0.1345	3.1292	1.1528	1.0624	0.6070	0.7994	41	47	52
8	0.1644	3.8382	1.4306	1.3064	0.6105	0.8193	49	56	63
7	0.1793	4.1947	1.5788	1.4372	0.6135	0.9308	53	61	68
5	0.2092	4.8949	1.8558	1.6707	0.6157	0.8485	61	70	79
3	0.2391	5.6104	2.1470	1.9166	0.6186	0.8689	70	80	90

Table 14-2 Ultimate Longitudinal Seam Strength of Offset-Type Liner Plates[1]

In Pounds*

PLATE GAGE	14	12	10	8	7	5	3
STRENGTH LB. FT.	20,000	30,000	47,000	55,000	62,000	87,000	92,000

* In 14 through 7 gage structures, longitudinal bolts are ASTM A-307, ⅝″ diameter by 1¼″ long. In 5 and 3 gage, ASTM A-449, ⅝″ diameter by 1½″ long. A ¼″ longer bolt is supplied for the center corrugation.

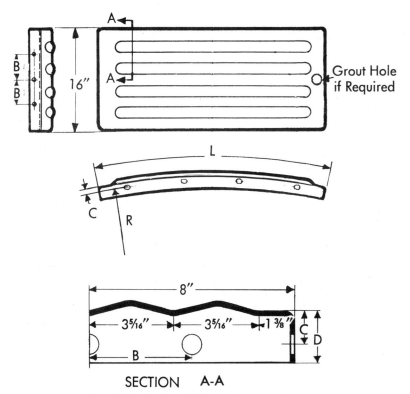

Fig. 14-5A. Details of 4-flange liner plate—Type 1.

Table 14-3   Sectional Properties and Weights of 4-Flange Tunnel Liner Plate—Type 1[2]

For 16-inch-wide Section

Gage	Uncoated Thickness T in In.	Area of Section A in In.²	Moment of Inertia I in In.⁴	Section Modulus S in In.³	Radius of Gyration r in In.	N. A. to Outer Fiber x in In.	Approximate Plate Weights Including Bolts, in Pounds	
							Full (37¹¹⁄₁₆″) Plate	Half Plate
11	0.1196	2.4375	0.7431	0.3890	0.5521	0.5849	27.7	14.7
7	0.1793	3.6093	1.0307	0.5516	0.5344	0.6314	40.9	21.7
3	0.2391	4.875	1.8638	0.9030	0.6183	0.6859	54.9	28.9
(⁵⁄₁₆ in.)	0.3125	6.0936	2.3845	1.1268	0.6255	0.7588	68.6	36.1
(³⁄₈ in.)	0.3750	7.3593	3.3854	1.5462	0.6781	0.8105	82.3	43.3

Engineers differ on the magnitude of loads bearing on the tunnel lining, and also on whether the lining should possess a low or high section modulus. Experience on the part of both the engineer and the contractor is the best guide for determining dimensions, shape and proper gages and type of plate under various conditions of soil, water and installation procedures.

Borings are helpful but not always reliable in determining the character of the underground conditions.

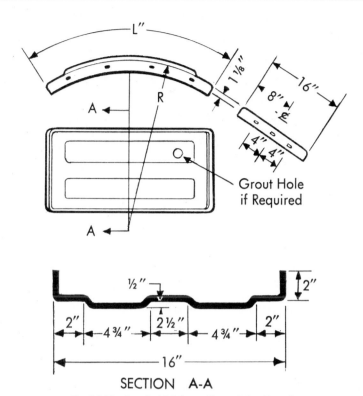

Grout Hole
if Required

SECTION A-A

Fig. 14-5B. Details of 4-flange liner plate—Type 2.

**Table 14-4   Sectional Properties and Weights of
4-Flange Liner Plate—Type 2[3]**

For 16-inch-wide Section

Gage	Uncoated Thickness T in In.	Area of Section A in In.^{2}	Moment of Inertia I in In.^{4}	Section Modulus S in In.^{3}	Radius of Gyration r in In.	N. A. to Outer Fiber x in In.	Approx. Plate Weights Including Bolts, in Pounds		
							Full* Plate	Half Plate	Quarter Plate
12	0.1046	2.1472	0.7347	0.3716	0.5850	0.0231	24.5	13.3	7.7
10	0.1345	2.7469	0.9283	0.4728	0.5813	0.0367	31.3	17.0	9.8
8	0.1644	3.3408	1.1156	0.5722	0.5779	0.0502	38.0	20.6	11.9
7	0.1793	3.6347	1.2066	0.6210	0.5762	0.0569	41.3	22.4	12.9
5	0.2092	4.2203	1.3849	0.7177	0.5729	0.0702	48.0	25.9	14.9
(¼ in.)	0.2500	5.0106	1.6196	0.8472	0.5685	0.0884	55.5	29.9	17.1
(⁵⁄₁₆ in.)	0.3125	6.2026	1.9616	1.0412	0.5624	0.1160	68.5	36.8	21.0
(⅜ in.)	0.3750	7.3724	2.2855	1.2310	0.5568	0.1434	81.3	43.5	24.6

* Full Plate 16″ wide x 37¹¹⁄₁₆″ long.

INSTALLATION NOTES

Steel liner plates are installed to support the ground exposed by the mining operations. The excavated opening should fit closely the outside shape of the liner plates.

Where too much ground is removed, the annular space between plates and ground should be backfilled promptly or temporarily packed with hay and later grouted. Backfill may consist of pneumatically placed pea gravel, lean grout, sand or other suitable material.

Some of the liner plates should be provided with grout holes, and a sufficient number of these installed so that grouting can be effectively done at various levels. Grout or backfill should be kept as close to the heading as possible, using grout stops behind the plates where necessary. When grout is used for backfill, it should be injected in lower holes first, moving up as the back space is filled. Plugs, preferably threaded, should be installed in holes after filling at each one.

With extremely heavy loads or a tunnel too large for practical use of liner plates alone, reinforcing rings of I-beam or T-section may be used. In unstable soils—where ground will not remain in place long enough to excavate for a liner plate—the ground can be held with steel poling plates, wood spiling boards, or a shield and breast boards in the face. Chemical stabilization of the soil is also practicable in some cases. Tunneling machines are useful for long lines and in uniform soils.

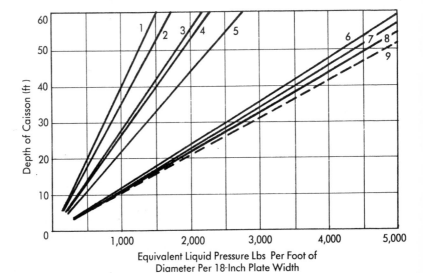

Fig. 14-6. Equivalent fluid pressure for caisson construction.

① Clay: Lumpy & dry.
  Earth: loose & either dry or slightly moist.

② Earth: Fairly moist & packed.

③ Earth: Perfectly dry & packed.

④ Clay, sand and gravel mixture.

⑤ Drained river sand.

⑥ Earth: Soft flowing mud.

⑦ Clay: Damp & plastic.

⑧ Earth: Soft, packed mud.

⑨ Hydrostatic pressure of water.

CAISSON CONSTRUCTION

The load to be carried by a caisson may be computed by known methods of determining horizontal pressure at a specified depth and multiplying this by one-half the caisson diameter. Unit pressures of some soils at various depths, assuming that pressure increases uniformly with depth, are shown in Fig. 14-6. The required thickness of liner plates may be selected from safe load tables for the type liner plate used.

Example

Soil: Damp plastic clay
Depth of caisson: 40 ft
Diameter of caisson: 20 ft
From the graph (Fig. 14-6):
  Load per 18-in. ring per ft of diameter = 3500 lb

$$3500 \times \frac{20 \text{ ft}}{2} = 35,000 \text{ lb per 18-in. lap joint}$$
     or 23,300 lb per ft of seam or joint.

Ultimate lap joint strength for No. 3 gage plates with ASTM A-449 high strength steel bolts = 92,000 lb per ft of seam*

Factor of safety $= \dfrac{92,000}{23,300} = 3.95$

---

*From Table 14-2, based on 2-flange offset-type plates.
For additional data on liner plate *underpasses*, see next chapter.

REFERENCES

1. *Armco Liner Plate*, Metal Products Div., Armco Steel Corp., Middletown, Ohio, Catalog LP-7865, 1965, 24 pp.
2. White, T. L., *Properties of Liner Plates*, Commercial Shearing & Stamping Co., Youngstown, Ohio, Catalog 300-Cl, 1958, 9 pp.
3. *Republic Tunnel Liner Plates*, Republic Steel Corp., Mfg. Div., Youngstown, Ohio. Catalog G-142, 1963, 14 pp.

Fig. 15-1A. *Above:* Giant sized vehicular steel underpass being constructed under an express highway.

Fig. 15-1B. *Right:* The shape of the underpass and the dimensions (in centimeters) is given in this sketch. The span and rise are 7140 and 6790 cm, respectively, or 23 ft 5 in. by 22 ft 3 in.

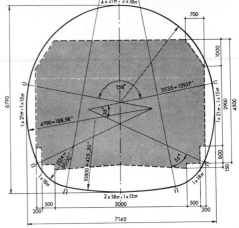

CHAPTER 15 **Underpasses and Service Tunnels**

GENERAL CONSIDERATIONS

Underground conduits serve practical purposes far beyond drainage, sewerage and water supply. As underpasses, they assure safe movement of people, vehicles, and livestock across busy highways, streets or railroads.

In industry, conveyance tunnels mean a smooth flow of merchandise, materials or equipment, with weather protection and freedom from surface interference. Service tunnels and conduits protect and provide access to vital utility lines.

VEHICULAR UNDERPASSES

Large underpasses serve as grade separations for automotive and railway traffic. For example, a county or local road can be carried under an Interstate Highway or railroad often at less cost than by building a bridge. Fig. 15-1.

UNDERPASSES FOR PEDESTRIANS AND LIVESTOCK

Pedestrian underpasses find their principal use in protecting people, including school children, who would otherwise be forced to cross dangerous railway tracks, streets or highways. The industrial organization that includes underpasses from parking lots to plant as part of its safety program benefits also in improved worker morale.

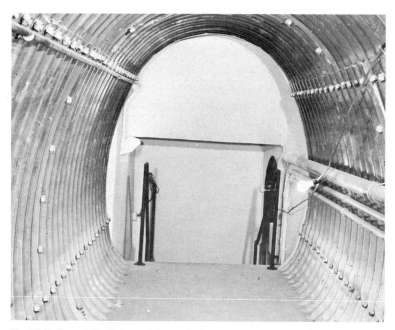

Fig. 15-2. Connection between a large city bank and a nearby drive-in banking facility and parking lot is provided by a structural plate steel underpass.

Fig. 15-3. Corrugated steel cattle pass under a local road. An earth floor is used.

Safety is not the only advantage. Where a business, industry or institution is divided by a busy street or railroad, an underpass is the most convenient and direct means of access from one part of the property to another. Lost time is avoided.

Farms and ranches, too, are more frequently than ever before divided by a highway or railroad, requiring livestock to make dangerous crossings. An opening or stock pass under the railroad is the most satisfactory solution.

Fig. 15-4. Giant structural steel plate reclaim tunnel houses belt conveyor equipment on large western dam construction. It is 1600 ft long, with a span of 16 ft 7 in. and a rise of 18 ft 3 in.

SERVICE TUNNELS AND CONDUITS

When a plant property is divided by a roadway or other barrier to efficient materials handling, a tunnel joins the property most economically. Examples include:

• A warehouse on the opposite side of a track from the plant
• Opening a new raw material pit beyond a roadway
• Contractors and aggregate companies make use of tunnels and belt conveyors under aggregate storage piles
• Mining companies use steel tunnel linings for entries, escapeways, shafts, haulageways, overcasts and other locations.

Where water, steam and gas lines, sewers or power cables must pass between buildings or beneath embankments or other surface obstacles, modern engineering practice most often places them within a conduit to protect against direct loading, impact, corrosion, temperature extremes, and against industrial or military sabotage.

When encasing sewers or high pressure lines, conduits help protect the fill and surface installations from damage in case of sudden breaks.

Circumstances will dictate tunnel or conduit size. If sufficiently large to walk through, better access for inspection and repairs results.

Brackets, hangers or cushioning bases are easily installed.

MATERIALS FOR CONSTRUCTION

Tunnels, underpasses and conduits can be built of steel, wood, concrete, vitrified clay or other materials. Of these, corrugated steel is perhaps most

Fig. 15-5. A missile plant is served by means of a large diameter steel underpass that connects various parts of the facility. A waterproof plastic envelope helps keep the interior bone-dry.

Fig. 15-6. Access tunnel of structural plate pipe on an overseas missile tracking site protects personnel from lethal radio frequency waves generated by radar transmitter.

widely accepted because of its superior strength-to-weight ratio, ease of installation and salvability on temporary installations.

The three basic types of corrugated steel structures are steel plate linings, structural plates and standard corrugated pipe.

STANDARD CORRUGATED PIPE AND PIPE-ARCHES

Sizes range from 8 to 96 in. diam. for full round pipe and from 18 x 11 to 85 x 54 in. for pipe-arches. For dimensional data and gages see Chapter 1.

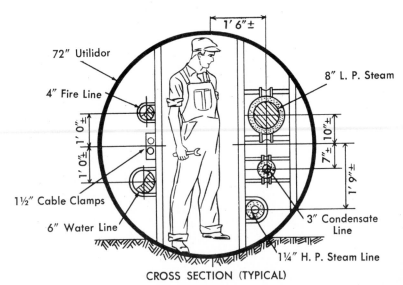

CROSS SECTION (TYPICAL)

Fig. 15-7. Cross-section of a 72-in. corrugated steel "utilidor" or service tunnel equipped with brackets and clamps for supporting various utility lines.

STRUCTURAL AND LINER PLATES

Structural Plates are available for diameters and spans of 5 to 20 ft or more. For dimensional data and gages, see Chapter 1.

Liner Plates for tunnel structures are available in circular, arch and other shapes particularly for lining old structures. Circular shapes range from 48 in. to 15 ft or more in diameter. For dimensions and available gages see Chapter 14.

For other shapes and dimensional data, consult the manufacturer. For conveyor covers and aerial conduits or overpasses, see Chapter 20 and Chapter 21.

END AND INTERIOR FINISH

Appearance and cost are the factors that usually govern the type of end treatment on an underpass or tunnel. Drainage, pavement, wall brackets, lighting and interior finish should be in keeping with the location and purpose of the installation.

Fig. 15-8. Roomy two-lane underpass under an important highway. For other views and data, see the beginning of this chapter.

Fig. 16-1. Driving corrugated steel sheeting through the ice for a float-plane base.

PART **III**

Construction
Products

CHAPTER 16 **Sheeting,
Light-Weight**

Steel sheeting or sheet piling is quite commonly used where bank erosion is to be prevented or earth retained, as in the case of trenches, cofferdams, bulkheads and cutoff walls. Comparatively light-weight corrugated steel sheets are now being used for these purposes where the loads do not exceed the strength limitations of the section. Fig. 16-1.

Advantages which sheeting offers are:

1. There are units to suit variou; service conditions
2. Because of size and weight they are easy to handle
3. Ease and speed of driving
4. Ample strength
5. Resistance to damage to the driving and leading edges
6. Ability to be salvaged readily and re-used frequently
7. Ease of storage and shipping

Because of the many uses to which steel sheeting is put, several types are needed to best meet varying conditions. Two widely used types are interlocking and flange. (See Table 16-1). The interlocking type is used where practical watertightness is desired, as in cutoff walls. Flange type is commonly used for sheeting trenches, particularly where watertightness is not essential. The flanges can butt against each other, or alternate sections can be reversed so that the flanges overlap.

Fig. 16-2. Overflow or spillway of steel sheeting for a small pond.

DIMENSIONAL DATA

Flange type units are 12 or 16 in. wide, depending on manufacturer, in 12 to 3 gage. Standard lengths are multiples of 2 ft, from 6 to 20 ft.

Interlocking type units have a nominal covering width of 14, 15 or 16 in. and are manufactured in 12, 10, 8 and 7 gage. Standard lengths are multiples of 2 ft, from 6 to 20 ft.

Sheeting used for temporary purposes is generally of black (uncoated) steel. For permanent dams and cutoff walls the sheeting may be galvanized or bituminous coated or both.

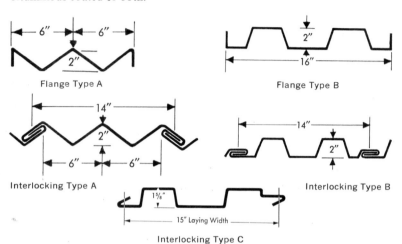

Flange Type A

Flange Type B

Interlocking Type A

Interlocking Type B

Interlocking Type C

Fig. 16-3. Types of lightweight corrugated steel sheeting or piling.

Table 16-1 Sectional Properties—Corrugated Steel Sheeting
Per Section Width

Type	Property	12 Ga.	10 Ga.	8 Ga.	7 Ga.	5 Ga.	3 Ga.
	Uncoated thickness	0.1046	0.1345	0.1644	0.1793	0.2092	0.2391
Flange—A 12 in. wide	Area of section, in.^{2}	1.785	2.295	2.805	3.059	3.570	4.080
	Weight per ft/length, lb	6.22	8.00	9.78	10.67	12.45	14.22
	Moment I—in.^{4}/Sect.	0.5653	0.7269	0.8885	0.9690	1.1306	1.2922
	Sect. mod. s—in.^{3}/Sect.	0.5180	0.6571	0.7924	0.8585	0.9889	1.1154
Flange—B 16 in. wide	Area of section, in.^{2}	2.406	3.094		4.124		
	Weight per ft/length, lb	8.27	10.781		14.375		
	Moment I—in.^{4}/Sect.	1.4937	1.9207		2.5604		
	Sect. mod. s—in.^{3}/Sect.	1.185	1.526		2.030		
Interlocking—A 14 in. wide	Area of section, in.^{2}	2.432	3.127	3.822	4.169	4.864	
	Weight per ft/length, lb	8.75	11.25	13.75	15.00	17.50	
	Moment I—in.^{4}/Sect.	0.6788	0.8783	1.0804	1.1820	1.3892	
	Sect. Mod. s—in.^{3}/Sect.	0.6258	0.8023	0.9776	1.0647	1.2399	
Interlocking—B 14 in. wide	Area of section, in.^{2}	2.406	3.094		4.124		
	Weight per ft/length, lb	8.27	10.78		14.375		
	Moment I—in.^{4}/Sect.	1.458	1.875		2.50		
	Sect. mod. s—in.^{3}/Sect.	1.190	1.531		2.040		
Interlocking—C 15 in. wide	Area of section, in.^{2}	2.29	3.00	3.68	4.00		
	Weight per ft/length	8.16	10.5	12.8	14.0		
	Moment I—in.^{4}/Sect.	0.881	1.162	1.42	1.55		
	Sect. mod. s per ft/wall	0.848	1.10	1.31	1.40		

Several types of *corner sections*, along with a T and X section for intermediate bulkheads and junctions, are available for the interlocking type. Sectional properties of interlocking and flange sheeting panels are given in Table 16-1.

WALES AND STRUTS FOR STEEL SHEETING

Steel sheeting without bracing will support earth loads if driven to sufficient depth and if strong enough. Generally, however, it is economical to use a lighter sheeting and support it with a system of wales and struts or anchors. When sheeting is used as a retaining wall, the wales are placed against the face of the wall and supported by ties extending through the wall to anchors placed in unyielding earth.

In trenches, the wales are placed on the trench side of the sheeting and are supported by struts extending across the trench from wale to wale. Fig. 16-5. Selection of the gage and cross section of sheeting and the design of the wales and supporting members are essentially the same problem in either a trench or wall condition.

Soil pressures vary with types of earth, moisture content and depth. Sheeting loads are commonly computed by means of equivalent fluid pressures, tables for which are available in many engineering handbooks.

Starting with the equivalent fluid pressure, the wale spacing for various gages of sheeting can be determined from Fig. 16-6. With wale spacing known, the loads on the wales, and the size of the wales and their supports, can be determined by the approximate method outlined below.

Often wale and strut material will be available on the job. The problem then becomes one of determining maximum spacing allowable for the material at hand.

Fig. 16-4. Elimination of unsightly and expensive erosion along lake shores and streams is a popular use of steel sheeting.

LOAD DISTRIBUTION ON WALES

The load per foot of wale (W) is computed this way:

Let: p = Equivalent fluid pressure
                              d = Depth below surface to wale (in ft)
Then: (1st Wale) $W_1 = p/8 \, (d_1 + d_2)^2$
                              (2nd Wale) $W_2 = p/4 \, (d_3 + d_1) \, (d_3 - d_1)$

Succeeding wales are figured similarly to W_2, substituting d_4 for d_3, d_2 for d_1 and so on. (Subnumbers refer to number of wale from surface.) The allowable total uniform load for any size of wale (wood or steel) and for any strut spacing may be obtained from standard beam tables.

Shear values often determine the maximum allowable load which, divided by the load per foot of wale, will give spacing of the struts in feet. The column load on each strut is the load per foot of wale multiplied by the spacing of the struts (in ft). The required size of struts can be obtained from the column loading tables in engineering handbooks.

Example: Assume a trench is to be dug to a depth of 20 ft in a wet earth soil. Equivalent fluid pressure is 40 psf. Available sheeting is 10 gage. Wales are to be spaced for equal stress in the sheeting, with the top of the sheeting loaded as a cantilever.
Then:
In the chart, Fig. 16-6, *Equal Stress in Sheeting*, locate the intersection of 40-lb fluid pressure and 10 gage line. Drop a vertical line from this point down through the lower chart, where the spacing of the wales is shown as 6, 12 and 17 ft below the ground line.

Compute load per foot on each wale:
(*1*) $W_1 = p/8 \, (d_1 + d_2)^2 = 40/8 \, (6 + 12)^2 = 1625$
(*2*) $W_2 = p/4 \, (d_3 + d_1) \, (d_3 - d_1)$
          $= 40/4 \, (17 + 6) \, (17 - 6) = 2530$
(*3*) $W_3 = p/4 \, (d_4 + d_2) \, (d_4 - d_2)$
          $= 40/4 \, (22 + 12) \, (22 - 12) = 3400$

With these loads known, it is possible to determine the required size of wales and size and spacing of struts.

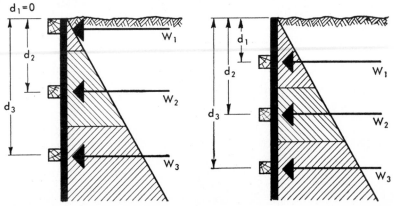

Fig. 16-5. Cross-sections of trench sheeting. Left, first wale at ground line. Right, first wale below ground line.

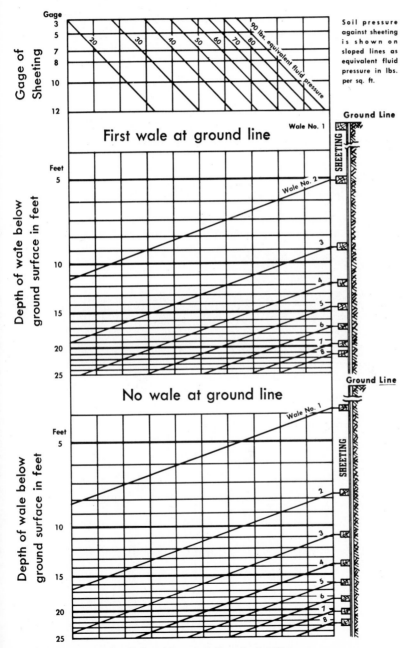

Fig.16-6. Wale spacing designed for equal stress in sheeting.

DRIVING

A hand maul or light pneumatic hammer is satisfactory for pushing metal sheeting or wood sheeting in a trench where the bottom can be excavated ahead of driving, and when the earth loads on the sheeting are light.

If the sheeting is to be driven in advance of excavation, Fig. 16-7, or the side pressures are heavy, then heavier equipment, such as a drop hammer or a pneumatic or steam pile-driver, will be needed. Under these conditions the use of heavy driving equipment will make for faster driving with less injury to the sheeting. Light equipment for this type of driving tends to batter the top edge of the sheeting and slow down the driving.

The driving equipment must be capable of supplying ample foot-pounds of energy to move the sheeting easily. A driver that strikes a heavy blow with a low velocity at impact will do the most work with least damage to the sheeting. A long, heavy sheet pile requires more energy to start it moving than a light, short section.

Soil friction on the sheeting surfaces and force required for penetration are factors hard to evaluate. Certainly, selecting the appropriate driving equipment requires knowledge of local conditions and experience with various types of equipment.

Driving heads are used when driving with hand tools or with light, narrow-driving-base pneumatic or gasoline drivers. They are generally unnecessary with gravity hammers or with larger air or steam hammers because these have a wide, flat base that will spread the blow over one or more widths of sheeting.

Fig. 16-7. Driving lightweight steel piling. It is easy to handle and has other advantages where heavy hot-rolled piling is not needed.

Fig. 16-8. Neat appearance with minimum maintenance is an important advantage of steel sheeting along the waterfront.

REFERENCES

1. *Armco Steel Sheeting*, Metal Products Div., Armco Steel Corp., Middletown, Ohio. Catalog SH-4664, 1964, 12 pp.

2. *USF Sheet Piling*, United Steel Fabricators, Inc., Wooster, Ohio, 1964.

3. *Foster Lightweight Steel Piling*, L. B. Foster Co., Pittsburgh, Pa., Catalog 900, 1964, 4 pp.

Fig. 17-1. Supplementing the abutment, a bin-type steel retaining wall provides valuable roadway space under a highway bridge.

CHAPTER 17 Retaining Walls

GENERAL

Soils and other materials have their own *angle of repose*. To maintain a steeper slope, some type of wall or support is necessary to prevent sloughing. Retaining walls are widely used for this purpose.

For low walls up to 20 ft, empirical methods are usually employed to determine earth pressures. For high walls, if a major item of a construction project, a complete soil survey and more thorough analysis of loads may be justified by possible savings.

USES OF WALLS

Retaining walls have the following uses:
1. To solve problems of limited right of way and to confine ground slopes within practical limits.
2. On road-widening and grade-separation projects.
3. To stabilize steep cut and embankment slopes (but not to stop landslides).
4. To repair breaks in roadway.
5. To prevent shore or bank erosion.
6. As wingwalls for abutments and headwalls.
7. As loading platforms or ramps.
8. For parking areas.
9. For cutoff walls or ditch checks in deep channels.
10. As aircraft splinter protection walls and barricades, or explosion walls in chemical plants.

Pressures which act upon a retaining wall tend to slide it forward, or to make it settle, or to overturn it. Determination of the magnitude, direction and point of application of pressure is a lengthy and involved procedure: the reader is directed to standard reference works on this subject.

Fig. 17-2. Retaining wall of corrugated steel lagging (bridge plank) behind a row of H piles.

Fig. 17-3. Bridge abutment of steel piles backed by corrugated steel sheeting.

An adequate foundation is necessary for satisfactory performance of a re-taining wall. Coarse-grained soils are generally satisfactory, with foundation piling used for only unusual cases.

Backfilling with predominantly clayey soils should be avoided, particularly if seepage exists in the slopes. Pervious granular soils, supplemented with pipe subdrains, ensure the most satisfactory backfill and stability of the wall.

TYPES OF WALLS

Retaining walls are of several types: gravity; cantilever (or counterfort); cribs or bins interlocked or bolted together; and wall faces supported by steel piling, wales or deadmen.

The simplest walls consist of steel piling driven to a suitable depth, and then faced or lagged with corrugated steel sheeting (see Chapter 16) or bridge plank (see Chapter 22), with or without the use of wales.

DESCRIPTION OF BIN-WALL[1]

Bin-type retaining walls are fabricated steel members, field-assembled into a series of connected closed-face bins, each 10 ft long. Component parts are bolted together at the installation site.

The various members comprising the wall are illustrated in Fig. 17-4. They consist of (1) steel base plates which support (2) vertical connectors with (3) S-shaped horizontal stringers connected to vertical units to form front and rear walls, and (4) S-shaped spacers or transverse members to separate front and rear walls. Miscellaneous parts include caps, top stringer stiffeners, connecting channels for attaching stringers to the verticals, and miscellaneous bolts, nuts and spring nuts.

Unit Number	Name	Description
1.	Vertical Connector	Vertical member connecting all other units
2.	Vertical Connector cap	Cover for front vertical connector
3.	Stringer Stiffener	Top flange protector
4.	Stringer	Horizontal longitudinal members in front and rear walls
5.	Connecting Channel	Connector for attaching stringers to vertical connectors
6.	Spacer	Transverse members that separate the front and rear vertical connectors
7.	Bottom Spacer	Special bottom transverse member
8.	Base Plate	Installation plate on which the vertical connector rests
9.	1¼" x ⅝" bolts	
10.	⅝" nuts	
11.	⅝" spring nuts	

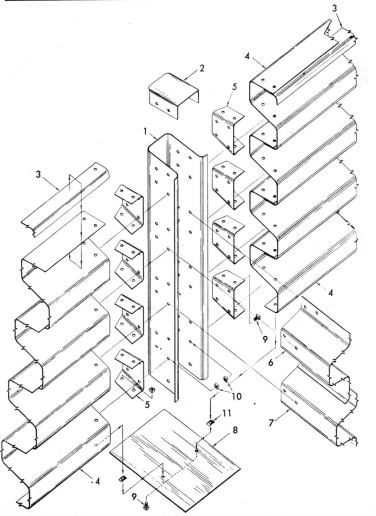

Fig. 17-4. "Exploded" view of a front panel joint of steel bin-type retaining wall, as seen from the rear.

Base plates serve primarily to build the wall to proper line, grade and batter. They are not intended to carry the load of the wall or its contents. If the soil within the bins settles, the wall may settle slightly and so relieve the stress in the units comprising the wall. When a wall is set on a solid rock foundation, a layer of compressible soil (8 to 12 in.) must be placed under each base plate. The transverse section of the wall is sufficiently rigid to minimize any possible bulging of the wall.

Stringer and spacer units are available in different gages. This makes it possible to design a wall with a uniform bin or panel length of 10 ft, regardless of wall height, and at the same time effect economies in design by varying the gage of metal required to resist pressure at various points. The units are shaped to eliminate voids in the fill material and to prevent water from standing on the face of the units.

Gages. The principal elements of steel bin-walls, the stringers along the face and back, are of progressively heavier gage from top to bottom of wall. See Table 17-2. The spacers, front to back of wall, are of heavier gage with greater lengths and higher wall designs, as shown in Table 17-3.

Coatings. Steel retaining walls are generally supplied with a galvanized finish, including fasteners. For particularly corrosive conditions, various panel units and vertical connectors may be ordered bonded with asbestos or may be suitably field coated.

DESIGN CONSIDERATIONS

A most important feature of the steel bin-wall is the U-shaped vertical connector to which other units are bolted. This design feature is to be contrasted to "cribbing" in which the units overlap at the corners. See Fig. 17-4.

Stability of a cellular crib or bin type wall is generally secured through weight of the fill material in the crib or bin.

A wall should be placed or driven deep enough (generally 1.5 to 3 ft) to resist sliding forward along the plane of the base. If located along a body of water, it may be necessary to set the wall deeper and to protect against erosion. The base width of the wall should be sufficient to resist overturning and settlement at the toe which can arise from overloading or crushing of the soil.

The units of a wall should have sufficient strength to resist shear, and the connections between units should resist bulging.

DESIGN WIDTHS AND HEIGHTS

In steel bin-walls, five basic design widths exist: *A, B, C, D, and E,* as shown in Fig. 17-5. Widths vary from 5.5 ft to 14.3 ft and in general are about one-half the height of the wall. (Wall height is measured over-all, not just ground level to top of wall.)

Table 17-1   Load Conditions for Retaining Walls

Batter	Level Surcharge	Slight Surcharge With Superimposed Load	Infinite Surcharge
Wall On 1:6 Batten	① R = .45	② R = .50	③ ·R = .55
Wall Vertical	③ R = .55	④ R = .60	⑤ R = .65

**Table 17-2 Gages and Number of Steel Bin-Wall Elements Required
for Walls of Various Heights*[1]**

Wall Height		Stringers				Stringer Stiffener
		16 Ga	14 Ga	12 Ga	10 Ga	
Feet	Feet–In.	9.5 Ft	9.5 Ft	9.5 Ft	9.5 Ft	9.5 Ft
4.00	4-0	4				1
5.33	5-4	6				1
6.67	6-8	8				1
8.00	8-0	10				1
9.33	9-4	12				1
10.67	10-8	14				1
12.00	12-0	14	2			1
13.33	13-4	14	4			1
14.67	14-8	14	6			1
16.00	16-0	14	8			1
17.33	17-4	14	8	2		1
18.67	18-8	14	8	4		1
20.00	20-0	14	8	6		1
21.33	21-4	14	8	8		1
22.67	22-8	14	8	10		1
24.00	24-0	14	8	12		1
25.33	25-4	14	8	14		1
26.67	26-8	14	8	14	2	1
28.00	28-0	14	8	14	4	1
29.33	29-4	14	8	14	6	1
30.67	30-8	14	8	14	8	1

*NOTE: This table gives the total number of stringers and stringer stiffeners for front and back of
a single 10-ft panel or element of standard bin-wall.
Gages apply to 1:6 batter walls only.

**Table 17-3 Gages and Lengths of Spacers (Front to Rear)
of Spacer Elements for Steel Bin-Walls[1]**

Design	A	B	C	D	E
Gage	16	16	14	12	12
Length in Feet	5.2	7.4	9.6	11.8	14.0

For cross-sections of DESIGNS A, B, C, D and E, see Figs. 17-6 and 17-7.

Where there is a limited or level surcharge, it is conservative practice to
specify base width equal to about 45 per cent of over-all height. With a heavily
surcharged wall, base width should be increased to at least 55 per cent of the
height. For recommended designs, see Figs. 17-6 and 17-7, and the chart on
loading conditions, Table 17-1.

To increase wall stability, a batter or inclination of 1 to 6 (or 2 in. per ft of
height) has been adopted in the accompanying design charts. If the wall is to
be installed without batter, additional stability can be obtained by selecting a
design with a greater base width.

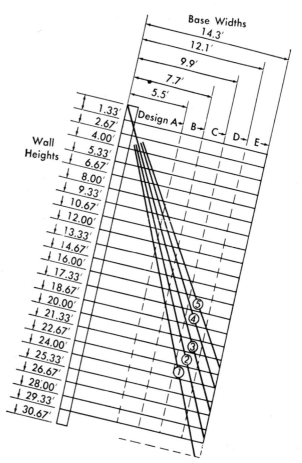

Fig. 17-5. Design chart for determining base widths for various designs and steel bin-wall heights.

Example:

Required: Find wall base width.

Assume a 20-ft high wall on a 1:6 batter. Surcharge, infinite.

Approach: In Table 17-1, these conditions are found in column 4.

In Fig. 17-5, line *3* intercepts the 20-ft height line about the midpoint of Design D, which has a base width of 12.1 ft.

The solution can also be obtained by using the formula:

$$R = base\ width \div height, or$$
$$base\ width = R \times height$$
$$= .55 \times 20 = 11$$

Nearest design is D, or 12.1 ft

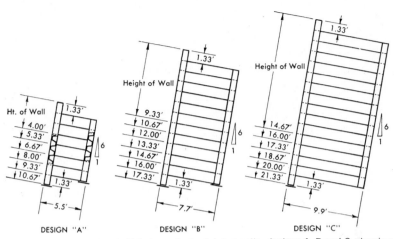

Fig. 17-6. Cross sections of bin-type steel retaining walls, designs A, B and C, showing some of the standard sizes available. Walls may be vertical as well as on a batter as shown.

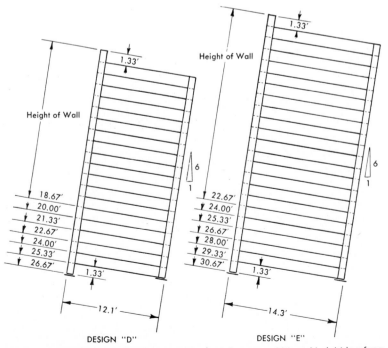

Fig. 17-7. Dimensions of designs D and E. The ratio between width and height is a function of surcharge and material behind the walls.

Fig. 17-8. How base width and height of bin-type retaining wall can be varied.

CHANGES IN ELEVATION

Stringers may be erected on a horizontal plane and stepped in multiples of 16 in. as in Fig. 17-8 to meet a change in grade. Where a change in wall height requires a change in the base width, a 'split' vertical unit is attached to the transverse spacers at an intermediate joint.

CURVED WALLS

Bin-type steel retaining walls can be built to almost any degree of curvature or with sharp change of direction tangentially. Four methods are illustrated in Fig. 17-10. The data applies to the five designs of walls (*A, B, C, D, and E*, (*continued on page 294*)

Fig. 17-9. Series of curved steel retaining walls. Purpose of this installation is to protect a micro-wave relay station on a mountain top.

Here is an example on the use of the curvature chart:

Required: Build a Design D wall 20 ft high on a 1400-ft radius curve.

Approach: Method 2 applies in this case. (Method 1 would apply only for very flat curves of 3900-ft radius. Methods 3 and 4 are required only for curves of 700 ft or less.) Use one set of short stringers for each five panel sections.

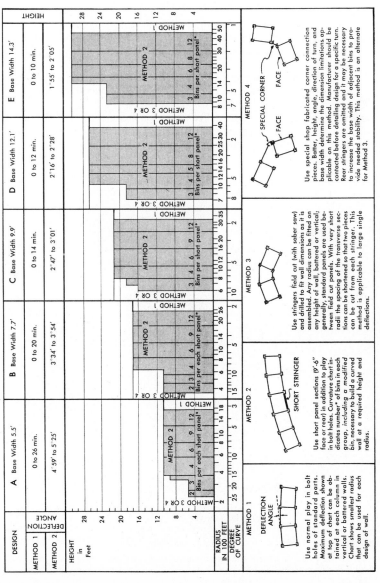

Fig. 17-10. Curvature chart for steel bin-type retaining walls on a 1 to 6 batter.

with varying base widths) in limited heights for 1:6 batter. For vertical walls, they apply without height restrictions. Consideration should be given to placing curved walls vertically instead of on a batter.

The second and third lines at the top of the chart, Fig. 17-10, show the deflection angles (between faces of adjacent stringers) that can be obtained at one vertical connector, using either Method 1 or 2. The first three methods use standard parts and are, therefore, more economical. Method 4 requires special shop drawings and fabrication.

Right angle turns in vertical walls can be made by starting a new wall at the rear of the first wall and using the end transverse section for a face panel. For battered walls, a special corner closure can be provided.

INSTALLATION CONSIDERATIONS

Retaining walls are more effective and less susceptible to failure if used near the top of a slope than at the bottom. Soundings or borings should be made to determine the subsoil, ground water and foundation conditions. A uniform foundation is best.

By trenching only for the walls of the bins, earth below the ground line need not be disturbed. Any earth that is excavated can be used to backfill the preceding bins.

Assembly of the wall can be handled either by building it piece by piece or by making a subassembly of the transverse section members, lifting them in place with a small crane, and then connecting with the stringers. Fig. 17-11.

Backfill should have a high percentage of graded granular material with a

Fig. 17-11. To widen an access road on the edge of a 100-ft cliff, a steel retaining wall was an economical solution. Careful compaction assures a sturdy installation.

Fig. 17-12. Revetments or steel retaining walls, set vertically and filled with earth, protect military planes in Vietnam against damage by mortar and rifle fire.

maximum size of 3 in. Bank-run gravel is ideal. No lumps, sod, cinders or frozen material should be used.

Tamp backfill carefully around the base of the wall and then place in 6-in. layers, with enough tamping to minimize settlement. It is not advisable to tamp fill into the stringers and spacers.

When a perforated metal underdrain is specified behind the wall, a properly graded pervious granular backfill must be used around the pipe and extended above the elevation of any seepage zones.

REFERENCE

1. Armco Bin-Type Retaining Walls, Metal Products Div., Armco Steel Corp., Middletown, Ohio, Catalog BW-3565, 1965, 16 pp.

Fig. 18-1. Steel saves lives. Out of control, a tractor trailer on an expressway during the rush hour, was stopped short of catastrophe by a steel median guardrail.

CHAPTER 18 Guardrail

INTRODUCTION

Efficient highway guardrail must perform several important safety functions. It warns drivers and protects out-of-control vehicles from disaster on high embankments, sharp curves, steep grades and slippery surfaces. On divided highways with narrow medians and large volumes of traffic, it helps prevent head-on or across-the-road collisions. Fig. 18-1. Guardrail also protects both vehicle and structure at bridges, grade separations, sign supports and other necessary obstacles. Guardrail helps keep minor accidents from becoming major ones.

"Every highway should be designed, through judicious arrangement and balance of geometric features, to preclude or minimize the need for guardrail."[1] Maximum roadside safety then is the direct and prime responsibility of the design engineer. The final check and adjustment of guardrail installations should be made through field inspection and operational experience.

In addition to highway installations, guardrail finds widespread and valuable use for parking lots, parking garages and ramps, and in industries where building walls, materials and equipment need protection from trucks and other conveyors.

TYPES OF GUARDRAIL

Various types of guardrail are available, and constant research should help to develop improved features and applications. Rectangular heavy gage steel tubing has been installed on a trial basis. Meanwhile, the type in predominant current use is the "beam-type" guardrail with the W-section of formed sheet steel. In a 1962 study by an AASHO committee, of 41 states reporting,

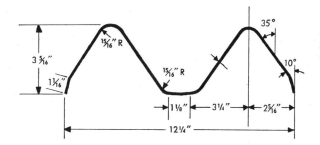

Table 18-1 Sectional Properties of Beam Guardrail[2]

per Unit Section*

Gage	Uncoated Thickness in Inches	Area of Section in Inches^2	Moment of Inertia in Inches^4	Section Modulus in Inches^3	Radius of Gyration in Inches
10	.1345	2.5555	2.9190	1.7322	1.0687
12	.1046	1.9874	2.2960	1.3640	1.0748

*Bolt holes not considered. Dimensions are nominal, subject to manufacturing tolerances. Weight of 10 gage galvanized rail is approximately 123 and 238 lb per 12½ and 25-ft lengths. Weight of 12 gage galvanized rail is approximately 97 and 186 lb per 12½ and 25-ft lengths.

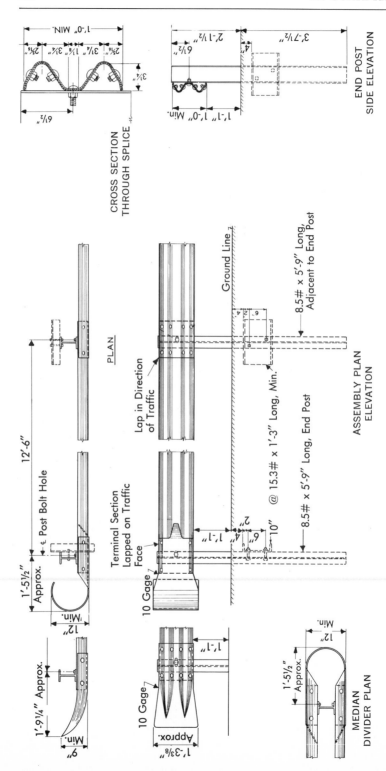

Fig. 18-2. Details of steel beam-type guardrail, showing simplicity of design and construction.

40 use beam-type rail; 24 states use it almost exclusively, and 15 also use cable type and other designs. For positive barriers on medians of various widths, some states use either (1) beam rail (plus hub rail) offset from the posts by wood blocks or (2) cables plus chain link fencing.

DESCRIPTION OF BEAM-TYPE RAIL

Cross Section. Beam-type guardrail has a W-shaped corrugated cross section 12¼ in. wide by 3¼ in. deep, of 12 gage steel sheet (class B) or 10 gage (class A).[2,3,4]

Lengths. Net lengths between posts are 12½ and 25 ft with a lap of 12½ in. See Fig. 18-2 for details and dimensions.

Sectional Properties such as end area, moment of inertia and section modulus are given in Table 18-1.

Strength of Material. Steel specified for the rail (and terminal) sections must meet AASHO Specification M 180—with a tensile strength of 80,000 and 100,000 psi for 12 gage (class B) and 10 gage (class A), and with a maximum deflection of 2 or 3 inches under the concentrated loads shown in Table 18-2

Table 18-2   Required Beam Strength For Highway Guardrail of Corrugated Sheet Steel (AASHO Spec. 180)

Class	Gage	Traffic Face Up		Traffic Face Down	
		Load in Pounds	Maximum Deflection in Inches	Load in Pounds	Maximum Deflection in Inches
A	10	2000	2.0	1600	2.0
A	10	3000	3.0	2400	3.0
B	12	1500	2.0	1200	2.0
B	12	2000	3.0	1600	3.0

when supported at 12-ft centers. Laboratory tests show that steel beam-type guardrail withstands more than three times the impact that aluminum does. See Fig. 18-3.[5]

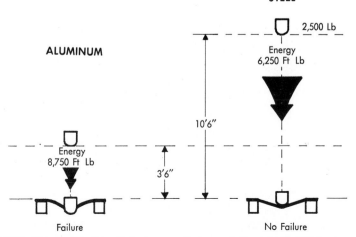

STEEL

2,500 Lb

ALUMINUM

Energy
6,250 Ft Lb

10'6"

Energy
8,750 Ft Lb

3'6"

Failure   No Failure

Fig. 18-3. Comparative strength tests prove that guardrail made of steel is stronger than those of other materials.

Coatings. The beam may be shop prime-painted. It may also be galvanized before or after fabrication with at least 2.0 oz per sq ft of spelter (total for both sides), meeting AASHO Specification M 111 or ASTM Specification A-525 (formerly A-93). ASTM A-123 applies to beams galvanized after fabrication. Terminal sections, bolts and other elements are furnished galvanized.

Vitreous-coated or reflective painted guardrail can be furnished on special order.

Guardrail test installations, nationwide, have been made since 1964 of unpainted high strength low-alloy steel that forms a dense, deep red, tightly adherent oxide coating which inhibits further corrosion.

Joints. Positive splices are achieved with a 12½-in. lap using eight specially designed splice bolts. If one section is stressed beyond its elastic limit, the load is transferred through the joint to adjacent sections; thus the rail functions as a continuous beam. Strength of the joint in moment resistance is greater than that of the rail itself. The post bolt is located in the center corrugation.

Posts. Beam guardrail can be installed with equal facility on a variety of steel, concrete or wood posts set in soil. Blocks to offset the beam 6 to 8 in. from the supporting posts are recommended to avoid a vehicle being snagged by the posts. Posts extend not more than ½ in. above the top of the beam, and about 24 to 26 in. above the ground.

Terminal Sections. Two general types of steel terminal sections are available —wing and "curled". The latter is used where end impact is possible; on median barriers, particularly, it may be supplemented by a curved vertical plate. Terminal sections on flared approaches may also consist of several types of buried anchorages.

CURVED RAILS

Beam guardrail can be installed on curves without loss of strength or safety and without tension. No special bolts are needed. Individual sections are curved in the shop to fit any radius from 20 ft to 150 ft, and beyond 150 ft are field fabricated. The traffic face of the rail can be curved either convex or concave. See Table 18-3 and Figs. 18-5 and 18-6.

Fig. 18-4. Median barriers are essential for separating traffic in opposing lanes and preventing head-on collisions which so often are fatal.

Fig. 18-5. Median rail, double-faced steel, on a sharp reverse curve and steep grade protects traffic from otherwise inevitable head-on collisions.

Table 18-3 Dimensions of Curved Guardrail[2]

L = 12' — 6"

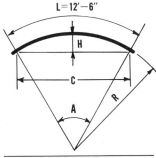

*Offsets for various degrees of curvature per 12½-ft length of guardrail.

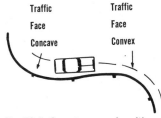

Traffic	Traffic
Face	Face
Concave	Convex

Fig. 18-6. Curvature can be either concave or convex toward traffic.

Radius R in Feet	Central Angle A Deg.-Min.	Chord C in Ft-In.	Rise* H in Inches
20	35—49	12—3⁹⁄₁₆	11⅝
25	28—39	12—4⁷⁄₁₆	9⁵⁄₁₆
30	23—52	12—4¹⁵⁄₁₆	7¹³⁄₁₆
35	20—28	12—5³⁄₁₆	6¹¹⁄₁₆
40	17—54	12—5⅜	5⅞
45	15—55	12—5½	5³⁄₁₆
50	14—19	12—5⅝	4¹¹⁄₁₆
55	13— 1	12—5¹¹⁄₁₆	4¼
60	11—56	12—5¾	3⅞
65	11— 1	12—5¾	3⅝
70	10—14	12—5¹³⁄₁₆	3⅜
75	9—33	12—5¹³⁄₁₆	3⅛
80	8—57	12—5⅞	2¹⁵⁄₁₆
85	8—26	12—5⅞	2¾
90	7—57	12—5⅞	2⅝
95	7—32	12—5⅞	2⁷⁄₁₆
100	7—10	12—5⅞	2⁵⁄₁₆
105	6—49	12—5¹⁵⁄₁₆	2¼
110	6—31	12—5¹⁵⁄₁₆	2⅛
115	6—14	12—5¹⁵⁄₁₆	2¹⁄₁₆
120	5—58	12—5¹⁵⁄₁₆	1¹⁵⁄₁₆
125	5—44	12—5¹⁵⁄₁₆	1⅞
130	5—31	12—5¹⁵⁄₁₆	1¾
135	5—18	12—5¹⁵⁄₁₆	1¾
140	5— 7	12—5¹⁵⁄₁₆	1¹¹⁄₁₆
145	4—56	12—5¹⁵⁄₁₆	1⅝
150	4—46	12—5¹⁵⁄₁₆	1⁹⁄₁₆

Fig. 18-7. Steel beam guardrail along embankments clearly marks limits of safe travel·

Bridge Installations. Beam rails are used to some extent on old truss-type bridges to protect bridge members or pedestrian walkways.

PERTINENT RECOMMENDATIONS

Following are some condensed conclusions, summaries and recommendations of the Highway Research Board Committee on need for, requirements and placement of guardrail.[1]

        1. Highways should be designed to preclude or minimize the need for guardrail

Fig. 18-8. Steel guardrails in parking lots prevent a lot of "fender bending" and broken car lights.

2. Guardrail need should be considered for (a) roadway sections on embankments, particularly high fills or with steep slopes; (b) divided highways with narrow medians, carrying large volumes of traffic; and (c) roadside hazards.

(a) *Embankment Conditions*

3. Omit guardrail on embankments with 4:1 slopes, or flatter.

4. Install on primary highways when height of fill exceeds 8 to 15 ft with slopes from 1½:1 to 3:1. For less favorable conditions, guardrail should be installed at lower heights of fill.

5. At about 20-ft fill, cost of slope flattening about equals the cost of installed guardrail.

6. A constant shoulder width is recommended on any one highway—a minimum of 4 or 5 ft.

7. For high-speed conditions, space posts with offset blocks at 6 ft 3 in. for W-section beam rail.

8. Guardrail should be in line with or in front of roadside obstructions or snag points.

9. Approach end of guardrail should be flared and anchored—offset not less than 4 ft from normal. Length of flare — 10 to 15 times end offset.

10. Guardrail ending near parapets, abutments, piers or retaining walls should be anchored to these elements.

(b) *Median Barriers*

11. Median barriers are recommended for median widths of 10, 20 and 30 ft where average daily traffic is (respectively) 15, 30, and 45 thousand vehicles or more. On medians 40 ft wide or more, omit barrier unless the two roadways are at different levels.

Fig. 18-9. Around structures, such as light standards, sign posts and bridge piers, guardrail deflects out-of-control vehicles away from the structures.

12. Median barriers on urban expressways with median 30 ft wide or less usually are blocked-out double-beam guardrail, 2 to 2.5 ft wide and 2.5 ft high.

13. At overpasses and underpasses, special treatment of the median and along the right side is recommended—particularly where twin overpass structures are used.

(c) *Highway*
    Appurtenances

14. Where both lighting and guardrail are used, light standards should be set behind the guardrail, preferably 2 ft from face of rail.

15. Sign supports on modern highways are formidable roadside obstacles and require treatment to protect supports and motorists. Length of guardrail in advance of a sign support should be 75 to 125 ft. Approach end should be flared and anchored.

16. Supports of side-mounted signs should be 2 to 4 ft behind the guardrail.

INSTALLATION NOTES

Location of Rail. On new construction, the proper location of guardrail is shown on the plans. Otherwise, local standards, preferably in line with the foregoing recommendations and printed report, could well be followed.

Posts should ordinarily be set in the ground and not rigidly imbedded in concrete unless no other choice exists—for example, set in a narrow curb in a median strip. This gives enough resistance to impact without letting the vehicle mash the rail and pass over it.

Steel posts can be driven; other post materials normally are set in excavated

Fig. 18-10. Assembling and bolting the joints of steel guardrail proceeds rapidly.

holes which may be drilled, depending on kind of soil and possible presence of rock or boulders.

Wood posts may be left high and later trimmed to a uniform height with a maximum of ½ in. showing above the rail.

Backfilling of holes should not be completed until the rail is in place and aligned. Backfill with dry earth or granular material, well tamped.

Assembling the Rail. Begin assembling rails at the far end and work back toward the point where traffic approaches the guardrail. In this way each succeeding panel is lapped so that no panel end is exposed to approaching traffic.

Splices are made before post bolts are inserted. Tightening of all bolts is done during the final aligning process. Terminal sections are bolted on last, always on top.

If special reflector tabs are used, these are generally inserted under the post bolt heads.

MAINTENANCE[6]

Well maintained guardrail is a credit to the whole highway organization. Panels or posts damaged by impact should be promptly repaired or replaced. Meanwhile, the rail can continue to provide effective protection.

Damaged panels can readily be unbolted and replaced by the maintenance crew. Earth around the posts should be thoroughly tamped as necessary.

Depending on whether the rail is painted or galvanized, the maintenance process may involve cleaning (scaling and washing), priming and painting, or may require removing the rail, galvanizing and replacing. The Illinois State Toll Road Commission has made a thorough study on these maintenance operations and their costs.[7]

REFERENCES

1. *Highway Guardrail—Determination of Need and Geometric Requirements*, Highway Research Board Special Report 81, 1964, 41 pp.
2. *Beam-Type Guard Rail*, Bethlehem Steel Corporation, Bethlehem, Pa. Booklet No. 1977.
3. *Highway and Bridge Guard Rail— Deep Beam Type*, Granco Steel Products Co., St. Louis, Mo., Cat. G-571, 1960, 8 pp.
4. *Armco FLEX-BEAM Guardrail for Safer Highways*, Metal Products Div., Armco Steel Corp., Middletown, Ohio, Cat. FB-3465, 1965, 14 pp.
5. Foreman, R. T., *A Comparison of the Energy Absorption Capacity of Steel and Aluminum Highway Beam Guardrail*, Bethlehem Steel Corp., Bethlehem, Pa., 1961, 29 pp.
6. Mallott, H. R., *Evaluating a New Guard Rail Coating System*, Indiana Toll Road Commission, Public Works Mag., New York, N. Y., April 1965, p. 124.
7. Kress, R. W., *Guardrail Maintenance*, Illinois State Toll Road Commission, Public Works Mag., New York, N. Y., Nov. 1964, p. 120.

Fig. 19-1. Testing tubular steel bridge rail at Lehigh University at Bethlehem, Pennsylvania.

CHAPTER 19 Bridge Railing

INTRODUCTION

Cautionary signs often placed near bridge approaches warn, "Bridge surface freezes before roadway." The danger can be great.

Safety is a prime purpose of a bridge railing—for out-of-control vehicles on the bridge, and for traffic below on waterways, highways or railways. A break-through can have disastrous results.

No longer is it necessary to have solid or heavy ornamental masonry railings. Specifications developed by AASHO Committee on Bridges and Structures[1] provides for more modern railings that are more open and afford excellent visibility to motorists, with ample strength and safety. Fig. 19-1.

SMOOTH FACE

According to AASHO Specifications: "Preference should be given to providing a smooth, continuous face of rail on the traffic side with the posts set back from the face of the rail. Structural continuity in the rail members, including anchorage of free ends is essential.

"The height of traffic railing shall be no less than 2'-3", measured from the top of the roadway, or curb, to the top of the rail member.

TRAFFIC RAILING LOADING

"Rail members shall be designed for a transverse load (P) of 10,000 lb divided between the various members as shown in Fig. 19-2 (AASHO Fig. 7). Rail members shall be designed for a moment at the center of the panel and at the posts of $PL/6$ for concentrated loads. The handrail members of combination railings (traffic plus pedestrian) shall be designed for a moment

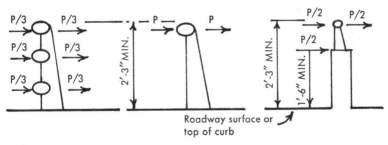

Traffic railing

Roadway surface or
top of curb

LEGEND

P = 10,000 lb.
L = Post spacing for
      traffic railing
W = 50 lb./lin. ft.
Rail load shown on left
Post load shown on right

NOTE
Rail members of
any material in
any configuration
may be used

Fig. 19-2. Minimum requirements for heights and loadings of bridge traffic railings and of combination traffic and pedestrian railings. — *Courtesy of AASHO.*

at center of panel and at posts of .1 wL^2, where $w = 50$ lb per lin ft and L is the post spacing."

Railing configurations that have been successfully tested by full scale impact tests are exempt from these provisions.

MULTIPLE RAILS—DESCRIPTION

Tubular or box channel bridge railing is made up of one-, two-, three- or four-rail sections of tubing or box channels of various shapes: rectangular, square, round, oval or others. These rails fit into recessed "notches" in the posts and fasten with special wedge bolts. The rail surface facing traffic is continuous and unbroken by posts. One- and two-rail posts mount on a parapet. Three- and four-rail posts are used on a low curb or sidewalk. Figs. 19-2, 19-3.

Post spacing depends on local conditions with a recommended maximum of 10 ft. Rails are furnished in multiple lengths for strength and ease of erection and are made continuous by means of overlapping splice joints and by expansion sections. The rails are flexible enough to be installed on any curve radius in common use today and on any grade up to 6 per cent—without special shop fabrication.

MATERIAL SPECIFICATIONS

Requirements for material should meet current AASHO Specifications.

Box-channel rails should be cold formed from 11 gage (or heavier) steel sheet, to conform to specification. For a rectangular 5 x 2 in. rail, ASTM Specification A 245 grade C applies.

Rails are galvanized to ASTM Specification A 123. The galvanizing of posts, bolts and nuts should conform with ASTM Specification A 153. Under normal conditions, the bridge railing will resist corrosion for many years without painting. If desired, the rail can be painted.

Fig. 19-3. Strength, neat appearance and freedom of view from passing vehicle are the advantages of tubular steel bridge rails set in sturdy posts at designed intervals.

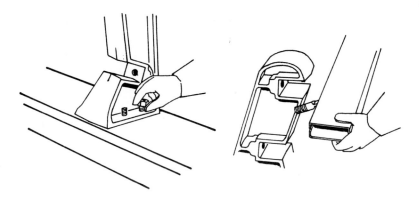

Fig. 19-4. Details of bolting box-channel rails to posts and attaching to floor. Installation of steel rails is accomplished rapidly by small crews.

INSTALLATION

Posts and rails arrive on the job ready for installation. No welding or riveting is required; after placing bolts in position, only a few nuts need be tightened. Fig. 19-4.

Post anchor bolts are set in concrete, using simple templates secured to the wall or parapet forms. Heavy anchor bolts hold each post in place.

Two men handle and place the rails and bolts while a third man handles the splices. One rail can be placed the full length of the structure. Alternatively, all the rails (two, three or four) can be installed simultaneously.

It is not necessary or recommended that all the bolts be tightened as the rail is installed, except at the end posts and posts on each side of expansion joints.

MAINTENANCE

Should a severe collision damage a rail or several rails, removal for repairs or replacement involves only loosening the rail bolts, opening the rail splices, removing the damaged portion, and inserting new rails.

MEDIAN BARRIER

For median barriers on multi-lane highway bridges, two-faced posts are available in several heights. These may be attached to the floor or to a curb of desired height and width. One, two or three rails placed on 10 to 12-in. centers complete the median barriers.

REFERENCE

1. American Association of State Highway Officials, Interim Specifications, Int. I (64), Committee on Bridges and Structures, Washington, D.C., 1964.

Fig. 20-1. Corrugated steel cover for conveyor from crusher station to stockpiles.—
Courtesy of Pit & Quarry.

CHAPTER 20 Conveyor Covers

INTRODUCTION

Transport of materials and manufactured products by belt conveyors is a major handling technique. This is especially true for metallic and non-metallic mining operations, quarries, waterside loading docks, and heavy construction and industrial projects. Many preparation, stockpiling, storage and shipping problems are handled economically for short or long overland distances by belt-conveyor. Fig. 20-1.

Numerous engineering concerns design conveyor systems. Manufacturers of equipment also have their own engineering staff who design conveyor systems to best utilize their equipment.

DESIGN CONSIDERATIONS

Belt conveyors are usually covered—mainly to prevent contamination or to protect the coal, ore, aggregates, minerals or other materials from rain and snow (and in some cases, wind). Coverings may consist of corrugated steel half-circle arch sections, horseshoe shapes, full circle or rectangular shapes, as described later. Often a walkway along one or both sides expedites repairs when needed.

Conveyor lines enjoy the advantage of flexibility, insofar as height, slope and change of direction and elevation are concerned. Belt width may vary from a few feet up to 6 ft, with 36 and 48 in. being quite common. Lengths of 2,500 ft are not unusual.

SUPPORTING STRUCTURES

Light-weight hot or cold rolled structural steel members are fabricated into trusses to carry the load between piers or bents, which also are fabricated steel. Catwalks and railings are usually added. Standard or pre-determined wind and material loadings, plus a safety factor, are used in the designs.

Fig. 20-2. Combination of conveyor cover of corrugated galvanized steel sheets and a conveyor tunnel of structural plate pipe.

Reserve strength must be provided at changes in direction and where booms, stackers or other equipment are injected in the line. Crossings over highways, railroads or buildings may require special trusses and screens.

Where conveyor lines cross flood plains, they must be elevated above the highest recorded crest of the stream.

CONVEYOR COVERS

Arch Sections. Perhaps the most commonly used cover is a half circle arch section, 48 in. long, supported on band sheets 10 in. wide. These band sheets in turn are supported by bolting to the conveyor frame. See Fig. 20-3.

Diameters of support bands and cover sheets are optional, to meet the conveyor equipment manufacturer's designs, but usually range from 36 to 72 in., in suitable gages. Cover sheets are secured by one bolt at each corner and can be quickly removed when necessary. Corrugations should preferably run transverse to the conveyor for greater strength with minimum framing.

Where the arch covers not only the conveyor belt but also the walkway, sheets with larger corrugations (6 in. x 2 in.) can be provided. Fig. 20-4.

Horseshoe or Full Round. The horseshoe shape finds use where weighing equipment or other facilities require a larger cover. A circular or elliptical shape can also serve as a beam to strengthen the span between bents. (See Chapter 21 *Aerial Conduits*)

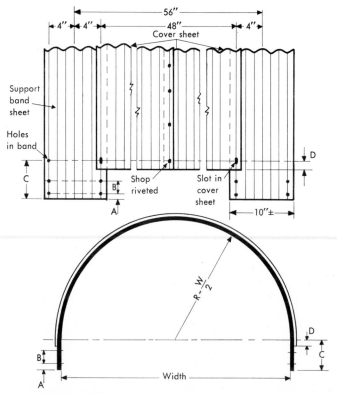

Fig. 20-3. Typical corrugated steel conveyor cover—with removable cover sheets supported by narrower band arches.

Fig. 20-4. Large conveyor cover of structural plate steel being installed at a steel mill operation.

If the conveyor extends under a stockpile, heavier construction is required. See Chapter 14 *Tunnels*, and Chapter 15 *Underpasses*.

Rectangular Housing. Large conveyor coverings may also consist of rectangular steel framing covered either with corrugated steel siding and roofing, or with interlocking steel panels. If required, light is provided by windows at intervals, or by electric lamps.

Materials. From the standpoint of strength, stiffness and resistance to damage, the designer's choice is most logically corrugated steel sheets, with suitable corrugations and gage of metal for the span selected. Exposure to corrosion-prone environment will call for specification of galvanized steel sheets, 2 oz/sq ft of zinc (total for both sides). Shop rivets and field bolts should be protected to the same extent as the corrugated sheets.

Fig. 21-1. Aerial bridges of structural plate between adjacent buildings of an industry or business·permit the efficient transfer of goods or equipment.

CHAPTER 21 Aerial Conduits

INTRODUCTION

Aerial conduits include at least two classes of structures. The first is exposed sewers, gravity water lines and service tunnels or "bridges". The second class includes ducts for air and various gases—for ventilation or circulation. Aerial access bridges for safe movement of humans or intra-plant materials handling also are described here. Fig. 21-1.

SEWERS AND WATER LINES

Often the need arises to establish a satisfactory gradient above ground for sanitary outfall sewers, and irrigation and gravity water lines that cross depressions, streams, or channels. These exposed lines may be supported on bents, suitably spaced, without need for beams or rails between piers. See Figs. 21-2 and 21-3. Safe spacing of bents is given in Table 21-1 for corrugated steel pipe flowing full of water. This table is based on the standard beam loading formula.

CANTILEVER STRENGTH

Where an unsupported corrugated steel pipe projects as a cantilever beyond an embankment or wall, it is customary to use, as a rough rule for strength, a maximum of *one half* of safe span shown in Table 21-1. Furthermore, the pipe length extending beyond the last coupling should at least equal the spans in this same table.

SERVICE TUNNELS

Rather than ground level crossings or subterranean passageways, aerial conduits can be a good choice in industry. Bridging between adjacent buildings of a manufacturing plant, Fig. 21-6, may be desirable for more direct access

Fig. 21-2. A sanitary sewer discharge line is carried by an aerial corrugated steel pipe. All seams and joints are watertight.

Table 21-1 Safe Spans or Bent Spacing[1]—in Feet
For Standard Corrugated Steel Pipe Flowing Full of Water

Diameter in Inches	Gage of Pipe				
	16	14	12	10	8
12	12	13.5	15.5		
15	12	13.5	15.5		
18	12.5	14	15.5		
21	12.5	14	16		
24	13	14.5	16.5		
30		14.5	16.5	19	20.5
36		14.5	17	19	21
42		14.5	17	19	21
48		15	17.5	19.5	21
54		15	17.5	19.5	21.5
60			17.5	19.5	21.5
66			17.5	20	21.5
72			17.5	20	22
84				20	22

for employees, materials, finished products, or utility lines. A variant is seen at mine tipples, quarries, or docks where the aerial lines may be quite lengthy.

Permissible loading will vary, depending on usage and whether belt conveyors, utility lines or other structures are added. Bents or other structural supports are designed by conventional methods but should be such as to maintain true pipe shape.

VENTILATION DUCTS

Mining, industry and construction operations require various degrees of ventilation to protect against health hazards arising from toxic gases, excessive

Fig. 21-3. Fastening rod-and-lug bands on a water-supply intake for a power station at a university.

Fig. 21-4. Providing fresh air for a tunneling or mining operation is often done by means of corrugated steel pipe as shown here.

heat, moisture, dust, and possible explosions. Ventilation codes and minimum standards are usually established and policed by state agencies and the U.S. Bureau of Mines.

The use of corrugated steel pipe and other steel products as important components of ventilating systems has been commonplace for many years. Fig. 21-4.

Use of explosives in tunneling or mining makes resistance to concussion, and ease of coupling and uncoupling, desirable characteristics of the ventilation pipe. Helically corrugated steel pipe and various forms of smooth wall pipe meet these requirements.

Friction factors for helically corrugated pipe are given in Table 21-2. These are actual test values for lengths of over 100 diameters.

Table 21-2   Coefficients of Friction for Galvanized Steel Pipe for Air Conduction[1]

Diam. of Pipe in Inches	Coefficient of Friction f^*	Diam. of Pipe in Inches	Coefficient of Friction f^*
6	.029–.033	12	.038–.044
8	.033–.038	15	.041–.047
10	.036–.041	18	.044–.050
		21	.047–.052

*From Darcy-Weisbach formula: $h_f = f \dfrac{l}{d} \dfrac{V^2}{2g}$ (1)

where

h_f = loss in head of fluid under conditions of flow, in ft
f = a dimensionless friction coefficient
l = length of pipe, in ft
V = velocity in ft per sec
g = acceleration due to gravity = 32.174 ft per sec²
d = internal diameter of pipe, in ft

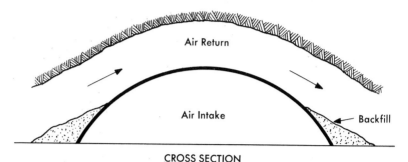

CROSS SECTION
Fig. 21-5. Typical structural plate or steel liner plate overcast.

FAN DUCTS

Mine ventilation conduits or "fan ducts" extend from the ventilating fan to the portal of the fresh air tunnel or air shaft. Corrugated steel ducts find wide use, in part due to their high strength-weight ratio. Further, they are fully salvable if a change of operations is necessary. They resist destruction from explosions and are fire resistant, and contribute to mine safety through confining explosion and fire in event of disaster. They may range from 36 to 84-in. diameter, with 48, 60 and 72-in. being common.

The duct is normally fabricated so that the fan opening is offset from the centerline of the main conduit to prevent damage to the fan in case of explosion. Spring-loaded explosion doors installed on the outlet end of the main duct serve to relieve pressures and minimize damage to ventilating equipment.

Air lock chambers can be installed on the side of the main conduit for entry into the air tunnel if desired.

OVERCASTS

The flow of ventilating air within the mine must often be directed when the main passageway is intersected or crossed by other passageways or drifts. Conditions change as the mining progresses, so it is neither necessary nor desirable

Fig. 21-6. An 84-in. corrugated steel aerial bridge or "grade separation" for an industrial plant.

Fig. 21-7. A corrugated steel tower serves to house some of the controlling equipment for an oil producing company.

that air crossovers or *overcasts* be permanent structures. For an economical and fully salvable overcast structure, low-ratio rise/span corrugated steel arches or pipe-arches are successfully used. Fig. 21-5.

HEAT MANIFOLDS AND STACKS

Concrete aggregates must, at times, be heated or cooled prior to mixing to obtain satisfactory working and setting properties of the concrete. Corrugated steel pipe inserted through aggregate piles have been commonly used as heat conduits. Heat transfer through pipe walls is rapid, and its adequate structural strength and complete salvability are advantageous.

Corrugated steel pipe is used for heat manifolds, ducts and stacks for smoke and fumes.

Galvanized steel is satisfactory except where the fumes are corrosive, in which case asbestos-protected steel can be specified.

REFERENCE

1. *Handbook of Drainage and Construction Products*, Armco
   Drainage & Metal Products, Inc., Middletown, Ohio.

Fig. 22-1. Reflooring an old bridge on a secondary school bus route. Top: The old timber floor was in poor condition. Center: Steel bridge flooring welded in place—awaiting asphalt pavement. Bottom: Completed, resurfaced bridge showing improvements.

CHAPTER 22 Steel Bridge Flooring or Planking

INTRODUCTION

Steel bridge flooring or planking is used as a structural support or deck and is normally surfaced with a bituminous pavement. It is frequently used to replace worn wood plank flooring on older bridges and overpasses. Steel bridge flooring can be used to replace obsolete concrete decks and to increase live load capacity of bridges.

Reflooring old truss or trestle-type bridges, whose decks are in poor condition but where supports are adequate, is readily done at low cost with steel bridge flooring. After the bridge flooring has been secured, a bituminous concrete surface is applied. This system will often add lateral stiffness to the entire bridge and may contribute less dead load than the deck system which it replaces. Successful use of steel bridge flooring in its present form has been a matter of record since 1946.[1]

DESCRIPTION

Steel bridge flooring in sheet and plate gages has trapezoidal corrugations, 6-in. pitch by 2-in. depth, with a 24-in. or an 18-in. net laying width. See Fig. 22-2. It is usually furnished in 6 to 18-ft maximum lengths for 10 and 12 gage, and shorter lengths for 7 gage and heavier. These lengths may be welded end-

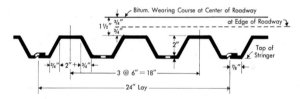

Fig. 22-2. Cross section of typical bridge flooring.

Table 22-1 Sectional Properties of Steel Bridge Flooring

Gage	Thick- ness T	Unit Section Modulus In. ³/Ft	Weight of Steel Bridge Floor		Resisting Moment and Max. Allowable Span for 20,000 PSI Fiber Stress	
			Pounds Per Lineal Foot of Section	Pounds Per Square Foot of Section	‡Resisting Moment Inch-Lb.	†Maximum Allowable Span L In.
12	7/64 "	1.176	12.4	6.2	39,300	22
10	9/64 "	1.488	16.0	8.0	49,800	25
7	3/16 "	1.944	21.4	10.7	64,900	30
	5/16 "	3.036	35.9	18.0	101,200	41

Formed steel bridge floor and end dam painted one shop coat of rust-inhibitive primer immediately after fabricating. Before paint is applied the steel is thoroughly cleaned.
†Based on H15 and on H20 loading for steel grid and timber floors. Assumed distribution of wheel load is 20 in. longitudinally and transversely.
‡Based on 20-in. width of floor section. References 2 through 6.

Fig. 22-3. Tack welding the seams, end dams and bridge plank units to the understructure of a steel bridge.

to-end to form continuous sections across the bridge floor. Physical properties and maximum allowable spans are shown in Table 22-1. Also, 9-in. pitch by 3-in. depth, 18-in. wide is available.

One coat of rust-inhibitive primer paint is applied before the steel bridge flooring leaves the shop; or the steel may be ordered with galvanized coating. Galvanized minimizes need for maintenance of the underside of the floor, and often eliminates it altogether.

Welded end dams retain the road surfacing material at the floor edges.

LOADS AND STRESSES

Each corrugation in the flooring transmits some of the superimposed load to adjacent corrugations as well as to its own supports. Wheel loads are distributed over an area 20 in. x 20 in. at the center of the flooring span and for stringer design, the load may be considered applied evenly over a 20-in. length of stringer.

Steel bridge flooring is designed to carry the live load plus 30 per cent for impact with a maximum allowable working stress of 20,000 psi for steels conforming to ASTM A 245, grade C, for sheet gages and ASTM A 283, grade D, for plate thicknesses. Maximum positive bending moments are computed as for a continuous beam with a uniform load symmetrically placed over a portion of one interior span.

INSTALLATION SUGGESTIONS

An A-frame derrick on a winch truck is a convenient way of removing the old flooring and carrying the new units from stockpile to bridge. Uniform support of the steel flooring over the old stringers is desirable to prevent excessive deflection and rupturing of the pavement. Steel shims are used to attain this support. If necessary, the old stringers should be strengthened or replaced.

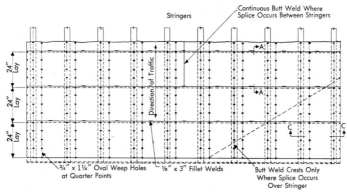

PLAN OF BRIDGE FLOOR

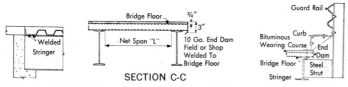

SECTION C-C

SECTION AT ABUTMENT　　　　　　　　**CURB AND GUARDRAIL DETAILS**

Fig. 22-4. Plan view showing method of attaching flooring to bridge stringers, and cross sections showing method of attaching steel curb and guard rail.

After proper positioning, the steel flooring is anchored to the stringers by a few scattered welds. When all flooring is in place, welding is completed by placing ⅛ in. x 1 in. fillet welds on each side of the slotted welding holes in the valley of each corrugation. Fig. 22-4. Adjacent plates are joined at the edges by overlapping and welding with a ⅛-in. x 3-in.-long fillet weld at approximately 24 in. center to center spacing.

When steel bridge flooring is applied over wood stringers, the plates are attached with lag screws and washers, and adjacent plates are welded together.

BITUMINOUS PAVEMENT

Bituminous pavements have been used successfully with steel bridge flooring. The only precautions necessary are to make the pavement smooth and of such consistency that it will not shove under the action of traffic. Densely graded mixes which are not too rich in bitumen and which are compacted in place, should provide trouble-free service. The best guide to proper pavement construction is the experience of the local highway department.

REFERENCES AND BIBLIOGRAPHY

1. American Road Builders' Association, *Formed Steel Structural Plate Bridge Plank*, Tech. Bull. No. 221, Washington, D. C., 1956, 32 pp.
2. *Bethlehem Formed Steel Bridge Flooring*, Bethlehem Steel Co., Bethlehem, Pa. Folder 781-A, 1963, 4 pp.
3. *USF Structural Plate Bridge Flooring*, United Steel Fabricators, Inc., Wooster, Ohio. Folder BF4, 1960, 8 pp.
4. Unpublished investigation, 1965.
5. *Sectional Properties of Steel Bridge Plank*, Research & Technology, Armco Steel Corp., Middletown, Ohio.
6. *Armco Bridge Plank*, Metal Products Div., Armco Steel Corp., Middletown, Ohio. Manual BP-8455.
7. Unpublished investigation, 1952. *Static Loads on Structural Plate Bridge Flooring*, Clayer, C. R. and Wolford, D. S., Research and Technology, Armco Steel Corp., Middletown, Ohio.

Fig. 23-1. Installing permanent steel bridge deck forms on Chesapeake Bay Bridge. Aligning the forms and fastening to supports is quickly done.

Fig. 23-2. Permanent steel bridge deck forms, with steel reinforcing bars installed, ready for pouring of concrete slab.

CHAPTER 23 Permanent Steel Bridge Deck Forms

BRIDGE DECK FORMING

A rising level of bridge construction since the start of the Interstate Highway system has created a great demand for faster, more efficient, and safer ways to form concrete slab bridge decks. A galvanized, permanent, steel form system has been developed to meet this demand and it is used today in many areas of the country. Fig. 23-1.

Permanent steel bridge deck forms are designed for placement over or between stringers, to speed up new construction or redecking of any concrete slab and stringer construction. Forming the deck slab and placing reinforcing steel and concrete is a smooth, uninterrupted, and consequently economical procedure. All work is carried out from the top side, which eliminates the usual erection and removal of conventional wood forms. In general, the use of steel bridge deck forms will result in a reduction of construction and fire hazards. Uninterrupted traffic flow can normally be maintained underneath the bridge during construction.

Permanent steel bridge deck forms are strong, deep ribbed, corrugated, galvanized steel sheets with a corrugation spacing specifically designed to match the reinforcing bar spacing and to carry the heavy construction loads with minimum deflection. Construction details permit field adjustment of form elevation. A uniform slab depth can be provided even though the concrete slab haunches over the stringers vary in height. Figs. 23-2 and 23-3.

The bridge deck form corrugation pattern permits the positive reinforcing steel bars to be placed over the troughs to obtain the required concrete cover for minimum slab depths. The positive reinforcing steel can be placed faster than with wood forming because the variety of available corrugation pitches eliminates the need for measuring and marking a bar layout on the forms.

The protected position of these permanent forms under bridge decks extends the anticipated life of the galvanized steel sheets significantly over that for similar sheets directly exposed to the elements.

PERMANENT BRIDGE FLOOR FORMS

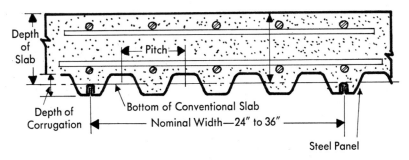

TYPICAL SECTION

Fig. 23-3. Conventional cross section: conventional slab vs. steel form slab.

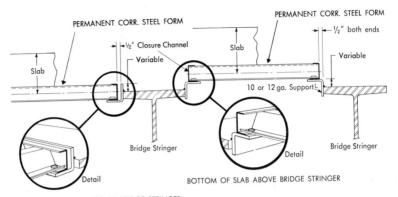

BOTTOM OF SLAB AT TOP OF BRIDGE STRINGER

Fig. 23-4. Permanent steel bridge deck forms showing angle supports for two conditions: left, with bottom of slab *at top* of stringers, and, right, *above* the stringers.

DESIGN AND MATERIALS

Permanent steel forms are designed in accordance with established engineering principles of flexural analysis and the requirements of the AISI "Specification for the Design of Light Gage Cold-formed Steel Structural Members."[1] The forms are designed to carry both the dead load of freshly poured concrete and any construction loads. The thickness and corrugation pitch of the form sheets are selected by considering: design span, design loads, limiting deflections, stresses, and reinforcing bar spacing of the slab. The form sheets are proportioned for a maximum bending stress under design load not to exceed 24,000 psi for steel conforming to ASTM A 446, grade C, or 30,000 psi for steel conforming to ASTM A 446, grade E. These stresses may be increased in accordance with Article 3.8.2 of the above AISI Specification for temporary construction loads.

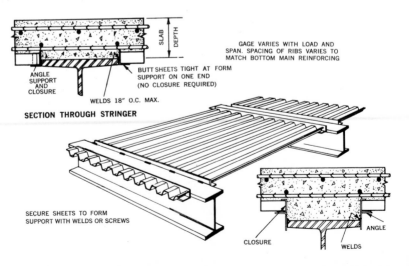

Fig. 23-5. Another variation of permanent bridge deck forms. The inset at the lower right differs from that at the left in that the angles are inverted and the bottom of the slab is higher.

Fig. 23-6. Placing steel bridge deck forms on a high arch bridge, fast and safely.

The maximum mid-span deflection of the form under uniform dead load of freshly poured concrete is usually limited to clear span divided by 180 or not more than approximately ½ inch. If the deflection exceeds these limits, camber may be required.

Form supports are 10, 12, or 14 gage steel angles or "zees" which are welded to the stringer flanges. Stringer details will usually determine the type of support to be used. Figures 23-4 and 23-5 show typical support positions.

All form sheets and exposed accessories are manufactured of galvanized steel conforming to ASTM Specification A 446, coating class 1.50 ounces. Form sheets are made from 22, 21, 20, 19, 18 17, or 16 gage steel sheet. Supports may be formed from steel conforming to ASTM A 446, grade A or C.

ERECTION

Permanent steel bridge deck forms are installed by a form erector in accordance with the placing plans, including installation instructions and approved details. Form supports are placed on or against the stringer top flange, adjusted to proper grade, then arc welded to the stringer at intervals not exceeding 18 inches on center or as shown on placing plans.

Steel forms are placed on the supports and securely welded or screw fastened in place after alignment across the bridge. To make a grout-tight form, corrugated or angle closures are placed tightly against the end of the sheets to prevent concrete leakage. Field cutting may be necessary to fit the forms at expansion joints, floor beams, diaphragms and end abutments. Cutting can be done with a steel cutting saw, cutting torch, electric arc welder or shears.

Normal construction practices are used in placement of reinforcing bars and concrete and in vibration of the freshly poured concrete.

REFERENCES AND BIBLIOGRAPHY

1. *Formed Steel Bridge Floor*, Bethlehem Steel Corp., Bethlehem, Pa., Folder 781-A.
2. *Bethlehem Bridgeform*, Bethlehem Steel Corp. Bethlehem, Pa., Booklet 2103.
3. *U. S. F. Leave-in-Place Forms*, United Steel Fabricators, Inc., Wooster, Ohio. Specification Bulletin No. 2, 1962.
4. *Stay-in-Place Bridge Forms*, Granco Steel Products Co., St. Louis, Mo., Manual No. 115-31, 1963, 16 pp.

Fig. 24-1. Bottom-lighted overhead steel signs at an exit on an Interstate highway.

INTRODUCTION

Well-designed, well-placed signs are essential for driver convenience and safety on all highways. This is particularly true on highspeed limited access highways. Fig. 24-1.

For improved visibility and more rapid scanning, today's signs have been greatly increased in size. Overhead signs are increasingly common. For the Interstate System, standards for letter size, message content and sign location have been established.[1]

Both larger sign area and more prominent location vastly increase problems of static and dynamic loading—notably wind loading.

One solution is *sheet steel*. The strength, economy and versatility of steel sheet merit the consideration of engineers concerned with the design, fabrication and maintenance of signs and sign supports.

Section I—SIGN FACES

Flat sheet steel is suitable for sign faces up to 3 ft wide with single support, and up to 6 ft wide with double support. Wider signs require stiffening or reinforcing of face panels to control vibration and deflection.

The unsupported width, wind load, and grade of steel determine the required thickness or gage of a flat-sheet sign.

Built-up Sign Faces. Various systems of built-up face panels may be designed for large directional signs. Panels may consist of flat steel sheet in panel sections, welded or bolted to light-gage, formed hot or cold rolled structural steel members. Flanged steel panels (butted or interlocked) are preferable, however, as they are lighter and stronger than flat sheets. Fig. 24-2.

Fig. 24-2. Back of steel highway sign comprised of bolted panels and supported on steel posts.

329

Outdoor advertising companies report favorable experience in assembling and mounting of large built-up steel poster panels. These need no welding and a minimum of bolting either to ground posts or to overhead bridges.

SURFACE FINISH[2]

AASHO Standard Specification for Highway Bridges covers materials and methods for painting sign faces and supports.

Steel provides an excellent flat sheet material for embossed signs. Steel sheets available include galvanized, galvannealed, aluminum coated, and stainless. For best paint adhesion, the sign should be suitably phosphatized. Hot-dip galvanizing (ASTM: A 525), although slightly higher in first cost, is a more durable and economical coating.

Galvanized steel signs can cost 30 per cent less than signs made of competitive materials of equal quality. They are also more salvable and adaptable to reuse.

Reflectorized sheeting can be applied easily to such sign blanks.

Large Sign Faces. The difficulty of maintaining large signs is ample justification for using A 374 or A 375 high strength steel or a steel suitable for vitreous enameling such as the very low carbon steels or aluminum-coated steel. Chief advantage of this last is its resistance to corrosion if the porcelain coating is damaged and the base exposed to air and moisture.

Post Selection Chart
for Sheet Signs

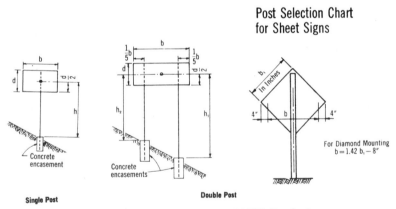

Fig. 24-3. Design of single and double post signs—AASHO Standards

Section II—SIGN SUPPORTS

Highway signs may be divided into two types according to location with respect to travel lanes: (1) roadside or ground-mounted signs, situated outside the usable roadway, and (2) overhead signs, located over the travel lanes or shoulders at sufficient elevation to provide vertical clearance for all vehicles.

SUPPORTS FOR GROUND-MOUNTED SIGNS

Regulatory and warning signs range from 12 x 18 in. to 4 x 6 ft. These, plus route markers, are small enough in horizontal dimension to mount on single steel supports without excessive deflection under wind loads. Sheet signs more than 4 ft wide can be designed for a more efficient combination of face and supports by using two posts rather than one. See Fig. 24-3.

Table 24-1   Allowable Sign Area for Single or Double Post Highway Signs

		ALLOWABLE SIGN AREA PER POST		
Wind Pressure		50 p.s.f.	40 p.s.f.	30 p.s.f.
h, h_1 or h_2 (in feet)		15 14 13 12 11 10 9 8	15 14 13 12 11 10 9 8	15 14 13 12 11 10 9 8
Standard Pipe Posts* A 53	2½(5.79)	5 5 6	6 7 7	8 9 10
	3(7.58)	5 6 6 7 8 9 10	7 8 8 9 10 11 12	9 10 11 12 13 15 17
	3½(9.11)	7 8 8 9 10 11 12 14	9 10 11 12 12 14 15 17	12 13 14 15 17 19 21 23
	4(10.79)	10 11 11 12 14 15 17 19	12 13 14 16 17 19 21 24	17 18 19 21 23 25 28 32
	5(14.62)	17 18 20 21 24 26 29 32	21 23 25 27 29 32 35	28 31 33 36 39
	6(18.97)	27 29 31 33	33 36	

*Standard pipe size is designated by nominal diameter in inches and weight per linear foot in pounds in parentheses.

Post selection data are given in Table 24-1 for single and double standard pipe posts of A 53 steel, for wind pressures of 50, 40 and 30 psf. For mounting heights from 10 to 26 ft, designs are available for pipe columns.

OVERHEAD SIGNS—BRIDGES AND CANTILEVER

Overhead signs are mounted either on sign bridges that span the roadway, or cantilevered over the roadway from a single column. A cantilever mount-

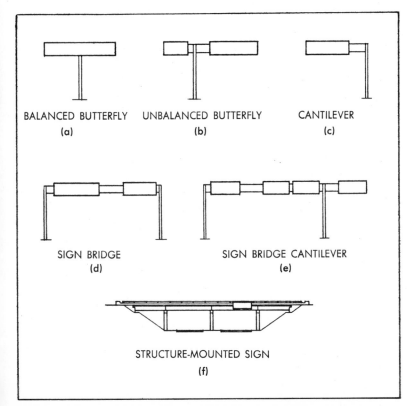

Fig. 24-4. Typical supporting structures for overhead signs—AASHO standards.

ing on which signs are extended from both sides of the column is called a "butterfly" installation.

Designs are commonly made to AASHO "Specifications for the Design and Construction of Structural Supports for Highway Signs," adopted June 1961[2].

Wind pressures of 35 and 55 lb per sq ft are often specified. These correspond to wind speeds of 80 and 100 mph. In areas subject to ice loading, this factor must be taken into account.

The AASHO specification requires that resonance of the structure at critical wind speeds should be generally avoided by limiting dead load vertical deflection to $d^2/400$ (in ft), where d is the sign depth in feet.

TYPES OF BRIDGES

Single horizontal steel members can be used for carrying relatively small signs over moderately wide roadways. However, large signs and heavier loadings require the strength, stiffness and economy of a truss structure—of planar, triangular or rectangular cross section across the roadway. These are supported at each end by single steel columns or column bents.

Butterfly and single cantilever designs include: single pipe, double pipe, planar trusses and rectangular trusses—supported by a single steel column.

Although structural members may consist of various hot or cold rolled shapes (angles, channels, I and H-beams), steel pipe in various diameters is predominant because of its ready availability from steel service centers and pipe distributors' stocks.

Pipe 4½ in. OD and under is commonly used for diagonals and verticals of trusses and bents. These conform to ASTM A 53, Type F, minimum yield strength 25,000 psi.

Pipe 4½ in. OD and larger is used for truss chords, columns for bents, single columns and cantilever arms. These conform to ASTM A 53, Types E and S, Grade B, minimum yield strength 35,000 psi. Other structural material conforms to ASTM A 36.

Fig. 24-5. Butterfly sign support, California

Fig. 24-6. Informational sign of steel panels on steel posts outside the traveled way.

This steel pipe is made by the open-hearth or basic oxygen process. It may be supplied black, black and painted, shop galvanized, or galvanized and painted.

STANDARD DESIGNS

Engineering departments can prepare their own standard designs or can supplement them with standard designs prepared by basic steel companies or sign fabricators.

One such group of standards available[3,4] consists of 47 drawings with various combinations such as:

Rectangular and triangular space truss spans 50 through 140 ft, on column bents

Triangular space truss spans 40 through 65 ft, on single poles

Planar truss spans 30 through 55 ft

Cantilevers and butterflies of arm lengths 10 through 36 ft

All of these are for 35 and 55 psf wind loads, and for painted and galvanized finishes.

These different types of modular highway sign support structures are adaptable to modular steel signs and to various lighting facilities.

REFERENCES

1. AISI, *Highway Construction Fact Sheets #4, #5*, New York, N. Y., 1964, 4 pp.
2. AASHO, *Specifications for the Design and Construction of Structural Supports for Highway Signs*, Washington, D. C., 1961, 21 pp.
3. *Highway Hardware Tech. Notebook Vol. 1*, U. S. Steel Corp. Pittsburgh, Pa., 1961.
4. *Design Drawings for Highway Sign Support Structures*, United States Steel Corp., Pittsburgh, Pa., June 1965, 47 dwgs.

Fig. 25-1. Simple light standard of galvanized steel pipe serving economically under coastal conditions.

Fig. 25-2. Double light standard approximately 30 ft high. Luminaire arm is 15 ft and signal arm 35 ft long.

CHAPTER 25 Light Standards

General agreement exists on when and how much lighting is warranted for streets and highways[1]. However, no such accord has been reached on lighting of limited access highways. Still needed is agreement which considers such conditions as interchange frequency, traffic volume and other factors.[2]

DESIGN CONSIDERATIONS

Structural design of light standards is based on dead weight, wind load and ice load on the standard and luminaire; also on loads imposed by overhead electrical wiring.[3] Luminaires in common use weigh from 15 to 150 pounds. Projected areas for luminaires range from 1.3 sq ft for filament units to 8 sq ft for large fluorescent fixtures.

Wind speed values (converted to pressure) are obtainable from maps from the U. S. Weather Bureau in cooperation with the Bureau of Public Roads. These pressures are expressed as "isotachs of extreme mile" at various heights above ground and at recurrence intervals. At heights of 15 to 30 ft above ground, and at speeds from 60 to 120 mph, pressures will vary from 16 to 62 psf (for a 50 year mean recurrence interval). The basic formula is $P = 0.00256$ $(1.3V)^2$, where V = wind speed. Gust speeds may reach $1.3V$.

Pole manufacturers are able to advise on shape factors for various cross sections of poles, brackets and luminaires.

Mounting heights for roadway lighting units range from 25 to 32½ ft for various locations and types of luminaires.[4] To achieve these heights, pole

Fig. 25-3. Attractive steel light standard at a highway interchange.

335

shafts usually range from 20 to 30 ft in length. Upsweep of the bracket arm achieves the desired luminaire height. Steel brackets range from 4 to 15 ft in length. Traffic signal arms range to 35 ft in length.

Traffic signals may be hung from independent poles or share the light standards with luminaires.

Most steel lightpoles are either anchor bolted to a concrete base or have a transformer base. Concrete foundations may be 4 to 7 ft deep depending on standard height and soil conditions.

MANUFACTURING PRACTICES

Steel shafts or poles are generally circular, square or octagonal in cross section. These shapes afford high resistance to torsion from wind load on the luminaire. Some shafts taper, usually at about 0.14 in. per ft, to provide greater resistance to bending at the base of the pole.

Properties of steel standards furnished by several manufacturers are shown in the accompanying Table 25-1:

Table 25-1   Characteristics of Steel Lightpole Shafts

Maker	Gage	Shape	Hot-Rolled Steel	Treatment	Yield Strength psi
A	11,7,3	Round	Mild	Cold rolled	48,000
B	10,7,3	Round	Mild	Cold rolled	33,000
C	11,3	Octagonal	High strength, low-alloy	Cold rolled	50,000
D	11,7,3	Octagonal	High strength, low-alloy	Press brake	50,000
E		Octagonal	High strength, nickel stainless		75,000

COATINGS

Steel light standards are thoroughly cleaned at the factory and then dip-prime coated with red oxide or red oxide chromate primer, or hot-dip galvanized for maximum durability. Paint-primed poles are finish-painted either prior to shipping or (more generally) after erection. Hot-dip galvanized standards are normally not painted and require practically no maintenance.

SPECIFICATIONS

Many agencies accept the specifications of lightpole manufacturers whereas others develop their own detailed designs and specifications. The latter procedure simplifies competitive bidding and permits describing any desired custom features.

Steel is preferred for lightpoles and brackets because of its resistance to impact and to torsion due to wind loads. Galvanized coatings practically eliminate the need for maintenance, but painting is highly satisfactory with proper surface preparation. Where stainless steel is used, maintenance of standards is practically eliminated.

REFERENCES

1. *American Standard Practice for Street and Highway Lighting*, D12-1, Illum. Eng. Soc., N. Y. 1953.
2. AASHO, *An Informational Guide for Lighting Controlled Access Highways*, Washington, D. C., 1960.
3. *Light Standards, Sect. III*, Technical Notebook, Vol. 2, U. S. Steel Corp., Pittsburgh, Pa., 1962.
4. *Designer's and Buyer's Guide to Preferred Lighting*, General Electric Co., Schenectady, N. Y., 1960.

Glossary

Definition of Terms:

Many terms in this handbook are common to drainage, highway, and other related design and construction disciplines. Most of these are defined, described or illustrated where they appear in the book. However, to aid the engineering student and to clear up unfamiliar words for the professional engineer, a number of terms are here defined even though they may be elementary. For other unfamiliar terms, many are keyed in the index of this book, particularly where the definitions already appear in the text.

Sources:

(1) Brown, V. J. and Runner, D. G. **Engineering Terminology,** Gillette Publishing Co., Chicago, Ill. 439 pp.

(2) American Society of Civil Engineers, **Nomenclature for Hydraulics,** Abbreviations, Units of Measurement, Symbols and Glossary. Task Force Report. New York, N. Y. 1962, 501 pp.

(3) American Society for Testing and Materials, **Standard Specifications.** Philadelphia, Pa. Current.

(4) Manufacturers' literature.

A

abutment—A wall supporting the end of a bridge or span, and sustaining the pressure of the abutting earth.

aerial sewer—An unburied sewer (generally sanitary type), supported on pedestals or bents to provide a suitable grade line.

angle of repose—The angle which the sloping face of a bank of loose earth, or gravel, or other material makes with the horizontal.

asbestos protection—Fibers of asbestos felt embedded in the galvanized coating of sheet steel to enable bituminous coatings to adhere more tenaciously, and to provide greater corrosion resistance.

B

backfill—Earth or other material used to replace material removed during construction, such as in culvert, sewer and pipeline trenches; and behind bridge abutments and retaining walls. Also refers to material placed in bin-walls or between an old structure and a new lining.

base (course)—A layer of specified or selected material of planned thickness, constructed on the subgrade (natural foundation) or subbase for the purpose of distributing load, providing drainage, or upon which a wearing surface or a drainage structure is placed.

batter—The slope or inclination from a vertical plane—as the face or back of a wall.

bedding—The earth or other material on which a pipe or conduit is supported.

berm—The space between the toe of a slope and excavation made for intercepting ditches or borrow pits.

—An approximately horizontal space introduced in a slope.

—Often used for word "shoulder" in road work.

bin-wall—A series of connected bins, generally filled with earth or gravel to serve as a retaining wall, abutment, pier, or as protection against explosions or gunfire. (See Chapt. 17)

bituminous (coating)—Of or containing bitumen; as asphalt or tar.

boring—An earth-drilling process used for installing conduits or pipelines.

bridge—A structure for carrying traffic over a stream or gulley, including the pavement directly on the floor of the structure. (A structure measuring 10 ft or more in clear span.)

bridge plank (deck or flooring)—A corrugated steel sub-floor on a bridge to support a wearing surface.

buoyancy—The power of supporting a floating body, including the tendency to float an empty pipe (by exterior hydraulic pressure).

buckling strength—see Chapt. 2 *Strength Design*, Formula (2).

C

caisson—A watertight box or cylinder used in excavating for foundations or tunnel pits—to hold out water so concreting or other construction can be carried on.

camber—Rise or crown of the center of a bridge, or flowline through a culvert, above a straight line through its ends. See *Index*.

cantilever—The part of a structure that extends beyond its support.

cathodic protection—Preventing corrosion of a pipeline by using special cathodes (and anodes) to circumvent corrosive damage by electric current. —Also a function of zinc coatings on iron and steel drainage products— galvanic action.

cofferdam—A barrier built in the water so as to form an enclosure from which the water is pumped to permit free access to the area within.

cohesive soil—A soil that when unconfined has considerable strength when air-dried, and that has significant cohesion when submerged.

combined sewer—A sewer that carries both storm water and sanitary or industrial wastes.

compaction—The densification of a soil by means of mechanical manipulation. See *consolidation*.

conduit—A pipe or other opening, buried or above ground, for conveying hydraulic traffic, pipelines, cables or other utilities.

consolidation—The gradual reduction in the volume of a soil mass resulting from an increase in compressive stress.

critical depth, flow, etc.—See Chapt. 4 *Hydraulics*.

culvert—see Chapt. 8 *Culverts*, and *Index*.

cutoff wall—A wall, collar or apron intended to prevent seepage or undermining. See *diaphragm*.

D

deadman—Buried anchorage for a guy, cable, etc.

deflection—Change in shape or decrease in diameter of a conduit, produced without fracture of the material.

diaphragm—A metal collar at right angles to a drain pipe for the purpose of retarding seepage or the burrowing of rodents.

discharge (Q)—Flow from a culvert, sewer, channel, etc.

ditch check—Barrier placed in a ditch to decrease the slope of the flowline and thereby decrease the velocity of the water.

drainage—Interception and removal of ground water or surface water, by artificial or natural means.

E

effluent—Outflow or discharge from a sewer or sewage treatment equipment.

embankment (or fill)—A bank of earth, rock or other material constructed above the natural ground surface.

end section—Flared metal attachment on inlet and outlet of a culvert to prevent erosion of the roadbed, improve hydraulic efficiency, and improve appearance. See *Index*.

energy gradient—Slope of a line joining the elevations of the energy head of a stream. (See Chapt. 4 *Hydraulics*)

energy head—The elevation of the

hydraulic gradient at any section, plus the velocity head.

equalizer—A culvert placed where there is no channel but where it is desirable to have standing water at equal elevations on both sides of a fill.

erosion—Wear or scouring caused by hydraulic traffic or by wind.

F

filter—Granular material placed around a subdrain pipe to facilitate drainage and at the same time strain or prevent the admission of silt or sediment.

flexibility—see *deflection.*

flexibility factor (*FF*)—Relative elastic deflection of a conduit. See Chapt. 2 *Strength Design.* Formula (3).

flume—An open channel or conduit of metal, concrete or wood, on a prepared grade, trestle or bridge.

ford—A shallow place where a stream may be crossed by traffic.

foundation—That portion of a structure (usually below the surface of the ground) which distributes the pressure to the soil or to artificial supports. *Footing* has similar meaning.

free outlet—(as pertaining to critical flow)—Exists when the backwater does not diminish the discharge of a conduit.

free water—Water (in soil) free to move by gravity (in contrast to capillary or hygroscopic moisture).

G

gage—Standard measurement of the thickness of metal sheets or wire (and bearing a relation to the weight of the metal).

—Also a term for the distance measured between railroad rails; (standard is 4 ft 8½ in).

gradation—Sieve analysis of aggregates.

grade—Profile of the center of a roadway, or the invert of a culvert or sewer. Also refers to slope, or ratio of rise or fall of the grade line to its length. (Various other meanings)

gradient—see *grade.*

granular—Technical term referring to

(the uniform size of) grains or crystals in rock. See *granular backfill* in *Index.*

groin—A jetty built at an angle to the shore line, to control the waterflow and currents, or to protect a harbor or beach.

ground water table (or level)—Upper surface of the zone of saturation in permeable rock or soil. (When the upper surface is confined by impermeable rock, the water table is absent.)

grout—A fluid mixture of cement, sand, and water that can be poured or pumped easily.

H

head—(static)—The height of water above any plane or point of reference. (The energy possessed by each unit of weight of a liquid, expressed as the vertical height through which a unit of weight would have to fall to release the average energy possessed.) See Chapt. 4 *Hydraulics.*

Standard unit of measure shall be the foot. Relation between pressure expressed in psi and psf of head is

$$\text{Head in feet} = \frac{\text{lb/sq in.} \times 144}{\text{Density in lb/cu ft}}$$

for water at 68°F

1 lb/sq in. = 2.310 ft

headwall—A wall (of any material) at the end of a culvert or drain to serve one or more of the following purposes: protect fill from scour or undermining; increase hydraulic efficiency, divert direction of flow, and serve as a retaining wall. See *Index.*

height of cover (*HC*)—Distance from crown of a culvert or conduit to the finished road surface or the base of rail.

hydraulic radius—The cross-sectional area of a stream of water divided by the length of that part of its periphery in contact with its containing conduit; the ratio of area to wetted perimeter.

hydraulics—That branch of science or engineering which treats of water or other fluid in motion. See Chapter 4 *Hydraulics.*

hydrogen ion (*pH*)—Refers to acidity

or alkalinity of water or soil. An ion is a charged atom or group of atoms in solution or in a gas. Solutions contain equivalent numbers of positive and negative ions.

I

impact—Stress in a structure caused by the force of a vibratory, dropping, or moving load. This is generally a percentage of the live load.

impervious—Impenetrable. Completely resisting entrance of liquids.

inlet control—See Chapt. 4 *Hydraulics*.

intercepting drain—A ditch or trench filled with a pervious filter material around a subdrainage pipe.

invert—That part of a pipe or sewer below the springing line—generally the lowest point of the internal cross section.

J

jacking (for conduits)—A method of providing an opening for drainage or other purposes underground, by cutting an opening ahead of the pipe and forcing the pipe into the opening by means of horizontal jacks. See Chapt. 7 *Installation*.

K

kip—A stress unit equal to 1000 lb.

L

ledge (rock)—Several beds of rock (or a single bed or stratum) occurring in a quarry or outcropping and exposed to view.

liner plate—Formed steel unit used to line or reinforce a tunnel or other opening. See Chapt. 14 *Tunnels, Shafts, Caissons*.

lock seam—Longitudinal seam in a pipe, formed by overlapping or folding the adjacent edges. Seam may be helical.

luminaire—In highway lighting, a complete lighting device consisting of a light source, plus a globe, reflector, refractor, housing, and such support as is integral with the housing. The light standard (bracket or pole) is not considered a part of the luminaire.

M

Manning's Formula—An equation for the value of coefficient C in the Chezy Formula, the factors of which are the hydraulic radius and a coefficient of roughness.

median barrier—A double-faced guardrail in the median or island dividing two adjacent roadways.

modulus of elasticity (E)—The stress required to produce unit strain, which may be a change of length (Young's modulus); a twist or shear (modulus of rigidity), or a change of volume (bulk modulus), expressed in dynes per square centimeter.

moment, bending—The moment which produces bending in a beam or other structure. It is measured by the algebraic sum of the products of all the forces multiplied by their respective lever arms.

moment of inertia—Function of some property of a body or figure—such as weight, mass, volume, area, length, or position, equal to the summation of the products of the elementary portions by the squares of their distances from a given axis.

N

neutral axis—An axis of no stress.

O

outfall (or outlet)—In hydraulics, the discharge end of drains and sewers.

outlet control—See Chapt. 4 *Hydraulics*.

P

parapet—Wall or rampart, breast high. Also, the wall on top of an abutment extending from the bridge seat to the underside of the bridge floor and designed to hold the backfill.

Pascal's Law—Pressure exerted at any point upon a confined liquid is transmitted undiminished in all directions.

pavement, invert—Lower segment of a corrugated metal pipe provided with a smooth bituminous material that completely fills the corrugations, intended to give resistance to scour and erosion, and to improve flow.

perched water table—In hydrology, the upper surface of a body of free ground water in a zone of saturation, separated by unsaturated material from an underlying body of ground water in a differing zone of saturation.

periphery—Circumference or perimeter of a circle, ellipse, pipe-arch, or other closed curvilinear figure.

permeability—Penetrability.

pile, bearing—A member driven or jetted into the ground and deriving its support from the underlying strata and/or by the friction of the ground on its surface. (See also *Sheeting*)

plate—A flat-rolled iron or steel product. See *structural plate*.

ponding—Jetting or the use of water to hasten the settlement of an embankment—requires the judgment of a soils engineer. In hydraulics, *ponding* refers to water backed up in a channel or ditch as the result of a culvert of inadequate capacity or design to permit the water to flow unrestricted.

precipitation—Process by which water in liquid or solid state (rain, sleet, snow) is discharged out of the atmosphere upon a land or water surface.

R

radian—An arc of a circle equal in length to the radius; or the angle at the center measured by the arc.

radius of gyration—The distance from the reference at which all of the area can be considered concentrated that still produces the same moment of inertia. Numerically it is equal to the square root of the moment of inertia, divided by the area. (See Chapt. 1 *Product Details*).

rainfall (*R*)—Precipitation in the form of water (usage includes snow and hail)—generally expressed in inches per hour.

retaining wall—A wall for sustaining the pressure of earth or filling deposited behind it. See Chapter 17 *Retaining Walls*.

revetment—A wall or a facing of wood, willow mattresses, steel units, stone, or concrete placed on stream banks to prevent erosion.

Reynolds number (aeronautic)—A non-dimensional coefficient used as a measure of the dynamic scale of a flow.

right bank—That bank of a stream which is on the right when one looks *downstream*.

riprap—Rough stone of various sizes placed compactly or irregularly to prevent scour by water or debris.

roadway—(highway)—Portion of the highway included between the outside lines of gutters or side ditches, including all slopes, ditches, channels and appurtenances necessary to proper drainage, protection and use.

—(railway)—That part of the right of way prepared to receive the track. (During construction the roadway is often referred to as the "grade.")

roughness coefficient (*n*)—A factor in the Kutter, Manning, and other flow formulas representing the effect of channel (or conduit) roughness upon energy losses in the flowing water. See Chapt. 4 *Hydraulics*.

runoff—That part of precipitation carried off from the area upon which it falls. Also, the rate of surface discharge of the above. That part of precipitation reaching a stream, drain or sewer. Ratio of runoff to precipitation is a "coefficient" expressed decimally.

S

safety factor (or factor of safety)—See Chapt. 2 *Strength Design;* Chapt. 4 *Hydraulics*.

saddle branch—See *Index*.

sectional properties—End area per unit of width, moment of inertia, section modulus, and radius of gyration. See Chapt. 1 *Product Details*.

section modulus—The moment of inertia of the area of a section of a member divided by the distance from the center of gravity to the outermost fiber. See Chapt. 1.

seepage—Water escaping through or emerging from the ground along some rather extensive line or surface, as contrasted with a spring, the water of which emerges from a single spot.

shaft—A pit or well sunk from the ground surface into a tunnel for the purpose of furnishing ventilation or access to the tunnel.

sheeting—A wall of metal plates or wood planking to keep out water, or soft or runny materials. See Chapt. 16 *Sheeting, Lightweight.*

siphon—(hydraulics)—A closed conduit, a part of which rises above the hydraulic grade line. It utilizes atmospheric pressure to effect or increase the flow of water through it.

—(inverted)—A conduit or culvert with a U or V shaped grade line to permit it to pass under an intersecting roadway, stream or other obstruction.

skew (or skew angle)—The acute angle formed by the intersection of the line normal to the centerline of the road improvement with the centerline of a culvert or other structure. See *Index.*

slide—Movement of a part of the earth under force of gravity.

span—Horizontal distance between supports, or maximum inside distance between the sidewalls of culverts.

spelter—Zinc or galvanized coating on steel products.

spillway—A low-level passage serving a dam or reservoir through which surplus water may be discharged; usually an open ditch around the end of a dam, or a gateway or a pipe in a dam.

—An outlet pipe, flume or channel serving to discharge water from a ditch, ditch check, gutter or embankment protector.

springing line—Line of intersection between the intrados and the supports of an arch. Also the maximum horizontal dimension of a culvert or conduit.

spun lining—A bituminous lining in a pipe, made smooth or uniform by spinning the pipe around its centerline or axis.

structural plate—Deeply corrugated steel plates or sheets, bolted together to form large pipes, pipe-arches, arches and other structures. See Chapt. 1 *Product Details.*

subdrain—A pervious backfilled trench containing a pipe with perforations or open joints for the purpose of intercepting ground water or seepage.

subgrade—The surface of a portion of the roadbed on which paving, or railroad track ballast, or other structure is placed.

T

tailwater—The water just downstream from a structure.

threading—The process of installing a slightly smaller pipe or arch within a failing drainage structure. See Chapt. 7 *Installation.*

time of concentration—(See Chapt. 4 *Hydraulics.*)

toe drain—A subdrain installed near the downstream toe of a dam or levee to intercept seepage.

U

underdrain—(See *subdrain*)

utilidor—(See *Index*)

V

velocity head (symbol H_v)—For water moving at a given velocity, the equivalent head through which it would have to fall by gravity to acquire the same velocity. See Chapt. 4 *Hydraulics.*

W

wale—Guide or brace of steel or timber, used in trenches and other construction.

water table—The upper limit of the portion of ground wholly saturated with water.

watershed—Region or area contributing to the supply of a stream or lake; drainage area, drainage basin, catchment area.

wetted perimeter—The length of the wetted contact between the water prism and the containing conduit, (measured along a plane at right angles to the conduit).

Symbols

Various disciplines of engineering, hydraulics, physics, chemistry, etc., have established standard symbols or letters to denote various factors or dimensions in formulas, tables, drawings and texts. Some of these are found in dictionaries; others have been published by technical associations. Some of the symbols used in this handbook are listed here. For others, reference should be made to sources such as are listed for the foregoing Glossary.

Symbol	*Definition or Use*	*Where Used in Handbook*	
a	area, cross-sectional, culvert	Ramser formula	Table 13-1
A	area, cross-sectional, of waterway, sq ft	Chezy formula	Ch. 4
A	drainage area, acres	Rational formula; subdrainage;	Ramser
A	area of section, sq in	Cross-section of corrugated plate	Ch. 1, 2, 14, 16
B	invert to spring line	pipe-arch	Ch. 1
c	coefficient, runoff	Burkli-Ziegler formula; Ramser	Table 13-1
c	coefficient of roughness drainage area	Chezy	Ch. 4
C	coefficient, runoff	Rational; Talbot; subdrainage	
₵	centerline		Ch. 8
C	ring compression, thrust, lb/ft		Ch. 2
d	depth of channel		Ch. 4
d	depth of wale from ground surface	Sheeting	Ch. 16
d	vertical height of sign		Ch. 23
d_c	critical depth		Ch. 4
D	diameter of conduit, inside—or maximum span	Ring compression formula (1)	Ch. 1, 2 Ch. 2
D_l	deflection lag	Iowa formula (4)	Ch. 2
△	delta, tangent angle, corrugation		Ch. 1
$△_x$	deflection, horizontal	Iowa formula	Ch. 2
DL	dead load		Ch. 2
E	modulus of elasticity, psi		Ch. 1, 2
E'	modulus of passive resistance of soil	Iowa formula	Ch. 2
f	friction factor	Darcy-Weisbach formula	Ch. 21
F	force		
FF	flexibility factor	Formula (3)	Ch. 2
f_b	buckling stress		Ch. 2
f_c	compressive stress		Ch. 2
FS	factor of safety		Ch. 2

Symbol	Definition or Use	Where Used in Handbook
g	gravitational acceleration	Ch. 4, 21
H	drop of water surface, inlet to outlet, in ft	Ch. 4
H	depth of weir notch, in ft	Table 12-2
h_o	tailwater depth (HW)	Ch. 4
H	head, total	Bernoulli formula, etc. Ch. 4
H_e	head, entrance loss	Ch. 4
H	height of remote point above outlet of drain	(charts) Ch. 4
H_f	head, friction loss	Ch. 4, 21
H_v	head, velocity	Ch. 4
HC	height of cover	Strength design Ch. 2
HW	headwater depth	Ch. 4
i	intensity, rainfall, in. per hr	Rational formula Ch. 4
I	imperviousness, relative	(see C)
I	moment of inertia, in⁴/unit of width	Ch. 1, 2
k	coefficient for filter (backfill materials)	Ch. 2, 10
K	soil stiffness factor	Ch. 2
K	bedding factor	Iowa formula Ch. 2
K_e	coefficient of head loss at entrance	Table 4-17
L	length of channel or travel	Ch. 4
l	length of pipe	Ch. 21
L	length of pipe barrel vs headwall	Ch. 5
L	length of weir notch in ft	Table 12-2
L	length of tunnel liner plate	Ch. 14
L	post spacing on bridge	Ch. 19
LL	live load	Ch. 2
M	area drained, acres	Talbot; Burkli-Ziegler Ch. 4
N	circumferential rivet space ($= 3\pi$ or 9.6 in.)	Periphery measure Ch. 1
n	roughness factor	Manning, Kutter Ch. 4, 9
P	pressure, wind, psf	Light standard Ch. 25
p	pressure, equivalent fluid	Ch. 16
p or P	pressure	Bridge rail formula, AASHO Ch. 19
pH	hydrogen ion concentration	Ch. 3
pi	$\pi = 3.1416$	
Q	discharge (peak volume rate of flow) cfs—(or quantity reaching a drain)	Rational; Chezy; Burkli-Ziegler, etc.

Symbol	Definition or Use	Where Used in Handbook	
r	radius of gyration		Ch. 1, 2, 14
r	factor for corrugation size	Buckling formula Formula (2)	Ch. 2
R	mean radius of pipe, in.	Iowa formula	Ch. 2
R	resistivity, electrical	Calif. corrosion test (Fig. 3-19)	Ch. 3
R	hydraulic radius	Chezy formula	Ch. 4
R	rainfall, rate in. per hr	(also runoff)	Ch. 4
R	ratio of base width to height	Bin-wall	Ch. 17
R	ratio of rise to span	Arch or pipe-arch	Ch. 1
R	radius of curvature	Guardrail cross-section or alignment	Ch. 18
R	rise of pipe-arch	Invert to crown	Ch. 1
R_b	radius of bottom (plates)	Pipe-arch	Ch. 1
R_c	radius of corner (plates)	Pipe-arch	Ch. 1
R_s	radius of side (plates)	Pipe-arch	Ch. 1
R_t	radius of top (plates)	Pipe-arch	Ch. 1
S	span of arch or pipe-arch (or max. horiz. diameter of any shaped structure)		
S	slope (of ground, channel, invert) ft/ft	Chezy, etc.	Ch. 4
S_c	slope, critical		Ch. 4
S_o	slope, bed (at outlet)		Ch. 4
S	section modulus, in.^{3}		Ch. 1
SF	safety factor (or FS)		Ch. 2
T	thrust, ring compression lb/ft		Ch. 2
T, t	thickness of sheet or plate, in.		Ch. 1
T_c	time of concentration of flow		Ch. 4
TL	tangent length		Ch. 1
t	time		
T	temperature		
TW	tailwater depth		Ch. 4
v	velocity, wind, mph		Ch. 24
V	velocity, mean, fps	Chezy	Ch. 4
W_c	weight or vertical load per unit length of pipe	Iowa formula	Ch. 2
W	width, bottom of channel		Ch. 4
W	load per foot of wale	Trench sheeting	Ch. 16
W	wetted perimeter		Ch. 4
X	distance from neutral axis to outer fiber		Ch. 14
x	horizontal coordinate	(in direction of flow)	
y	vertical coordinate	(normal to flow)	
z	horizontal coordinate	(normal to flow)	

Conversion Tables

Table C-1 Length

Ordinary Units

1 foot = 12 inches
1 yard = 3 feet
1 mile = 5280 feet
1 nautical mi = 1.1516 statute mi
1° of latitude at the equator = 69.16 statute mi
$\qquad\qquad\qquad\qquad\qquad\qquad$ = 60 nautical mi
1 acre = 208.71 ft on one side of square

Metric Units

10 millimeters (mm) = 1 centimeter (cm)
100 cm = 1 meter (m)
1000 m = 1 kilometer (km) (about ⅝ mi)

Equivalents

1 inch $\quad\quad$ = 2.5400 centimeters
1 foot $\quad\quad$ = 0.3048 meter
1 statute mi $\;$ = 1.60935 kilometers
1 nautical mi = 1.853 kilometers
1 centimeter = 0.39370 inch
1 meter $\quad\;$ = 3.28 feet
1 kilometer $\;$ = 3280.83 feet = 0.62137 mile

Table C-2 Area

Ordinary Units

1 square foot = 144 square inches
1 square yard = 9 sq ft
$\qquad\qquad\qquad$ = 1296 sq in.
1 acre $\qquad\;\;$ = 43,560 sq ft
$\qquad\qquad\qquad$ = 4840 sq yds
1 sq mile $\quad\;$ = 640 acres
$\qquad\qquad\qquad$ = 1 section of land (U.S.)

Equivalents

1 square centimeter = 0.155 square inch
1 square meter $\qquad$ = 10.76 square feet
$\qquad\qquad\qquad\qquad\;\;$ = 1.196 square yards
1 square kilometer $\;$ = 0.386 square mile
1 square inch $\qquad\;\;$ = 6.45 square centimeters
1 square foot $\qquad\;\;$ = 0.0929 square meter
1 square yard $\qquad\;$ = 0.836 square meter
1 square mile $\qquad\;$ = 2.59 square kilometers

Table C-3   Volume and Capacity

Ordinary Units

1 cu ft of water at 39.1° F = 62.425 lbs
1 United States gallon = 231 cu in.
1 imperial gallon = 277.274 cu in.
1 cubic foot of water = 1728 cu in.
                            = 7.480519 U. S. gallons
                            = 6.232103 imperial gallons
1 cubic yard = 27 cu ft = 46,656 cu in.
1 quart   = 2 pints
1 gallon   = 4 quarts
1 U. S. gallon = 231 cu in.
                     = 0.133681 cu ft
                     = 0.83311, imperial gallon
                     = 8.345 lbs
1 barrel = 31.5 gallons = 4.21 cu ft
1 U. S. bushel = 1.2445 cu ft
1 fluid ounce = 1.8047 cu in.
1 acre foot = 43,560 cu ft
                 = 1,613.3 cu yds
1 acre inch = 3,630 cu ft
1 million U. S. gallons = 133,681 cu ft
                              = 3.0689 acre-ft
1 ft depth on 1 sq mi = 27,878, 400 cu ft
                         = 640 acre-ft

Equivalents

1 cu in. = 16.387 cu cm
1 cu ft = 0.0283 cu m
1 cu yd = 0.765 cu m
1 cu cm = 0.0610 cu in.
1 cu m = 35.3 cu ft
        = 1.308 cu yds
1 liter = 61.023378 cu in. (about 1 quart)
        = 0.264170 U. S. liquid gallon
        = 0.2201 imperial gallon
1 U. S. liquid quart = 0.946 liter
1 U. S. liquid gallon = 3.785 liters

Table C-4   Weight

Ordinary Units

1 pound   = 16 ounces (avoirdupois)
1 ton   = 2000 lbs
1 long ton = 2240 lbs
1 lb of water (39.1° F) = 27.681217 cu in.
                            = 0.016019 cu ft
                            = 0.119832 U. S. gallon
                            = 0.453617 liter

Equivalents
1 kilogram   = 2.205 avoirdupois pounds
1 metric ton   = 0.984 gross or long ton
                       = 1.102 net or short tons
1 avoirdupois ounce = 28.35 grams
1 avoirdupois pound = 0.4536 kilogram

Table C-5 Pressure

Comparison of Heads of Water in Feet with Pressures in Various Units

One foot of water at 39.1° F = 62.425 pounds per square foot (psf)
              = 0.4335 pound per square inch
              = 0.0295 atmosphere
              = 0.8826 inch of mercury at 30° F
              = 773.3 feet of air at 32° F and atmospheric pressure
One foot of water at 62° F = 62.355 pounds per square foot
              = 0.43302 pound per square inch
One pound of water on the square inch at 62° F = 2.3094 feet of water
One ounce of water on the square inch at 62° F = 1.732 inches of water
1 atmosphere at sea level (32° F) = 14.697 lbs per sq in.
              = 29.921 in. of mercury
1 inch of mercury (32° F) = 0.49119 lb per sq in.

Table C-6 Flowing Water

cfs   = cubic feet per second, or second feet
gpm = gallons per minute
1 cfs = 60 cu ft per min
       = 86,400 cu ft per 24 hrs
       = 448.83 U. S. gals per min
       = 646,317 U. S. gals per 24 hrs
       = 1.9835 acre-foot per 24 hrs (usually taken as 2)
       = 1 acre-inch per hour (approximate)
       = .028317 cu meter per second
1 U. S. gpm = 1440 U. S. gals per 24 hrs
             = 0.00442 acre-foot per 24 hrs
             = 0.0891 Miners inches, Ariz., Calif.
1 million U. S. gal per day = 1.5472 cfs
                        = 3.07 acre-feet
                        = 2.629 cu meters per min

Table C-7 Miscellaneous

Temperature

Freezing point of water = 32° Fahrenheit
                     = 0° Centigrade
Boiling point of water (at normal air pressure) = 212° Fahrenheit
                                               = 100° Centigrade
1 degree Fahrenheit = 0.5556 degree (Centigrade)
1 degree Centigrade = 1.8 degrees Fahrenheit

Circular Measure

1 minute (′)   = 60 seconds (″)
1 degree (°)   = 60 minutes
1 right angle   = 90 degrees
1 circumference = 360 degrees

Time Measure

1 minute = 60 seconds
1 hour   = 60 minutes = 3600 seconds
1 day   = 24 hours = 1440 minutes
1 week   = 7 days
1 year   = 365 days, 5 hr, 48 min, 48 sec

Ice and Snow

1 cubic foot of ice at 32° F weighs 57.50 pounds; 1 pound of ice at 32° F has a volume of 0.0174 cubic foot = 30.067 cubic inches (Clark).

1 cubic foot of fresh snow, according to humidity of atmosphere, weighs 5 pounds to 12 pounds. 1 cubic foot of snow moistened and compacted by rain weighs 15 pounds to 50 pounds (Trautwine).

Table C-8 Inches and Fractions Expressed in Decimals of a Foot

Inches	Fractions of Inches							
	0	⅛	¼	⅜	½	⅝	¾	⅞
0	.0000	.0104	.0208	.0313	.0417	.0521	.0625	.0729
1	.0833	.0937	.1042	.1146	.1250	.1354	.1458	.1562
2	.1667	.1771	.1875	.1979	.2083	.2188	.2292	.2396
3	.2500	.2604	.2708	.2813	.2917	.3021	.3125	.3229
4	.3333	.3437	.3542	.3646	.3750	.3854	.3958	.4062
5	.4167	.4271	.4375	.4479	.4583	.4688	.4792	.4896
6	.5000	.5104	.5208	.5313	.5417	.5521	.5625	.5729
7	.5833	.5937	.6042	.6146	.6250	.6354	.6458	.6562
8	.6667	.6771	.6875	.6979	.7083	.7188	.7292	.7396
9	.7500	.7604	.7708	.7813	.7917	.8021	.8125	.8229
10	.8333	.8437	.8542	.8646	.8750	.8854	.8958	.9062
11	.9167	.9271	.9375	.9479	.9583	.9688	.9792	.9896
12	1.0000							

From King's "Handbook of Hydraulics."

Table C-9 Slope in Inches Reduced to Feet

In. per 100 Ft	Ft per 100 Ft	Ft per Mile	In. per 100 Ft	Ft per 100 Ft	Ft per Mile
¼	.0208	1.098	¼	.5208	27.498
½	.0417	2.202	½	.5417	28.602
¾	.0625	3.300	¾	.5625	29.700
1	.0833	4.398	7	.5833	30.798
¼	.1042	5.502	¼	.6042	31.902
½	.1250	6.600	½	.6250	33.000
¾	.1458	7.698	¾	.6458	34.098
2	.1667	8.802	8	.6667	35.202
¼	.1875	9.900	¼	.6875	36.300
½	.2083	10.998	½	.7083	37.398
¾	.2292	12.102	¾	.7292	38.502
3	.2500	13.200	9	.7500	39.600
¼	.2708	14.298	¼	.7708	40.698
½	.2917	15.402	½	.7917	41.802
¾	.3125	16.500	¾	.8125	42.900
4	.3333	17.598	10	.8333	43.998
¼	.3542	18.702	¼	.8542	45.102
½	.3750	19.800	½	.8750	46.200
¾	.3958	20.898	¾	.8958	47.298
5	.4167	22.002	11	.9167	48.402
¼	.4375	23.100	¼	.9375	49.500
½	.4583	24.198	½	.9583	50.598
¾	.4792	25.302	¾	.9792	51.702
6	.5000	26.400	12	1.0000	52.800

General Tables

Table G-1   Areas of Plane Figures

Triangle:
Base $\times$ ½ perpendicular height

$$\sqrt{s(s - a)\ (s - b)\ (s - c)}$$
$s = $ ½ sum of the three sides a, b and c

Trapezium:
Sum of areas of the two triangles

Trapezoid:
½ sum of parallel sides $\times$ perpendicular height

Parallelogram:
Base $\times$ perpendicular height

Regular Polygon:
½ sum of sides $\times$ inside radius

Circle:
$\pi r^2\ = 0.78540 \times \text{dia}^2 = 0.07958 \times \text{circumference}^2$

Sector of Circle:
$\dfrac{\pi r^2\ A^\circ}{360} = 0.0087266\ r^2 A^\circ = \text{arc} \times$ ½ radius

Segment of Circle:
$\dfrac{r^2}{2}\left(\dfrac{\pi A^\circ}{180} - \sin A^\circ\right)$

Circle of same area as square: diameter $= $ side $\times 1.12838$

Square of same area as circle: side $= $ diameter $\times 0.88623$

Ellipse:
Long diameter $\times$ short diameter $\times 0.78540$

Parabola:
Base $\times$ ⅔ perpendicular height

Table G-2   Trigonometric Formulas

Radius, $1 = \sin^2 A + \cos^2 A$
$= \sin A \cosec A = \cos A \sec A$
$= \tan A \cot A$

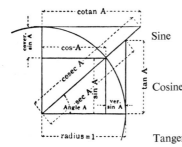

Sine
$A = \dfrac{\cos A}{\cot A} = \dfrac{1}{\cosec A} = \cos A \tan A$
$= \sqrt{1 - \cos^2 A}$

Cosine
$A = \dfrac{\sin A}{\tan A} = \dfrac{1}{\sec A} = \sin A \cot A$
$= \sqrt{1 - \sin^2 A}$

Tangent
$A = \dfrac{\sin A}{\cos A} = \dfrac{1}{\cot A} = \sin A \sec A$

Cotangent
$A = \dfrac{\cos A}{\sin A} = \dfrac{1}{\tan A} = \cos A \cosec A$

Secant
$A = \dfrac{\tan A}{\sin A} = \dfrac{1}{\cos A}$

Cosecant
$A = \dfrac{\cot A}{\cos A} = \dfrac{1}{\sin A}$

Table G-3   Natural Trigonometric Functions

Angle	Sin	Cosec	Tan	Cotan	Sec	Cos	
0°	0.000	......	0.000	......	1.000	1.000	90°
1°	0.017	57.30	0.017	57.29	1.000	1.000	89°
2°	0.035	28.65	0.035	28.64	1.001	0.999	88°
3°	0.052	19.11	0.052	19.08	1.001	0.999	87°
4°	0.070	14.34	0.070	14.30	1.002	0.998	86°
5°	0.087	11.47	0.087	11.43	1.004	0.996	85°
6°	0.105	9.567	0.105	9.514	1.006	0.995	84°
7°	0.122	8.206	0.123	8.144	1.008	0.993	83°
8°	0.139	7.185	0.141	7.115	1.010	0.990	82°
9°	0.156	6.392	0.158	6.314	1.012	0.988	81°
10°	0.174	5.759	0.176	5.671	1.015	0.985	80°
11°	0.191	5.241	0.194	5.145	1.019	0.982	79°
12°	0.208	4.810	0.213	4.705	1.022	0.978	78°
13°	0.225	4.445	0.231	4.331	1.026	0.974	77°
14°	0.242	4.134	0.249	4.011	1.031	0.970	76°
15°	0.259	3.864	0.268	3.732	1.035	0.966	75°
16°	0.276	3.628	0.287	3.487	1.040	0.961	74°
17°	0.292	3.420	0.306	3.271	1.046	0.956	73°
18°	0.309	3.236	0.325	3.078	1.051	0.951	72°
19°	0.326	3.072	0.344	2.904	1.058	0.946	71°
20°	0.342	2.924	0.364	2.747	1.064	0.940	70°
21°	0.358	2.790	0.384	2.605	1.071	0.934	69°
22°	0.375	2.669	0.404	2.475	1.079	0.927	68°
23°	0.391	2.559	0.424	2.356	1.086	0.921	67°
24°	0.407	2.459	0.445	2.246	1.095	0.914	66°
25°	0.423	2.366	0.466	2.145	1.103	0.906	65°
26°	0.438	2.281	0.488	2.050	1.113	0.899	64°
27°	0.454	2.203	0.510	1.963	1.122	0.891	63°
28°	0.469	2.130	0.532	1.881	1.133	0.883	62°
29°	0.485	2.063	0.554	1.804	1.143	0.875	61°
30°	0.500	2.000	0.577	1.732	1.155	0.866	60°
31°	0.515	1.942	0.601	1.664	1.167	0.857	59°
32°	0.530	1.887	0.625	1.600	1.179	0.848	58°
33°	0.545	1.836	0.649	1.540	1.192	0.839	57°
34°	0.559	1.788	0.675	1.483	1.206	0.829	56°
35°	0.574	1.743	0.700	1.428	1.221	0.819	55°
36°	0.588	1.701	0.727	1.376	1.236	0.809	54°
37°	0.602	1.662	0.754	1.327	1.252	0.799	53°
38°	0.616	1.624	0.781	1.280	1.269	0.788	52°
39°	0.629	1.589	0.810	1.235	1.287	0.777	51°
40°	0.643	1.556	0.839	1.192	1.305	0.766	50°
41°	0.656	1.524	0.869	1.150	1.325	0.755	49°
42°	0.669	1.494	0.900	1.111	1.346	0.743	48°
43°	0.682	1.466	0.933	1.072	1.367	0.731	47°
44°	0.695	1.440	0.966	1.036	1.390	0.719	46°
45°	0.707	1.414	1.000	1.000	1.414	0.707	45°
	Cos	Sec	Cotan	Tan	Cosec	Sin	Angle

Table G-4 Properties of the Circle*

Circumference of Circle of Dia 1 = π = 3.14159265

Circumference of Circle = $2\,\pi\,r$

Dia of Circle = Circumference × 0.31831

Diameter of Circle of equal periphery as square = side × 1.27324

Side of Square of equal periphery as circle = diameter × 0.78540

Diameter of Circle circumscribed about square = side × 1.41421

Side of Square inscribed in Circle = diameter × 0.70711

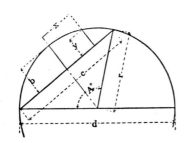

Arc, $a = \dfrac{\pi\,r\,A°}{180} = 0.017453\,r\,A°$

Angle, $A = \dfrac{180°\,a}{\pi\,r} = 57.29578\,\dfrac{a}{r}$

Radius, $r = \dfrac{4\,b^2 + c^2}{8\,b}$ Diameter, $d = \dfrac{4\,b^2 + c^2}{4\,b}$

Chord, $c = 2\sqrt{2\,b\,r - b^2} = 2\,r\sin\dfrac{A°}{2}$

Rise, $b = r - \tfrac{1}{2}\sqrt{4\,r^2 - c^2} = \dfrac{c}{2}\tan\dfrac{A°}{4} = 2\,r\sin^2\dfrac{A}{4}$

Rise, $b = r + y - \sqrt{r^2 - x^2}$ $y = b - r + \sqrt{r^2 - x^2}$ $x = \sqrt{r^2 - (r + y - b)^2}$

$\pi = 3.14159265,\ \log = 0.4971499$

$\dfrac{1}{\pi} = 0.3183099,\ \log = \bar{1}.5028501$

$\pi^2 = 9.8696044,\ \log = 0.9942997$

$\dfrac{1}{\pi^2} = 0.1013212,\ \log = \bar{1}.0057003$

$\sqrt{\pi} = 1.7724539,\ \log = 0.2485749$

$\sqrt{\dfrac{1}{\pi}} = 0.5641896,\ \log = 1.7514251$

$\dfrac{\pi}{180} = 0.0174533,\ \log = \bar{2}.2418774$

$\dfrac{180}{\pi} = 57.2957795,\ \log = 1.7581226$

*From Carnegie's "Pocket Companion."

Table G-5   Areas of Circles

Diameter in Inches	Area		Diameter in Inches	Area		Diameter in Inches	Area	
	Square Inches	Square Feet		Square Inches	Square Feet		Square Inches	Square Feet
1.0	0.7854	.005454	4.0	12.5664	.087266	7.0	38.4845	.267254
.1	0.9503	.006599	.1	13.2025	.091684	.1	39.5919	.274944
.2	1.1310	.007854	.2	13.8544	.096211	.2	40.7150	.282743
.25	1.2272	.008522	.25	14.1863	.098516	.25	41.2825	.286684
.3	1.3273	.009218	.3	14.5220	.100847	.3	41.8539	.290652
.4	1.5394	.010690	.4	15.2053	.105592	.4	43.0084	.298669
.5	1.7671	.012272	.5	15.9043	.110446	.5	44.1786	.306796
.6	2.0106	.013963	.6	16.6190	.115410	.6	45.3646	.315032
.7	2.2698	.015763	.7	17.3494	.120482	.7	46.5663	.323377
.75	2.4053	.016703	.75	17.7205	.123059	.75	47.1730	.327590
.8	2.5447	.017671	.8	18.0956	.125664	.8	47.7836	.331831
.9	2.8353	.019689	.9	18.8574	.130954	.9	49.0167	.340394
2.0	3.1416	.021816	5.0	19.6350	.136354	8.0	50.2655	.349066
.1	3.4636	.024053	.1	20.4282	.141863	.1	51.5300	.357847
.2	3.8013	.026398	.2	21.2372	.147480	.2	52.8102	.366737
.25	3.9761	.027612	.25	21.6475	.150330	.25	53.4562	.371223
.3	4.1548	.028852	.3	22.0618	.153207	.3	54.1061	.375736
.4	4.5239	.031416	.4	22.9022	.159043	.4	55.4177	.384845
.5	4.9087	.034088	.5	23.7583	.164988	.5	56.7450	.394063
.6	5.3093	.036870	.6	24.6301	.171042	.6	58.0880	.403389
.7	5.7256	.039760	.7	25.5176	.177205	.7	59.4468	.412825
.75	5.9396	.041247	.75	25.9672	.180328	.75	60.1320	.417584
.8	6.1575	.042760	.8	26.4208	.183477	.8	60.8212	.422370
.9	6.6052	.045869	.9	27.3397	.189859	.9	62.2114	.432024
3.0	7.0686	.049087	6.0	28.2743	.196350	9.0	63.6173	.441786
.1	7.5477	.052414	.1	29.2247	.202949	.1	65.0388	.451658
.2	8.0425	.055851	.2	30.1907	.209658	.2	66.4761	.461640
.25	8.2958	.057609	.25	30.6796	.213053	.25	67.2006	.466671
.3	8.5530	.059396	.3	31.1725	.216475	.3	67.9291	.471730
.4	9.0792	.063050	.4	32.1699	.223402	.4	69.3978	.481929
.5	9.6211	.066813	.5	33.1831	.230438	.5	70.8822	.492237
.6	10.1788	.070686	.6	34.2119	.237583	.6	72.3823	.502654
.7	10.7521	.074667	.7	35.2565	.244837	.7	73.8981	.513181
.75	11.0447	.076699	.75	35.7847	.248505	.75	74.6619	.518486
.8	11.3411	.078758	.8	36.3168	.252200	.8	75.4296	.523817
.9	11.9459	.082958	.9	37.3928	.259672	.9	76.9769	.534561

The above table may be used for finding the areas of circles whose diameters are not within the limits of the table. Since the areas vary as the squares of their diameters, the given diameter may be divided (or multiplied) by 10, and the area found from the table under the resulting diameter corrected by moving the decimal point two places to the right (or left). Thus to find the area of a 22-inch circle:

From table, area of 2.2-inch circle = 3.8013 sq in. = .026398 sq ft

Therefore area of 22-inch circle = 380.13 sq in. = 2.64 sq ft

Again, to find the area of a 0.75-inch circle:

From table, area of 7.5-inch circle = 44.1786 sq in. = 0.306796 sq ft

Therefore area of 0.75-inch circle = 0.4418 sq in. = 0.00307 sq ft

It will also be apparent that the *first two* columns in the table may be used for any unit of measure.

Table G-6 Functions of Numbers 1 to 99

No	Square	Cube	Square Root	Cubic Root	Loga- rithm	1000 × Reciprocal	No = Diameter	
							Circum	Area
1	1	1	1.0000	1.0000	0.00000	1000.000	3.142	0.7854
2	4	8	1.4142	1.2599	0.30103	500.000	6.283	3.1416
3	9	27	1.7321	1.4422	0.47712	333.333	9.425	7.0686
4	16	64	2.0000	1.5874	0.60206	250.000	12.566	12.5664
5	25	125	2.2361	1.7100	0.69897	200.000	15.708	19.6350
6	36	216	2.4495	1.8171	0.77815	166.667	18.850	28.2743
7	49	343	2.6458	1.9129	0.84510	142.857	21.991	38.4845
8	64	512	2.8284	2.0000	0.90309	125.000	25.133	50.2655
9	81	729	3.0000	2.0801	0.95424	111.111	28.274	63.6173
10	100	1000	3.1623	2.1544	1.00000	100.000	31.416	78.5398
11	121	1331	3.3166	2.2240	1.04139	90.9091	34.558	95.0332
12	144	1728	3.4641	2.2894	1.07918	83.3333	37.699	113.097
13	169	2197	3.6056	2.3513	1.11394	76.9231	40.841	132.732
14	196	2744	3.7417	2.4101	1.14613	71.4286	43.982	153.938
15	225	3375	3.8730	2.4662	1.17609	66.6667	47.124	176.715
16	256	4096	4.0000	2.5198	1.20412	62.5000	50.265	201.062
17	289	4913	4.1231	2.5713	1.23045	58.8235	53.407	226.980
18	324	5832	4.2426	2.6207	1.25527	55.5556	56.549	254.469
19	361	6859	4.3589	2.6684	1.27875	52.6316	59.690	283.529
20	400	8000	4.4721	2.7144	1.30103	50.0000	62.832	314.159
21	441	9261	4.5826	2.7589	1.32222	47.6190	65.973	346.361
22	484	10648	4.6904	2.8020	1.34242	45.4545	69.115	380.133
23	529	12167	4.7958	2.8439	1.36173	43.4783	72.257	415.476
24	576	13824	4.8990	2.8845	1.38021	41.6667	75.398	452.389
25	625	15625	5.0000	2.9240	1.39794	40.0000	78.540	490.874
26	676	17576	5.0990	2.9625	1.41497	38.4615	81.681	530.929
27	729	19683	5.1962	3.0000	1.43136	37.0370	84.823	572.555
28	784	21952	5.2915	3.0366	1.44716	35.7143	87.965	615.752
29	841	24389	5.3852	3.0723	1.46240	34.4828	91.106	660.520
30	900	27000	5.4772	3.1072	1.47712	33.3333	94.248	706.858
31	961	29791	5.5678	3.1414	1.49136	32.2581	97.389	754.768
32	1024	32768	5.6569	3.1748	1.50515	31.2500	100.531	804.248
33	1089	35937	5.7446	3.2075	1.51851	30.3030	103.673	855.299
34	1156	39304	5.8310	3.2396	1.53148	29.4118	106.814	907.920
35	1225	42875	5.9161	3.2711	1.54407	28.5714	109.956	962.113
36	1296	46656	6.0000	3.3019	1.55630	27.7778	113.097	1017.88
37	1369	50653	6.0828	3.3322	1.56820	27.0270	116.239	1075.21
38	1444	54872	6.1644	3.3620	1.57978	26.3158	119.381	1134.11
39	1521	59319	6.2450	3.3912	1.59106	25.6410	122.522	1194.59
40	1600	64000	6.3246	3.4200	1.60206	25.0000	125.66	1256.64
41	1681	68921	6.4031	3.4482	1.61278	24.3902	128.81	1320.25
42	1764	74088	6.4807	3.4760	1.62325	23.8095	131.95	1385.44
43	1849	79507	6.5574	3.5034	1.63347	23.2558	135.09	1452.20
44	1936	85184	6.6332	3.5303	1.64345	22.7273	138.23	1520.53
45	2025	91125	6.7082	3.5569	1.65321	22.2222	141.37	1590.43
46	2116	97336	6.7823	3.5830	1.66276	21.7391	144.51	1661.90
47	2209	103823	6.8557	3.6088	1.67210	21.2766	147.65	1734.94
48	2304	110592	6.9282	3.6342	1.68124	20.8333	150.80	1809.56
49	2401	117649	7.0000	3.6593	1.69020	20.4082	153.94	1885.74

(*Continued on next page*)

Table G-6 Functions of Numbers 1 to 99 (Continued)

No	Square	Cube	Square Root	Cubic Root	Logarithm	1000 × Reciprocal	No = Diameter Circum	No = Diameter Area
50	2500	125000	7.0711	3.6840	1.69897	20.0000	157.08	1963.50
51	2601	132651	7.1414	3.7084	1.70757	19.6078	160.22	2042.82
52	2704	140608	7.2111	3.7325	1.71600	19.2308	163.36	2123.72
53	2809	148877	7.2801	3.7563	1.72428	18.8679	166.50	2206.18
54	2916	157464	7.3485	3.7798	1.73239	18.5185	169.65	2290.22
55	3025	166375	7.4162	3.8030	1.74036	18.1818	172.79	2375.83
56	3136	175616	7.4838	3.8259	1.74819	17.8571	175.93	2463.01
57	3249	185193	7.5498	3.8485	1.75587	17.5439	179.07	2551.76
58	3364	195112	7.6158	3.8709	1.76343	17.2414	182.21	2642.08
59	3481	205379	7.6811	3.8930	1.77085	16.9492	185.35	2733.97
60	3600	216000	7.7460	3.9149	1.77815	16.6667	188.50	2827.43
61	3721	226981	7.8102	3.9365	1.78533	16.3934	191.64	2922.47
62	3844	238328	7.8740	3.9579	1.79239	16.1290	194.78	3019.07
63	3969	250047	7.9373	3.9791	1.79934	15.8730	197.92	3117.25
64	4096	262144	8.0000	4.0000	1.80618	15.6250	201.06	3216.99
65	4225	274625	8.0623	4.0207	1.81291	15.3846	204.20	3318.31
66	4356	287496	8.1240	4.0412	1.81954	15.1515	207.35	3421.19
67	4489	300763	8.1854	4.0615	1.82607	14.9254	210.49	3525.65
68	4624	314432	8.2462	4.0817	1.83251	14.7059	213.63	3631.68
69	4761	328509	8.3066	4.1016	1.83885	14.4928	216.77	3739.28
70	4900	343000	8.3666	4.1213	1.84510	14.2857	219.91	3848.45
71	5041	357911	8.4261	4.1408	1.85126	14.0845	223.05	3959.19
72	5184	373248	8.4853	4.1602	1.85733	13.8889	226.19	4071.50
73	5329	389017	8.5440	4.1793	1.86332	13.6986	229.34	4185.39
74	5476	405224	8.6023	4.1983	1.86923	13.5135	232.48	4300.84
75	5625	421875	8.6603	4.2172	1.87506	13.3333	235.62	4417.86
76	5776	438976	8.7178	4.2358	1.88081	13.1579	238.76	4536.46
77	5929	456533	8.7750	4.2543	1.88649	12.9870	241.90	4656.63
78	6084	474552	8.8318	4.2727	1.89209	12.8205	245.04	4778.36
79	6241	493039	8.8882	4.2908	1.89763	12.6582	248.19	4901.67
80	6400	512000	8.9443	4.3089	1.90309	12.5000	251.33	5026.55
81	6561	531441	9.0000	4.3267	1.90849	12.3457	254.47	5153.00
82	6724	551368	9.0554	4.3445	1.91381	12.1951	257.61	5281.02
83	6889	571787	9.1104	4.3621	1.91908	12.0482	260.75	5410.61
84	7056	592704	9.1652	4.3795	1.92428	11.9048	263.89	5541.77
85	7225	614125	9.2195	4.3968	1.92942	11.7647	267.04	5674.50
86	7396	636056	9.2736	4.4140	1.93450	11.6279	270.18	5808.80
87	7569	658503	9.3274	4.4310	1.93952	11.4943	273.32	5944.68
88	7744	681472	9.3808	4.4480	1.94448	11.3636	276.46	6082.12
89	7921	704969	9.4340	4.4647	1.94939	11.2360	279.60	6221.14
90	8100	729000	9.4868	4.4814	1.95424	11.1111	282.74	6361.73
91	8281	753571	9.5394	4.4979	1.95904	10.9890	285.88	6503.88
92	8464	778688	9.5917	4.5144	1.96379	10.8696	289.03	6647.61
93	8649	804357	9.6437	4.5307	1.96848	10.7527	292.17	6792.91
94	8836	830584	9.6954	4.5468	1.97313	10.6383	295.31	6939.78
95	9025	857375	9.7468	4.5629	1.97772	10.5263	298.45	7088.22
96	9216	884736	9.7980	4.5789	1.98227	10.4167	301.59	7238.23
97	9409	912673	9.8489	4.5947	1.98677	10.3093	304.73	7389.81
98	9604	941192	9.8995	4.6104	1.99123	10.2041	307.88	7542.96
99	9801	970299	9.9499	4.6261	1.99564	10.1010	311.02	7697.69

Table G-7 Two-thirds Powers of Numbers

No	.00	.01	.02	.03	.04	.05	.06	.07	.08	.09
.0	.000	.046	.074	.097	.117	.136	.153	.170	.186	.201
.1	.215	.229	.243	.256	.269	.282	.295	.307	.319	.331
.2	.342	.353	.364	.375	.386	.397	.407	.418	.428	.438
.3	.448	.458	.468	.477	.487	.497	.506	.515	.525	.534
.4	.543	.552	.561	.570	.578	.587	.596	.604	.613	.622
.5	.630	.638	.647	.655	.663	.671	.679	.687	.695	.703
.6	.711	.719	.727	.735	.743	.750	.758	.765	.773	.781
.7	.788	.796	.803	.811	.818	.825	.832	.840	.847	.855
.8	.862	.869	.876	.883	.890	.897	.904	.911	.918	.925
.9	.932	.939	.946	.953	.960	.966	.973	.980	.987	.993
1.0	1.000	1.007	1.013	1.020	1.027	1.033	1.040	1.046	1.053	1.059
1.1	1.065	1.072	1.078	1.085	1.091	1.097	1.104	1.110	1.117	1.123
1.2	1.129	1.136	1.142	1.148	1.154	1.160	1.167	1.173	1.179	1.185
1.3	1.191	1.197	1.203	1.209	1.215	1.221	1.227	1.233	1.239	1.245
1.4	1.251	1.257	1.263	1.269	1.275	1.281	1.287	1.293	1.299	1.305
1.5	1.310	1.316	1.322	1.328	1.334	1.339	1.345	1.351	1.357	1.362
1.6	1.368	1.374	1.379	1.385	1.391	1.396	1.402	1.408	1.413	1.419
1.7	1.424	1.430	1.436	1.441	1.447	1.452	1.458	1.463	1.469	1.474
1.8	1.480	1.485	1.491	1.496	1.502	1.507	1.513	1.518	1.523	1.529
1.9	1.534	1.539	1.545	1.550	1.556	1.561	1.566	1.571	1.577	1.582
2.0	1.587	1.593	1.598	1.603	1.608	1.613	1.619	1.624	1.629	1.634
2.1	1.639	1.645	1.650	1.655	1.660	1.665	1.671	1.676	1.681	1.686
2.2	1.691	1.697	1.702	1.707	1.712	1.717	1.722	1.727	1.732	1.737
2.3	1.742	1.747	1.752	1.757	1.762	1.767	1.772	1.777	1.782	1.787
2.4	1.792	1.797	1.802	1.807	1.812	1.817	1.822	1.827	1.832	1.837
2.5	1.842	1.847	1.852	1.857	1.862	1.867	1.871	1.876	1.881	1.886
2.6	1.891	1.896	1.900	1.905	1.910	1.915	1.920	1.925	1.929	1.934
2.7	1.939	1.944	1.949	1.953	1.958	1.963	1.968	1.972	1.977	1.982
2.8	1.987	1.992	1.996	2.001	2.006	2.010	2.015	2.020	2.024	2.029
2.9	2.034	2.038	2.043	2.048	2.052	2.057	2.062	2.066	2.071	2.075
3.0	2.080	2.085	2.089	2.094	2.099	2.103	2.108	2.112	2.117	2.122
3.1	2.126	2.131	2.135	2.140	2.144	2.149	·2.153	2.158	2.163	2.167
3.2	2.172	2.176	2.180	2.185	2.190	2.194	2.199	2.203	2.208	2.212
3.3	2.217	2.221	2.226	2.230	2.234	2.239	2.243	2.248	2.252	2.257
3.4	2.261	2.265	2.270	2.274	2.279	2.283	2.288	2.292	2.296	2.301
3.5	2.305	2.310	2.314	2.318	2.323	2.327	2.331	2.336	2.340	2.345
3.6	2.349	2.353	2.358	2.362	2.366	2.371	2.375	2.379	2.384	2.388
3.7	2.392	2.397	2.401	2.405	2.409	2.414	2.418	2.422	2.427	2.431
3.8	2.435	2.439	2.444	2.448	2.452	2.457	2.461	2.465	2.469	2.474
3.9	2.478	2.482	2.486	2.490	2.495	2.499	2.503	2.507	2.511	·2.516
4.0	2.520	2.524	2.528	2.532	2.537	2.541	2.545	2.549	2.553	2.558
4.1	2.562	2.566	2.570	2.574	2.579	2.583	2.587	2.591	2.595	2.599
4.2	2.603	2.607	2.611	2.616	2.620	2.624	2.628	2.632	2.636	2.640
4.3	2.644	2.648	2.653	2.657	2.661	2.665	2.669	2.673	2.677	2.681
4.4	2.685	2.689	2.693	2.698	2.702	2.706	2.710	2.714	2.718	2.722
4.5	2.726	2.730	2.734	2.738	2.742	2.746	2.750	2.754	2.758	2.762
4.6	2.766	2.770	2.774	2.778	2.782	2.786	2.790	2.794	2.798	2.802
4.7	2.806	2.810	2.814	2.818	2.822	2.826	2.830	2.834	2.838	2.842
4.8	2.846	2.850	2.854	2.858	2.862	2.865	2.869	2.873	2.877	2.881
4.9	2.885	2.889	2.893	2.897	2.901	2.904	2.908	2.912	2.916	2.920

From King's "Handbook of Hydraulics."

Table G-8 Square Roots of Decimal Numbers
For Use in Manning's Formula

Number	.−0	.−1	.−2	.−3	.−4	.−5	.−6	.−7	.−8	.−9
.00001	.003162	.003317	.003464	.003606	.003742	.003873	.004000	.004123	.004243	.004359
.00002	.004472	.004583	.004690	.004796	.004899	.005000	.005099	.005196	.005292	.005385
.00003	.005477	.005568	.005657	.005745	.005831	.005916	.006000	.006083	.006164	.006245
.00004	.006325	.006403	.006481	.006557	.006633	.006708	.006782	.006856	.006928	.007000
.00005	.007071	.007141	.007211	.007280	.007348	.007416	.007483	.007550	.007616	.007681
.00006	.007746	.007810	.007874	.007937	.008000	.008062	.008124	.008185	.008246	.008307
.00007	.008367	.008426	.008485	.008544	.008602	.008660	.008718	.008755	.008832	.008888
.00008	.008944	.009000	.009055	.009110	.009165	.009220	.009274	.009327	.009381	.009434
.00009	.009487	.009539	.009592	.009644	.009695	.009747	.009798	.009849	.009899	.009950
.00010	.010000	.010050	.010100	.010149	.010198	.010247	.010296	.010344	.010392	.010440
.0001	.01000	.01049	.01095	.01140	.01183	.01225	.01265	.01304	.01342	.01378
.0002	.01414	.01449	.01483	.01517	.01549	.01581	.01612	.01643	.01673	.01703
.0003	.01732	.01761	.01789	.01817	.01844	.01871	.01897	.01924	.01949	.01975
.0004	.02000	.02025	.02049	.02074	.02098	.02121	.02145	.02168	.02191	.02214
.0005	.02236	.02258	.02280	.02302	.02324	.02345	.02366	.02387	.02408	.02429
.0006	.02449	.02470	.02490	.02510	.02530	.02550	.02569	.02588	.02608	.02627
.0007	.02646	.02665	.02683	.02702	.02720	.02739	.02757	.02775	.02793	.02811
.0008	.02828	.02846	.02864	.02881	.02898	.02915	.02933	.02950	.02966	.02983
.0009	.03000	.03017	.03033	.03050	.03066	.03082	.03098	.03114	.03130	.03146
.0010	.03162	.03178	.03194	.03209	.03225	.03240	.03256	.03271	.03286	.03302
.001	.03162	.03317	.03464	.03606	.03742	.03873	.04000	.04123	.04243	.04359
.002	.04472	.04583	.04690	.04796	.04899	.05000	.05099	.05196	.05292	.05385
.003	.05477	.05568	.05657	.05745	.05831	.05916	.06000	.06083	.06164	.06245
.004	.06325	.06403	.06481	.06557	.06633	.06708	.06782	.06856	.06928	.07000
.005	.07071	.07141	.07211	.07280	.07348	.07416	.07483	.07550	.07616	.07681
.006	.07746	.07810	.07874	.07937	.08000	.08062	.08124	.08185	.08246	.08307
.007	.08367	.08426	.08485	.08544	.08602	.08660	.08718	.08775	.08832	.08888
.008	.08944	.09000	.09055	.09110	.09165	.09220	.09274	.09327	.09381	.09434
.009	.09487	.09539	.09592	.09644	.09695	.09747	.09798	.09849	.09899	.09950
.010	.10000	.10050	.10100	.10149	.10198	.10247	.10296	.10344	.10392	.10440
.01	.1000	.1049	.1095	.1140	.1183	.1225	.1265	.1304	.1342	.1378
.02	.1414	.1449	.1483	.1517	.1549	.1581	.1612	.1643	.1673	.1703
.03	.1732	.1761	.1789	.1817	.1844	.1871	.1897	.1924	.1949	.1975
.04	.2000	.2025	.2049	.2074	.2098	.2121	.2145	.2168	.2191	.2214
.05	.2236	.2258	.2280	.2302	.2324	.2345	.2366	.2387	.2408	.2429
.06	.2449	.2470	.2490	.2510	.2530	.2550	.2569	.2588	.2608	.2627
.07	.2646	.2665	.2683	.2702	.2720	.2739	.2757	.2775	.2793	.2811
.08	.2828	.2846	.2864	.2881	.2898	.2915	.2933	.2950	.2966	.2983
.09	.3000	.3017	.3033	.3050	.3066	.3082	.3098	.3114	.3130	.3146
.10	.3162	.3178	.3194	.3209	.3225	.3240	.3256	.3271	.3286	.3302

From King's "Handbook of Hydraulics."

Table G-9 U. S. Standard Gages for Sheet and Plate Iron and Steel (Black)

Established by Act of Congress, July 1, 1893
(With revisions, 1945)

Number of Gage	Approximate Thickness				Weight		
	Fractions of an Inch	Decimal Parts of an Inch		Milli-meters	per Square Foot in Ounces Avoir-dupois	per Square Foot in Pounds Avoir-dupois	per Square Meter in Kilo-grams
	Wrought Iron*	Wrought Iron*	Steel†	Steel†			
000	3–8	.375	.3587	9.111	240	15.	73.24
00	11–32	.34375	.3288	8.352	220	13.75	67.13
0	5–16	.3125	.2989	7.592	200	12.50	61.03
1	9–32	.28125	.2690	6.833	180	11.25	54.93
2	17–64	.265625	.2541	6.454	170	10.625	51.88
3	1–4	.25	.2391	6.073	160	10.	48.82
4	15–64	.234375	.2242	5.695	150	9.375	45.77
5	7–32	.21875	.2092	5.314	140	8.75	42.72
6	13–64	.203125	.1943	4.935	130	8.125	39.67
7	3–16	.1875	.1793	4.554	120	7.5	36.62
8	11–64	.171875	.1644	4.176	110	6.875	33.57
9	5–32	.15625	.1495	3.797	100	6.25	30.52
10	9–64	.140625	.1345	3.416	90	5.625	27.46
11	1–8	.125	.1196	3.038	80	5.	24.41
12	7–64	.109375	.1046	2.657	70	4.375	21.36
13	3–32	.09375	.0897	2.278	60	3.75	18.31
14	5–64	.078125	.0747	1.897	50	3.125	15.26
15	9–128	.0703125	.0673	1.709	45	2.8125	13.73
16	1–16	.0625	.0598	1.519	40	2.5	12.21
17	9–160	.05625	.0538	1.367	36	2.25	10.99
18	1–20	.05	.0478	1.214	32	2.	9.765
19	7–160	.04375	.0418	1.062	28	1.75	8.544
20	3–80	.0375	.0359	0.912	24	1.50	7.324

By Act of Congress, the gage numbers are based on the weight per square foot in ounces (sixth column) and not on thickness.

*The thickness given in the Congressional table is for wrought iron and not for steel.

†The thickness for steel is from tables compiled by American Iron and Steel Institute, November 1942, based on 41.82 pounds per square foot per inch thick.

Example: A 16 gage sheet of either wrought iron or steel weighs 40 ounces per square foot. The wrought iron is approximately .0625 inch thick whereas the steel is .0598 inch thick.

General Index

The scope of this handbook can best be determined by a look at the CONTENTS, page 5
The chapters, along with sections and prime references, are shown in bold face.

Tables are indicated by T followed by chapter, table no. and page number (T6-1, 51).

NAMES of individuals, places, organizations, colleges and industries are listed at the end of the GENERAL INDEX.

Items listed in the GLOSSARY, page 337, and SYMBOLS, page 343, are partly cross-referenced to this GENERAL INDEX.

(Corrections or suggestions are invited)

Index of Names